Introduction to Wood Design

2011 Edition

A learning guide
to complement
the Wood Design Manual

Canadian
Wood
Council

Conseil
canadien
du bois

© 2011 Copyright
Canadian Wood Council
Conseil canadien du bois
Ottawa, Ontario, Canada

ISBN 978-0-9783213-8-3

Printed in Canada

1.5M399, 2.5M796, 2M702, 1.5M107, 1.0M709, 1.5M911

Printing:

Gilmore Printing Services
Ottawa, ON

Design and production:

Accurate Design & Communication Inc.,
Nepean, ON

Photos:

Front cover: **Scott Alpen**
Back cover: **Tim Swanky**, centre photo
Page 1-2: **Scott Alpen**
Page 1-4: **David Schaeffer**, bottom photo
Page 1-6: **Peter Powles**, top photo

Published and distributed by:

Canadian Wood Council
99 Bank St., Suite 400
Ottawa, ON
K1P 6B9

General Inquiries
1-800-463-5091

Internet
www.cwc.ca

Table of Contents

Introduction

1.1 General Information

PURPOSE

Introduction to Wood Design has been prepared to facilitate and encourage the instruction of wood engineering at Canadian universities and colleges. The information has been prepared in consultation with professors to ensure its relevance to the way wood engineering is taught.

These notes focus on the engineering aspects of wood design, which are of primary concern to students of engineering. The information is also of value to architecture students for developing an understanding of structural design principles.

Courses are most often custom tailored by each professor. The course content at each university or college will vary depending on the lecture time available and the personal style and preferences of each professor. These course notes are meant to cover a wide range of subjects. For some courses, all the material may be relevant. For other courses, the professor is of course at liberty to select those subject areas which best suit the time available and the level of familiarity of the students.

Introduction to Wood Design is intended to be continually upgraded to meet changing needs. If students or professors have suggestions for additions, corrections or additional design examples, please contact the Canadian Wood Council.

CANADIAN WOOD COUNCIL

The Canadian Wood Council (CWC) is privately funded by the manufacturers of Canadian wood and engineered wood products. CWC prepares and distributes technical information to facilitate the use of wood products, and is active in the development and improvement of building codes and standards throughout North America.

CWC maintains products for facilitating design and construction, including:

- *Wood Design Manual*
- *WoodWorks® Design Software*
- *Permanent Wood Foundations*
- *The Span Book*
- *Engineering Guide for Wood Frame Construction*

CWC also publishes a variety of technical bulletins, workbooks and fact sheets that include examples of wood buildings, design details and comparisons between wood and other framing materials. These smaller publications can be downloaded free from CWC's web site at www.cwc.ca. The web site also contains design tools and general information for students and designers wanting to learn more about wood and wood design.

Every effort has been made to ensure that the data and information in *Introduction to Wood Design* are accurate and complete. The CWC does not, however, assume any responsibility for errors or omissions in the book nor from any designs or plans prepared from it.

CWC provides technical assistance to designers. If you require information about products, design, or publications, you may contact CWC as follows:

Email: info@cwc.ca
Web Site: www.cwc.ca

Errata available at:
www.tools.cwc.ca/books

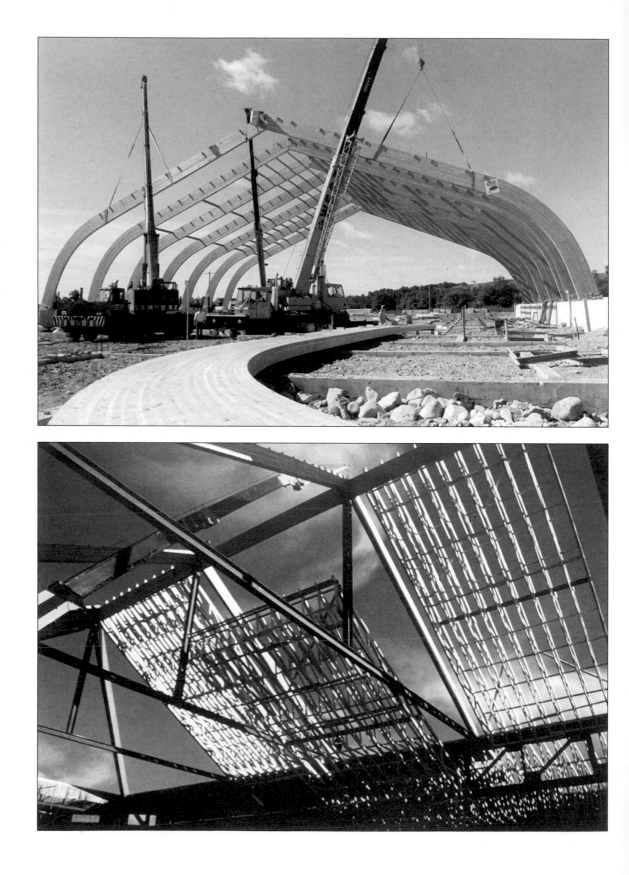

REFERENCE MATERIALS

Introduction to Wood Design is intended to be used in conjunction with the *Wood Design Manual 2010*. This manual includes CSA O86-09 *Engineering Design in Wood*. It also includes information and selection tables which simplify the design process for the examples used in this textbook. The manual is also the reference wood design document which is used by practising Canadian engineers.

The *National Building Code of Canada* (NBCC) is the model building code in Canada that forms the basis of most building design in the country. In terms of structural design, the NBCC specifies loads, while material resistance is referenced through using the material Standards. In the case of wood, CSA Standard O86 provides the designer with the means of calculating the resistance values of wood. Additional information on loads is found in the companion document to the NBCC – *NBC 2010 Structural Commentaries (Part 4)*.

In the design examples, references will be noted as follows:

WDM   – *Wood Design Manual 2010*

CSA O86   – CSA O86-09 *Engineering Design in Wood*

NBCC   – *National Building Code of Canada*

NBCC-SC – *User's Guide – NBC 2010 Structural Commentaries (Part 4)*

The Canadian Wood Council wishes to assist students to become familiar with wood design by having them attain an understanding of the basic properties of wood, and learning design from first principles. CWC also recognizes that wood design is made easier with design aids. Once students have learned the basics, the *Wood Design Manual* offers many shortcuts for member selection.

WoodWorks® is a family of software design programs. *WoodWorks® Sizer* offers a conceptual design mode for initial sizing and options analysis. It also offers detailed design capability for beams and columns including the generation of shear and moment diagrams. *WoodWorks® Connections* provides detailed designs for wood beam and wood column connections. *WoodWorks® Shearwalls* is the module that designs shearwalls and connections for lateral wind and seismic loads.

It is suggested that once students are accustomed to using the member selection tables in the *Wood Design Manual*, they become acquainted with *WoodWorks®* programs to check designs and investigate alternative solutions.

In this way, students will learn the basics, while also learning methods for facilitating the design procedures they will apply during their careers.

WoodWorks® programs are available to schools. For more information, contact the Canadian Wood Council.

SAMPLE BUILDING

The design examples in Chapter 13 of this publication are based on a sample building. In this Chapter, the assignment of loads and the design of members and connections are interdependent, thus allowing students to develop an understanding of the design process for all structural aspects of a building design.

WOOD AS AN ENGINEERING MATERIAL

Wood has a long history in Canada as a building material.

The main use for wood products is in the construction of residential and commercial buildings.

Wood is by far the preferred building material for residential construction in North America, and is becoming increasingly popular in commercial and industrial construction. The photographs in this section show just some examples of wood construction for commercial and industrial buildings. Except for a few high hazard occupancies which severely restrict the use of wood products, a host of building types including schools, warehousing and manufacturing facilities, offices, stores, recreational facilities, firehalls and many others can efficiently be constructed of wood.

THE ENVIRONMENTAL EFFECTS OF BUILDING MATERIALS

All building materials are derived from natural resources. The management of natural resources and the effect of manufacturing and using building materials is undergoing increased scrutiny.

Increasingly, environmental considerations are influencing the choice of structural materials. Although specific results may vary between studies, research indicates that wood has environmental advantages when compared to the three other major building materials – masonry, concrete and steel.

Evolving technology has provided more sophisticated methods to evaluate the environmental impacts associated with alternative building materials.

Life-Cycle Analysis (LCA) is gaining acceptance worldwide as the method of choice for this purpose. The process involves evaluating the direct and indirect environmental burdens associated with a product, process or activity, by measuring energy and material usage and environmental releases at each stage of a product's life cycle.

ATHENA™ is a North American life cycle assessment tool developed by the ATHENA™ Sustainable Materials Institute. Using peer-reviewed data, the ATHENA™ software program is able to assess the environmental effects of the mainstream building systems. Any student or designer interested in reviewing life cycle assessment further can download a trial version of the ATHENA™ software free from the website: www.athenasmi.ca.

Resource Management

Wood is the only renewable building material, harvested and replanted in a continually regenerating cycle. To ensure long-term viability of supply, the Canadian forest industry is continually improving forest practices and is actively supporting the development of sustainable forestry certification standards.

The Canadian forestry industry has become a world leader in adopting forest certification to demonstrate that forests are managed sustainably and meet public expectations. Forest certification is the process of having a qualified third-party audit a company's forest management system, practices and performance against a predetermined standard. Certification embraces the following general objectives:

- conservation of the biodiversity (plant and animal species) and representative forests;
- conservation of soil and water quantity and quality;
- regulation of harvest levels with regard to long-term productivity;
- continual improvement of forest management and public involvement; and integration of timber and non-timber values.

Certification of Canadian forests began in 1998 and by 2011, Canadian companies had achieved third-party certification on over 149 million hectares of the Canadian working forests, representing 42% of certified forests in the world.

Operating and Embodied Energy

The operating energy use in buildings represents a major contributor to fossil fuel use for space heating and cooling, lighting and the operation of appliances. Fossil fuels release greenhouse gases such as carbon dioxide and nitrous oxide. For this reason, the need to save energy by reducing operating energy consumption in buildings is widely recognized throughout the world.

Wood is a good and natural insulator. Due to its cellular structure, wood traps air resulting in low conductivity and good insulating properties. Other commonly used framing materials conduct heat faster than wood. High conductivity causes thermal bridging leading to increased energy use for heating and cooling.

While it is easier to focus solely on the conservation of operating energy, the effects of embodied energy in structures are significant. Of the major building materials, wood requires the least energy to produce.

Less attention has been given to the need to reduce the embodied energy of structures because the amount of embodied energy is small in comparison to the amount of operating energy over a building's lifetime cycle. However, as buildings become more energy-efficient, the ratio of embodied energy to lifetime operating energy consumption becomes more significant.

Conclusion

Life-cycle analysis provides the basis for responsible choices of building materials by specifiers and users. While some products are obviously better suited for one application than another, the effects of these choices on the environment can be minimized by specifying a product that:

• comes from a renewable resource

• is energy conserving in manufacture and use

FIRE SAFETY ASPECTS OF WOOD CONSTRUCTION

At the present time, the NBCC and other North American building codes categorize wood buildings as combustible construction.

Despite being termed combustible, construction techniques can give wood frame construction fire-resistance ratings up to 2 hours.

In addition, post and beam construction meeting certain criteria qualifies as Heavy Timber construction (Section 4.4), and is assigned an equivalency to wood frame or noncombustible construction having a 45-minute fire-resistance rating.

The provision of fire safety in a building is a complex matter; far more complex than the relative combustibility of the main structural materials used in a building. To develop safe code provisions, prevention, suppression, movement of occupants, mobility of occupants, building use, and fuel control are but a few of the factors that must be considered in addition to the combustibility of the structural components.

Fire-loss experience shows that building contents play a large role in terms of fuel load and smoke generation potential in a fire. The passive fire protection provided by the fire-resistance ratings on the major floor and wall assemblies in a building assures structural stability in a fire. However, this does not necessarily control the movement of smoke and heat which can have a large impact on the level of safety and property damage resulting from fire.

Sprinklers typically operate very early in a fire thereby quickly controlling the damaging effects. For this reason, the provision of automatic sprinkler protection within a building greatly improves the life safety and property protection prospects of all buildings including those constructed of noncombustible materials.

Wood buildings must of course meet building code requirements which have already accounted for the nature of wood as a suitable material in assigning maximum permissible heights and areas. Wood has been used for schools, warehouses, fire stations, apartment buildings, and research facilities – virtually all types of buildings. When designed and built to code requirements, these buildings provide the same level of life safety and property protection required for comparably sized buildings constructed of steel or concrete.

When meeting the area and height limits for the various NBCC building categories, wood frame construction can meet the NBCC life safety requirements by making use of wood assemblies (usually protected by gypsum wallboard) that are tested for fire-resistance ratings.

The allowable height and area restrictions can be extended by using fire walls to break a large building area into smaller separate building areas. The recognized positive contribution to both life safety and property protection which comes from the use of automatic sprinkler systems can also be used to increase the permissible area of wood buildings.

In-depth discussion and commentary on the complex topic of fire protection for buildings in general and wood buildings in particular is found in other CWC publications on Fire Safety.

HOUSING AND SMALL BUILDINGS

Structural design of wood building in Canada is undertaken using the loads defined in Part 4 of the NBCC and the resistance values obtained using CSA Standard O86. Housing and other small buildings in Canada can be built without a full structural design using the Housing and Small Building requirements (Part 9) of the NBCC.

Part 9 of the NBCC was developed to provide prescriptive solutions covering the design of residential, mercantile, business, personal service and some industrial buildings, 3 stories or less in building height and 600 m² or less in building area. Some of the prescriptive requirements in Part 9 are based on calculation – others are based on construction practices that have a proven performance history over time. There may be structural members or connections in Part 9 buildings that are beyond the scope of the prescriptive requirements. These elements may be designed according to Part 4 using the loads, deflection and vibration limits specified in Part 9 or Part 4.

The Canadian Wood Council has developed the *Engineering Guide for Wood Frame Construction* that is referenced in the NBCC as providing good engineering practice for the structural design of Part 9 buildings. The Guide provides guidance in defining situations where engineering design is required to supplement the Part 9 prescriptive requirements, outlines design procedures and provides design aids.

DURABILITY OF WOOD CONSTRUCTION

Throughout history, wherever wood has been available as a resource, it has found favour as a building material for its strength, economy, workability and beauty. The longevity of wood has been demonstrated again and again. From the ancient temples of Japan and the great stave churches of Norway to the countless North American buildings built in the 1800s, wood construction has proven it can stand the test of time.

The longevity of wood structures is dependent on the wood members remaining intact and sound. In the forest, fallen trees are broken down by wood destroying fungi. In a building, deterioration by fungi can be prevented through selection of materials and by careful detailing of the structure.

Fungi require air and water to deteriorate wood. By keeping wood members dry, decay is prevented. Increasingly, attention is being paid to the design and detailing of the building envelope (exterior walls and roof). Proper detailing of the building envelope can prevent rainwater from wetting the wood structure and causing decay. Information on wood durability can be found at DURABLE-WOOD.COM.

SYNOPSIS OF THIS GUIDE

The following is a brief description of the chapters which comprise the *Introduction to Wood Design*:

2. **Safety, Reliability and Serviceability**
   This chapter describes the design philosophies and the statistical approach used to establish safety, reliability and serviceability of materials and the structures they comprise.

3. **Loads**
   Good design begins with careful assessment of the loads and load combinations acting on a structure. This chapter describes the various dead and live loads, and provides guidance for their calculation.

4. **Structural Form**
   There are many ways to design a given structure, and many factors which determine the best solution. This chapter looks at many of these factors, and provides basic information for the selection of a structural solution.

5. **Design Properties of Wood**
   Wood is the only major structural material which originates from a living organism. This gives it special properties such as anisotropy and hygroscopicity. An understanding of these and other properties will assist the designer to undertake designs which maximize favourable attributes, and minimize unfavourable attributes.

6. **Wood Products**
   A host of traditional and engineered wood products are available to the designer. This chapter describes the grades, properties, and methods of manufacture for the most common structural wood products.

7. **Bending Members**
   This chapter describes the action of bending members and the design of bending members.

8. **Compression Members**
   This chapter describes members loaded in axial compression.

9. **Tension Members**
   This chapter describes members loaded in axial tension.

10. **Combined Axial Loads and Bending Members**
    This chapter describes members that are loaded axially in compression and laterally in bending, such as an exterior column that is subject to wind load.

11. **Connections**
    There are many different products used to join wood members, from nails to bolted shear plates. This chapter describes the most common fasteners and connectors, and gives design guidelines.

12. **Lateral Load Resisting Systems**
    This chapter describes the wood shearwall and diaphragm action used to provide the required rigidity to resist lateral loads from wind or earthquake.

13. **Sample Building**
    The sample building, a combination office and warehouse facility, is used to demonstrate the determination of loads, and the design of the members required to resist the loads. The design examples range from wind load determination, to the design of joists, beams, columns, and shearwalls.

Safety, Reliability and Serviceability

2.1 General Information

A structure must be designed to resist all the loads expected to act on the structure during its service life. Under the effects of the expected applied loads, the structure must remain intact and perform satisfactorily. In addition, a structure must not require an inordinate amount of resources to construct. Thus, the design of a structure is a balance of necessary reliability and reasonable economy.

The reliability of a structure depends on a variety of factors that can be categorized as follows:

- external influences such as loads and temperature change
- modelling and analysis of the structure, code interpretations, design assumptions and other judgements which make up the design process
- strength and consistency of materials used in construction
- quality of the construction process

The reliability of the design process is affected by:

- errors and omissions (these can be minimized by checking procedures)
- systematic and coincidental errors (these are accounted for on a statistical basis)

A design process which results in an economical, safe and serviceable design must:

- be founded on knowledge contained in applicable building and material codes
- be based on experience, research data, and judgement where there is no code guidance
- enable comparison of different designs
- be practical

The *National Building Code of Canada* (NBCC) provides overall guidance for the design of all buildings. It is through this document and all related codes and standards that the accepted balance between reliability and economy is established. One of these related standards, CSA O86 *Engineering Design in Wood*, provides specific information for the design of wood components and connections.

In addition to the CSA O86 standard which assigns specified strengths and methods for the design of components and connections, there are many other product specific standards (Table 2.1) which govern the quality of the manufacturing and fabrication of materials used in wood buildings.

2.2   Design Methods

INTRODUCTION

During the 1980s, the design of wood structures in Canada, as directed by the NBCC and CSA O86, changed from working stress design (WSD) to limit states design (LSD), making the design approaches for wood similar to those for steel and concrete.

All design methods require the following for both strength and serviceability:

Member resistance ≥ Effects of design loads

WORKING STRESS DESIGN (WSD)

In WSD (also called allowable stress design), the overall structure and its individual structural components are analyzed under the assumption of elastic behaviour. The stresses and deflections that are induced in structural members by the specified design load must not exceed prescribed allowable stresses and deflection limits. Specified design loads are high estimates of the loads that are likely to occur in service, and allowable stresses are fractions of estimated strengths.

The design equation is written as

Applied stress ≤ Allowable stress

where

$$\text{Allowable stress} = \frac{\text{material strength}}{\text{safety factor}}$$

The specified design loads used to determine the applied stresses are not factored despite varying levels of predictability for different loads. As a result, working stress design may result in varying levels of safety. For example, live loads resulting from wind and snow are more variable and less predictable than the dead load of a piece of equipment. Working stress design does not account for this variability, and therefore, the margin of safety may vary depending on the nature of the load. As well, differences in failure modes are not explicitly considered in the WSD method.

LOAD AND RESISTANCE FACTOR DESIGN

A more rational method for incorporating safety into design is to use the full resistance of a member associated with a specific limit state for the resistance side of the equation. This limit state could be a failure or a limit on deflection or vibration. Suitable factors are applied to the loads side of the equation to account for variability and to consider the limit state that it is checked against.

In this approach, factors are applied to both the load and resistance sides of the equation. This load and resistance factor design approach is the basis for the LSD design format which is used in Canada for wood and other principal structural materials.

This design format uses a probabilistic approach that considers the variability in loads and material properties, as well as the consequences of failure.

Limit States Design (LSD)

Using the LSD design method, the structure and its individual components are characterized by their resistance to the effects of the applied loads.

The design equation (NBCC Clause 4.1.2.) for the LSD design format is

Factored resistance $\geq$ Factored load effect

The load effect is calculated using the same units as the resistance (i.e. kN, kN/m) and is governed by the most unfavourable effect considering all possible load combinations. For strength calculations,

$$\phi R \geq \Sigma(\alpha_i SL_i)$$

where

ϕ = resistance factor applied to the resistance or specified material property which takes into account variability of material properties and dimensions, workmanship, type of failure (for example, brittle versus ductile) and uncertainty in the prediction of resistance

R = calculated resistance of a member, connection or structure based on the specified material properties

α_i = load factor specific to the specified load and the load combination

SL_i = the specified loads - D, L, S, W, E, H, P, T (dead, live, snow, wind, earthquake, earth pressure, prestress and effects due to contraction, expansion or deflection). Dead load, D, is based on the calculated weight of the structure. Other specified loads are estimates of the higher loads that the structure would be exposed to. For example, the snow and wind loads are based on a 1 in 50 (2%) probability of occurring in a year.

The left side of the equation, ϕR, is the factored resistance. For many wood products the nominal resistance, R, for strength, is based on the fifth percentile of the resistance population (this will be explained in more detail in Section 2.4).

The right side of the equation is the effect of the factored loads acting alone or in combination. The 2005 edition of the NBCC adopted a companion action format for load combinations. In this format, load cases consider principal loads and companion loads. The principal loads consist of the permanent loads acting alone or the permanent loads acting in combination with a transient load on the structure. Except where the dead load counteracts the transient load effects, the principal load factors are 1 or greater. The companion loads are transient loads that may also occur at the same time as the principal loads. The companion load factors are less than one to account for the low probability of having two transient design loads occurring at the same time.

The resistance of the structure or part thereof is determined based on the appropriate failure mechanism, taking into account the variability of such factors as material strength, construction methods, and design calculations. It is important to note that although it is not necessary to assume that any or all elements behave elastically up to their limit states, it is still customary for indeterminate structures to be analysed under the assumption of elastic behaviour.

Limit States

A structure is considered to have failed or to be unfit for use when it reaches a limit state, beyond which its performance or use is impaired. The limit states for wood design are classified into the following two categories:

- Ultimate limit states concern safety and correspond to the maximum load-carrying capacity and include such failures as loss of equilibrium, loss of load-carrying capacity, instability and fracture.

- Serviceability limit states concern restrictions on the normal use of a structure. Examples of serviceability limit states include durability, deflection, localized damage and vibration.

It is the responsibility of the structural designer to determine all of the limit states which apply to the structure being designed, and to ensure that for each limit state, the factored resistance is not less than the effect of the factored loads, considering all applicable loads and load combinations.

Both the ultimate and serviceability limit states described in the following sections are set to meet minimum acceptable requirements. In some situations, minimum requirements will not be adequate and a higher standard will have to be met. For instance, issues outside the scope of the codes may be encountered such as appearance factors or simply a desire to provide a higher than usual level of resistance.

Ultimate limit states usually fall within fairly narrow limits. Efficient designs meet the strength requirements of the structure without using excess material.

Serviceability limit states are more subjective and there is more latitude for interpretation. For example, a floor which meets all the strength limit states might be designed to be stiffer than minimum requirements so that the floor will better meet the performance requirements for a particular building use.

2.3   Ultimate and Serviceability Limit States

ULTIMATE LIMIT STATES

The design process must assess all of the strength limit states. The LSD equation at ultimate limit state is given by:

$$\phi R \geq \Sigma(\alpha_i SL_i)$$

where

$\Sigma(\alpha_i SL_i)$ is summarized by 5 load cases provided in the NBCC:

Case	Principal loads	Companion loads
1	1.4D	
2	(1.25D or 0.9D) + 1.5L	0.5S or 0.4W
3	(1.25D or 0.9D) + 1.5S	0.5L or 0.4W
4	(1.25D or 0.9D) + 1.4W	0.5L or 0.5S
5	1.0D + 1.0E	0.5L + 0.25S

The companion load approach takes into account the reduced probability that a number of loads from different sources will be acting simultaneously at their full values. For example, the probability of high wind loads occurring coincidentally with extreme live loads is low, and the load combination factor allows a reduction in recognition of the low probability. Wind and earthquake loads are never combined due to the extremely low probability of both design levels occurring at the same time.

SERVICEABILITY LIMIT STATES

Serviceability limit states are considered in the design process to ensure that structural performance is satisfactory when the specified loads are applied under day to day conditions. Vibration, deflection, and slippage in a joint are examples of occurrences which might not cause collapse, but might cause inconvenience or deficiencies other than a failure.

While vibration of a certain magnitude might be acceptable in a warehouse floor, the same degree of vibration in a laboratory floor where precise measurements are an important part of the business, might cause the building to be unuseable for that occupancy.

Serviceability limit states are considered in the design process to ensure that the application of the specified loads does not restrict the required degrees of service.

The LSD equation at the serviceability limit state is given by:

$$R \geq \Sigma(\alpha_i SL_i)$$

The left side of this equation might be a force resulting in slippage in a joint, or unacceptable deflection or vibration. R is typically the mean resistance for the serviceability property being considered.

For wood design, CSA O86 specifies 4 serviceability limit state load combinations:

Case	Principal loads	Companion loads
1	1.0D	
2	1.0D + 1.0L	0.5S or 0.4W
3	1.0D + 1.0S	0.5L or 0.4W
4	1.0D + 1.0W	0.5L or 0.5S

2.4 Structural Reliability

INTRODUCTION

No two similar samples of lumber, structural steel, or any other material are exactly alike in strength. In any manufacturing process it is necessary to recognize that each manufactured piece will be unique.

Manufacturing quality control procedures set limits on the deviation from the norm. This is done by continually testing samples to ensure that quality remains acceptable and that the number of rejects is controlled.

Loads are also variable. For instance, the variability of weather patterns is well recognized. Snow drift patterns on a roof will never be identical from one storm to another, or from one winter to another. Wind direction, the properties of snow, and many other factors establish how a drift is deposited and the actual snow load.

Therefore, structural design must recognize that loads and resistances are really groups of data rather than single values. Like any group of data, there are statistical attributes such as mean, standard deviation, and coefficient of variation.

The goal of design is to find a reasonable balance between reliability and such factors as economy and practicality. While a hockey stick could be manufactured so that is would never break under any foreseeable game conditions, such a stick would likely be too heavy or too cumbersome to give the player any chance of being effective. Therefore the hockey stick manufacturer makes a stick which performs well and which will only break under certain circumstances.

In the same way, the structural failure of a nuclear reactor has much greater potential for human consequence than the failure of a cattle barn and therefore requires a higher reliability. Society does not require that the barn be built to the same standard. In fact, the farmer could not afford to build to this standard.

Therefore, the design of a structure is a statistical problem since neither loads nor resistances are entirely predictable and can at best be described by a statistical distribution. The probability of failure reflects a risk factor that the public is prepared to accept for a particular type of structure.

In most cases, the designer need not consider the statistical analysis of loads or specified strength because the codes have already done so, resulting in the publication of single values. It is still useful to have a basic understanding of how such values are established.

DISTRIBUTIONS OF LOADS AND RESISTANCES

To determine the safety level of a structure, it is necessary to examine the populations of load and resistance values. The following statistical expressions are used to characterize groups of data.

For a sample of n data points each with a value "x", the mean value is:

$$m_x = \frac{1}{n}\sum x_i$$

the standard deviation from the mean is:

$$\sigma_x = \sqrt{\frac{1}{(n-1)}\sum (x_i - m_x)^2}$$

and the coefficient of variation, COV, which characterizes the distribution about the mean, is:

$$COV = \frac{\sigma_x}{m_x}$$

Samples of data can often be characterized by mathematical models called distribution functions. Several functions are used in reliability analysis with the aim of obtaining a model that best fits the data. Many occurrences (such as the stiffness of lumber, the diameter of grapefruits, class scores, or any other attribute of interest to the statistician) can be idealized with a normal distribution curve (Figure 2.1).

Often a distribution is also expressed as the probability of a value being below a given value x. This is the integral of the distribution function and is called the probability density function. Some data sets are better described with other types of distribution functions. While a normal (or Gaussian) distribution is suitable for dead loads, Gamma distributions are often used for occupancy loads, and snow loads are best modeled with a lognormal distribution. Wood member strengths are typically represented with Weibull 2-Parameter or 3-Parameter distribution.

If the curve in Figure 2.2 were showing the frequency distribution of lumber bending strength, the curve would indicate that strength values approximately equivalent to the mean occur quite frequently, and very strong pieces and very weak pieces occur less frequently. A normal distribution also suggests symmetry, but wood strength properties are often skewed to the right; that is, there is a lower limit on the weakest pieces.

Similarly, a load distribution as shown in Figure 2.3 may have the odd extreme value that may coincide or exceed a low strength value, resulting in failure. The shaded area where the load and resistance curves overlap relates to the probability of failure. The objective is to minimize this area, keeping in mind the associated costs and practical considerations.

To illustrate this procedure, let us use the bending strength of small wood specimens. The bending strength value below which a certain percentage, p, of all samples fall is called the p-th percentile or fractile (Figure 2.3). When a normal distribution

curve is used for the lumber test results (or any other material or attribute), a relation between the strength property, x, at the p-th percentile, mean value, m_x, and standard deviation, σ_x, is given as:

$$x_p = m_x \pm k \, \sigma_x$$

with the values for k at the percentages, p, of:

Percentile, p	k
20	0.842
10	1.282
5	1.645
2.5	1.960
2.275	2.000
1.000	2.326
0.135	3.000
0.003	4.000
0.000	5.000

This means that the 5th percentile is the mean value minus 1.645 σ_x (standard deviation) or the 2.275th percentile is the mean value minus 2.0 σ_x, and the 50th percentile is the mean value.

In structural design, the 5th percentile is often used to characterize the resistance (Figure 2.3) and this is used in the reliability analysis and calibration procedure.

This normal 5th percentile is given as

$$x_{5\%} = m_x - 1.645 \, \sigma_x$$

Supposing that the specified strength for a given code was established as the normal 5th percentile and that the testing data for bending showed a mean value of 15.6 MPa and a standard deviation of 2.3 MPa. Then the specified strength to be used for design would be

$$15.6 - 1.645 \, (2.3) = 11.8 \text{ MPa}$$

In the same way, the 95th percentile could be used for determining the specified loads. For example, in establishing the ground snow load for a given area, the historical data would be reviewed to establish means and standard deviations, and the specified load would be determined by adding the product

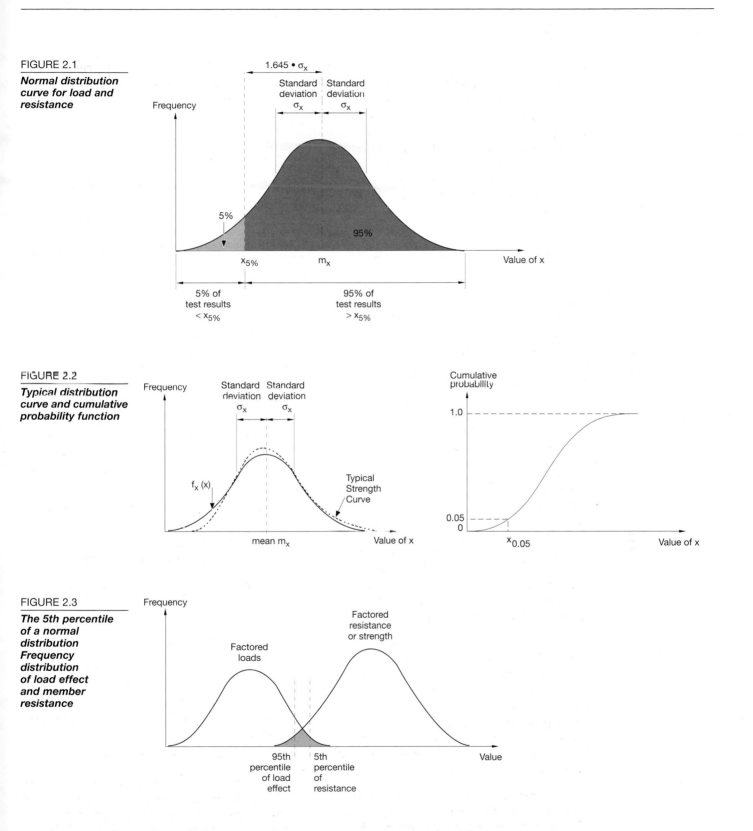

FIGURE 2.1

Normal distribution curve for load and resistance

FIGURE 2.2

Typical distribution curve and cumulative probability function

FIGURE 2.3

The 5th percentile of a normal distribution Frequency distribution of load effect and member resistance

of the standard deviation and the k factor (k = 1.645) to the mean snow load. Similar procedures are used when a distribution function other than a normal (or Gaussian) function is used.

SAFETY MARGINS

The probability of failure is related to the overlapping area of the load and resistance distributions. Since it is very difficult to obtain information about the tail ends of the populations, statistical methods have to be used to establish an acceptable safety standard.

The simplest safety measure is the global safety factor, Y_o, which is the ratio between the mean value of resistance and the mean value of load (Figure 2.4).

$$Y_o = \frac{m_r}{m_s}$$

This factor gives a poor indication of the possibility of failure since it does not include any information on the spread of the distributions, and a wide variety of safety margins is possible.

In fact, for distributions having the same global safety factors, Y_o, the occurrence of failure will be inconsistent because the actual safety depends not only on the mean values, but also on the variability, which is not considered in the global safety factor.

The nominal safety factor, Y_p, is a more accurate way to describe the overlapping area of the load and resistance curves (Figure 2.5). It is the ratio of a certain percentile of the resistance, r_p, to a certain percentile of the load, s_p:

$$Y_p = \frac{r_p}{s_p}$$

In the normal distribution example, the 95th percentile of the load and the 5th percentile of the resistance are typically used for structural design in which case:

$$Y_p = \frac{r_{5\%}}{s_{95\%}}$$

Exact knowledge of the distribution function in the asymptotic regions (tail areas) of the curves is essential, but unfortunately data for those regions is usually not available or is sparse. For more complex distributions, major numerical difficulties exist, and there is no mechanism to take experience into account.

These problems can partially be resolved by using a probability density distribution, f_z, of the safety parameter, z, which is obtained by subtracting the load, s, from the resistances, r, for every possible combination of r and s (Figure 2.6).

$$z = r - s$$

FIGURE 2.4

Global safety factor, Y_o

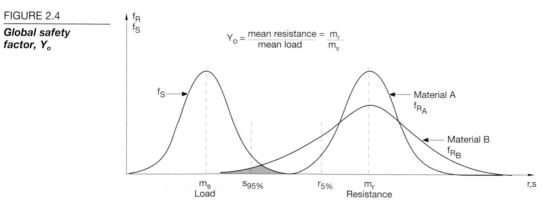

Notes:
1. The normal distribution for material B is wider than for material A and therefore material B is less consistent
2. Material A does not overlap the load curve and therefore there is no risk of failure
3. Because the global safety factor, Y_o, is a ratio of mean values, material A and B have the same global safety factor although it is apparent from the curves that the possibility of failure of material B is greater
4. The nominal safety factor, Y_p, is a more accurate way of describing safety margins.

This results in a new distribution of the performance parameter, z. All negative values of the function f_z indicate failure, while positive values indicate survival. The probability of failure is then represented by the area underneath the curve and left of the origin, given by:

$$P_f = \int_{-\infty}^{0} f_z(z)\, dz$$

When both distributions are normal, the mean value m_z and the standard deviation s_z are obtained from the load and resistance distributions as follows:

$$m_z = m_R - m_s$$

$$\sigma_z = \sqrt{\sigma_R^2 + \sigma_S^2}$$

FIGURE 2.5

Nominal safety factor, Y_p

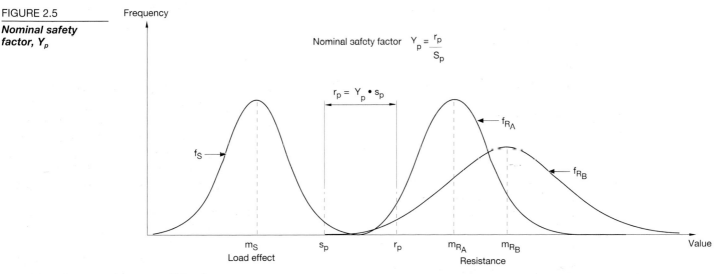

Notes:
1. The nominal safety factor relates load and resistance values in the tail portions of their respective curves
2. For structural design, the 95th percentile of the load and the 5th percentile of the resistance are typically used

FIGURE 2.6

Normal Distribution density of loads, S, resistance, R, and safety zone, Z

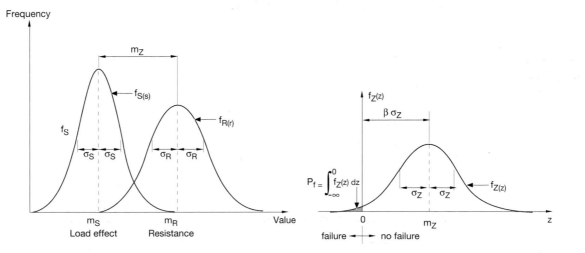

The inverse coefficient of variation of the function f_z is defined as the safety index:

$$\beta = \frac{m_z}{\sigma_z}$$

The safety index, β, characterizes the probability of failure in a more appropriate way than the safety factor, Y, because it takes the distribution of load and resistance into account. The appropriate safety index is chosen in accordance with the consequence of failure and should be the same for all materials.

To obtain a consistent safety index, the code design equations have to be calibrated with a reliability analysis that considers all of the relevant factors such as the load and the variability of the member strength based on species, grade and type of application. Generally, the 5th percentile of the strength test data is used for the resistance side, while the load statistics are obtained from extensive studies of structures in all climatic zones and with different occupancies. The load data are common to structures built from any material and can thus not be adjusted in the analysis. The only factor that remains flexible is thus the performance or resistance factor ϕ.

The reliability analysis is very sensitive to the model used to describe the strength distribution of the material. Figure 2.7 illustrates the relationship between reliability index, β, and performance factor, ϕ. The resistance is the bending strength of 2×8 lumber and is modeled with four different distributions that are fit as closely as possible to a complete data set of full-sized test results.

As can be seen from the plots, in order to have a β of 2.6, ϕ would range between 0.55 and 1.0 depending on which distribution model is used. The mathematical model chosen must represent the weaker pieces of material. A careful inspection of the strength data (Figure 2.8) reveals that, while the distribution curve fits the overall data reasonably well, the mathematical curve does not necessarily represent the lower end of the data set at all. This is, however, the most important portion of the population, since the low strength members are the ones most vulnerable to failure. Typically, a curve that better represents the lower end of the data set (the lower 15%) is chosen for the reliability analysis.

A variety of load distributions have to be considered in the analysis. Figure 2.9 shows that for a resistance factor, ϕ, of 0.85, the safety index varies between 2.6 and 2.8 when a variety of load conditions are considered. This falls within the acceptable range and such a ϕ-factor could then be adopted in the code design equation.

Other factors that have a significant impact on the resistance of a wood member are the load duration, service condition (wet or dry), whether a member forms part of a load

FIGURE 2.7

$\phi - \beta$ **relation for four distribution types (100% data)**

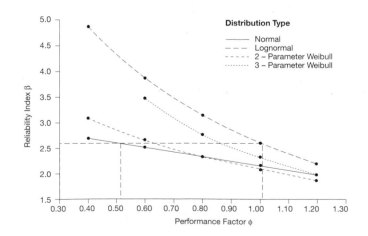

sharing system, the size of a member and the effects of preservative and fire treatment. Since it is desirable to have only one φ-factor for a given design equation, these are dealt with by applying strength modification factors to the resistance calculations directly. For particular applications, such as where stability or connector configurations have to considered, special factors are applied that are derived from theory or test results.

The procedure described in this section to calibrate the code values with a probability analysis is not typically a design issue. It is useful, however, to be aware of the background to the design rules to gain a better understanding of the issues affecting safety and reliability, and in some cases to make rational decisions where the code does not provide direction.

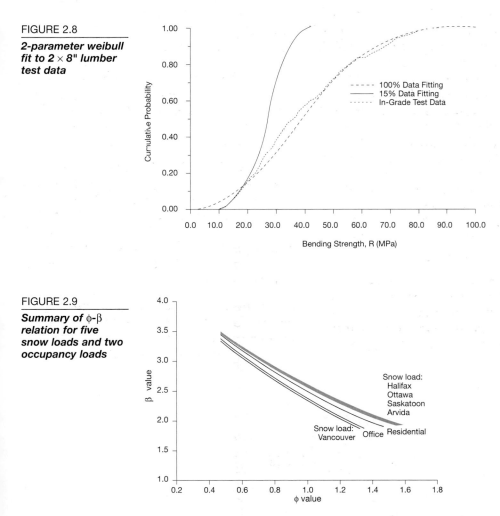

FIGURE 2.8

2-parameter weibull fit to 2 × 8" lumber test data

FIGURE 2.9

Summary of φ-β relation for five snow loads and two occupancy loads

2.5   Reliability of Wood and Engineered-Wood Products

INTRODUCTION

Previous sections relate to the statistical methods that form the basis for the reliability analysis for structural design. This section describes briefly the approach to assigning design values to wood products.

LUMBER

For many years, wood design in Canada followed the WSD format, using allowable stresses which were derived from the testing of small clear samples.

Due to questions about the suitability of using small clear samples to estimate the capability of full size members to carry in-situ loads, a comprehensive lumber testing program was undertaken during the 1980s. This resulted in data for dimension lumber based on the testing of full size specimens in actual grade categories.

In an earlier testing program, a proof-loading arrangement designed to break approximately the weakest 15% of each sample of 200 pieces was used. The unbroken 85% of the pieces was returned to stock for use. By arranging the strength values of the broken pieces in order of increasing modulus of rupture (MOR), it was possible to determine directly the fifth percentile of the sample population. These test values were later confirmed in a more comprehensive test program coordinated by the Canadian Wood Council.

The incorporation of this important new information on dimension lumber into the NBCC and CSA O86 increased the reliability of engineering design for wood.

In general, it was found that the S-P-F and Hem-Fir species combinations were stronger and stiffer than had been calculated using data from small clear specimens, and that the D Fir-L combination had been overrated. It was also found that, while Select Structural was clearly stronger than the other grades, and No.3 weaker, there was no significant difference between No.1 and No.2. Thus, these grades now have the same specified strengths.

It should also be noted that because of the variability in values for the No.3 grade, it is rarely used for single member designs (that is, it is used mainly in load-sharing systems).

The test data showed a pronounced size effect in strength, but not in modulus of elasticity. The fifth percentile strength values are higher for the smaller depths than for the larger depths. This applies to all depths and species and has been reflected in CSA O86 by the modification factor, K_Z, in Table 5.4.5. This phenomenon may be explained by the weak link theory which predicts that the strength of a member subject to a uniform load will be limited by the weakest part of the member. For example, the strength of a chain loaded in tension will be controlled by the weakest link. A long chain with more links is more likely to be weaker than a short chain with fewer links. In wood, the theory predicts that a larger volume of wood is more likely to have a strength-limiting defect that will cause it to be weaker than a smaller volume.

The actual use of these specified strength values in design, together with the CSA O86 modification factors and the resistance factors mentioned in this chapter, will be described in detail in Chapter 5.

Canadian dimension lumber is graded in accordance with the National Lumber Grades Authority (NLGA). The grading associations undergo routine inspections to ensure that lumber grading is consistent with NLGA standards.

TIMBER

Only dimension lumber was tested in the full-size lumber testing program. However, the specified strength data for larger size timbers was reviewed and modified in light of the data from the lumber test program so that the values for specified strengths and performance factors in CSA O86 are a refinement on the previous data. There was some limited data on Douglas Fir timbers, so the design values were calibrated to that species group.

GLULAM

Specified strength values for glued-laminated timber come from a small number of test results. Over the past 40 and more years, Canadian glulam manufacturing standards have been improved and full-size beams have been tested to validate the design values used for the different stress grades.

Glulam is manufactured according to CAN/CSA O122-06 *Structural Glued-Laminated Timber*.

PLYWOOD

CSA O86 gives specified strength capacities only for standard constructions of regular grades of unsanded Douglas Fir Plywood (DFP) and Canadian Softwood Plywood (CSP). (Sanded grades of plywood are intended for non-structural uses). The specified strength for unsanded plywood is based on test results, and manufacturing and quality control are done in accordance with CSA O121-08 *Douglas Fir Plywood* and CSA O151-09 *Canadian Softwood Plywood*.

ORIENTED STRANDBOARD (OSB)

In the 2001 edition of CSA O86, design values were introduced for OSB manufactured in accordance with CSA O325 *Construction Sheathing*. This standard sets performance ratings for specific end uses such as floor, roof and wall sheathing in light-frame construction. Although this standard may also be used to manufacture plywood, the CSA O325 design values in CSA O86 are currently limited to OSB.

TRUSSES

Light frame trusses are manufactured according to standards established by the Truss Plate Institute of Canada. The capacities for the plates vary with manufacturer, and they are established through testing.

OTHER WOOD PRODUCTS

There are several structural wood products which are proprietary and are not covered by a performance code. Rather, each product varies somewhat from one manufacturer to another. In some cases, the product is unique and protected by patents.

For these products, specified strengths are determined through testing by an independent agency, and an approval of the values based on an evaluation listing or report from the Canadian Construction Materials Center.

Laminated veneer lumber (LVL), wood I-joists, and parallel strand lumber are examples of proprietary products. Clauses 13 and 14 of CSA O86 provide design procedures for these products. For more information on these and other wood products, refer to Chapter 6.

2.6   Tables

TABLE 2.1

CSA standards relevant to design with wood

Number	Title
CSA B111-1974 (R2003)	Wire Nails, Spikes and Staples
CSA O80 Series-08	Wood Preservation
CSA O121-08	Douglas Fir Plywood
CSA O122-06	Structural Glued-Laminated Timber
CSA O141-05	Canadian Softwood Lumber
CSA O151-09	Canadian Softwood Plywood
CSA O177-06	Qualification Code for Manufacturers of Structural Glued-Laminated Timber
CSA O322-02 (R2007)	Procedure for Certification of Pressure Treated Wood Materials for Use in Preserved Wood Foundations
CSA O437.0-93 (R2011)	OSB and Waferboard
CSA S347-99 (R2009)	Method of Test for Evaluation of Truss Plates Used in Lumber Joints
CSA S406-92 (R2008)	Construction of Preserved Wood Foundations

Loads

3.1 General Information

INTRODUCTION

Structures must be designed to carry the loads likely to be imposed on them. For common occurrences, the magnitude and nature of these loads are specified in the *National Building Code of Canada* (NBCC).

Using limit states design (as outlined in Chapter 2), the designer strives to prevent the attainment of a limit state, either strength or serviceability, with a common safety and serviceability criterion for all materials and types of construction. The goal of limit states design is to design and construct a structure that has sufficient strength and stability such that:

Effect of factored loads ≤ Factored resistance

Different loading conditions and their likelihood of occurrence are described in the following load combinations which are factored according to their probability distribution. The basic load cases are:

D = specified dead load

L = specified live load

S = specified snow load

W = specified wind load

E = specified earthquake load

T = specified load due to contraction, expansion or deflection

H = specified load due to lateral earth pressure

P = specified load due to prestress

The specified dead load includes the weight of all permanent materials of construction and stationary equipment.

The specified live load consists of all loads due to use and occupancy of the building, such as people and movable equipment.

The specified snow load includes load due to snow, ice and associated rain.

In typical wood frame structures, wind and earthquake loads must be considered in lateral design.

Some conditions induce displacements that creates stresses in a structure. These include temperature changes (contraction or expansion), shrinkage or creep of component materials, and differential settlements.

Permanent loads due to lateral earth pressure, including groundwater, depend on many factors such as the soil properties, interaction of the soil and structure, and groundwater conditions.

Permanent prestress loads consist of predetermined stresses that are placed in members to enhance their resistance to service loads.

LOAD EFFECTS

The effects of loads, their combination and likelihood of occurrence were introduced in Section 2.3, and are now discussed in more detail.

Importance Factors

Importance factors take into account the consequences of collapse based on the type of load and the use and occupancy of the structure. The specified snow, earthquake and wind loads incorporate the importance factors shown in Table 3.1. Note that separate importance factors are provided for ultimate and serviceability limit states.

The importance of the survival of the structure in major loading conditions is reflected by these factors. Post-disaster buildings have to be functional after earthquakes and major storms, and are designed for values of 1.5 times the regular load for earthquake loads, and 1.25 times the regular load for snow and wind loads. Post-disaster buildings include, for example, hospitals, fire halls, and communication facilities. Schools are used as shelters following major storms and are assigned importance factors of 1.3 for earthquake loads and 1.15 for snow and wind loads. Normal and Low importance buildings have importance values of 1.0 and 0.8 respectively for all load types.

Load Combinations

Load combinations take into account the reduced probability of simultaneous occurrence of variable loads. For ultimate limit states load combinations, the effect of principal plus companion loads is determined using the load combinations in the building code as shown in Table 3.2.

Considering serviceability limit states, the effect of principal plus companion loads is determined using the load combinations specified in CSA O86 as shown in Table 3.3.

Design must be based on the most severe load combination, which is determined by considering all possible load combinations. Note that the load effect should be in the same units as the resistance (e.g. kN, kN•m).

3.2 Structural Loads

DEAD LOAD

The dead load, D, as specified in the NBCC (subsection 4.1.4) must include the following:

- the weight of the member itself
- the weight of all materials of construction incorporated into the building to be supported permanently by the member
- the weight of partitions
- the weight of permanent equipment
- the vertical load due to earth, plants and trees

In addition, allowance must be made for the weight of partitions which might be added in the future, or for the weight of temporary partitions. The partition weight to be used is the actual or anticipated weight of the partitions placed in any probable position, but must not be less than 1.0 kPa over the area of floor being considered.

The weights of common construction and stored materials used to determine dead weight are shown in Table 11.25 of the *Wood Design Manual*.

Tables 11.26 and 11.27 of the *Wood Design Manual* show the weights of lumber and sheathing products.

LIVE LOAD DUE TO USE AND OCCUPANCY

The live load L includes the loads due to intended use and occupancy.

The specified live load on an area of floor or roof depends on the intended use and occupancy of the building. Minimum uniformly distributed loads for common occupancies are given in Table 3.4. These loads are to be applied over the entire area, or over a portion of the area, whichever produces the most critical effects in the members concerned.

In general, the uniformly distributed loads are critical for the major load carrying members, while the concentrated loads are critical to the design of smaller details such as fastenings and cladding.

For cases that are not included in Table 3.4, the specified live loads due to the use and occupancy of the area shall be determined by:

- the weight of the probable assembly of persons
- the weight of the probable accumulation of equipment and furnishings
- the weight of the probable storage of materials

SNOW LOAD

The specified load on a roof or any other building surface subject to snow and associated rain is either the snow load or the rain load, whichever produces the greater effect.

Snow loads on roofs vary according to geographical location, exposure, and roof shape and type. To account for these varying conditions, the specified snow load on a roof or other surface is expressed as follows from NBCC 4.1.6.2.:

$$S = I_s [S_s (C_b C_w C_s C_a) + S_r]$$

where

I_s = importance factor for snow loads

S_s = ground snow load

C_b = basic roof snow load factor

C_w = wind exposure factor

C_s = roof slope factor

C_a = shape factor

S_r = associated rain load (not greater than $S_s [C_b C_w C_s C_a]$)

The ground snow load reflects the expected weight of dry snow and is based on a return period of 50 years while the associated rain load allows for the increase in the load caused by rainwater absorbed by the snow.

The values for major Canadian locations are given in the table *Design Data for Selected Locations in Canada* in Appendix C of NBCC. Design data for some major Canadian locations is summarized in Table 3.5. Detailed information on snow distributions and loads is in the Structural Commentaries of the NBCC.

The NBCC does not allow a reduction in snow load even where regular snow removal practices will be implemented. It can not be guaranteed that snow will be removed in a timely fashion, and there is no control of maintenance practices as a result of a change in building ownership.

It should be noted that while most provincial building codes adopt the NBCC design procedures, in some cases, loads specified by local jurisdictions are different than those shown in the NBCC. Check local requirements before proceeding to final design.

Basic Roof Snow Load Factor, C_b

The basic roof snow load factor, C_b, is usually equal to 0.8. The factor is based on the result of a country-wide survey of snow loads on roofs which found that the amount of snow on roofs is generally less than the ground snow load, (Figure 3.1).

The C_b factor may be higher where roofs have a plan dimension greater than 70 m.

Wind Exposure Factor, C_w

Observations show that where a roof is exposed to wind, some of the snow blows away or is prevented from accumulating, thereby reducing the average snow load.

The wind exposure factor, $C_w = 1.0$, may be reduced to 0.75 when a building is in an exposed location, such that the roof is exposed to the winds on all sides. No obstruction higher than the roof can be located within a distance equal to ten times the height of the obstruction above the roof. The reduction of C_w only applies to buildings in the Low and Normal Importance Categories.

Engineering judgement is required whenever a reduction in the exposure factor is contemplated, and designs must anticipate the effects of changes in exposure conditions due to future construction.

Roof Slope Factor, C_s

Under most conditions, snow accumulates less on steep roofs than on flat roofs because of sliding, creep, and improved drainage (Figure 3.1). The roof slope factor, C_s accounts for these effects by reducing the snow load linearly from $C_s = 1.0$ for roof slopes up to 30°, to $C_s = 0$ for roof slopes at 70°. For slippery roofs such as glass or metal, $C_s = 1.0$ at 15° and $C_s = 0$ at 60°.

Shape Factor, C_a

Shape factors have been developed to forecast the deposition of snow on roofs of different shapes and orientations. Judgement is required to determine the factor which applies, and the factor that might apply as a result of future construction.

The shape factor, C_a, is dependent upon roof shape. For complicated projects, models or scaled drawings may be used to more accurately determine snow loads resulting from drifting.

Figure 3.2 shows values of C_w, C_s, and C_a factors for gable, flat, and shed roofs. Values for other roof shapes are given in the NBCC-SC. The factors used in the NBCC are based on:

- non-uniform snow loads on gabled, arched or curved roofs
- increased snow loads in valleys
- increased non-uniform snow loads due to snow drifting onto a roof, which is at a level lower than other parts of the same building or at a level lower than another building within five metres of it
- increased non-uniform snow loads on areas adjacent to roof projections, such as penthouses, large chimneys and equipment
- increased snow or ice loads owing to snow sliding or drainage of meltwater from adjacent roofs.

FIGURE 3.1

Snow deposition

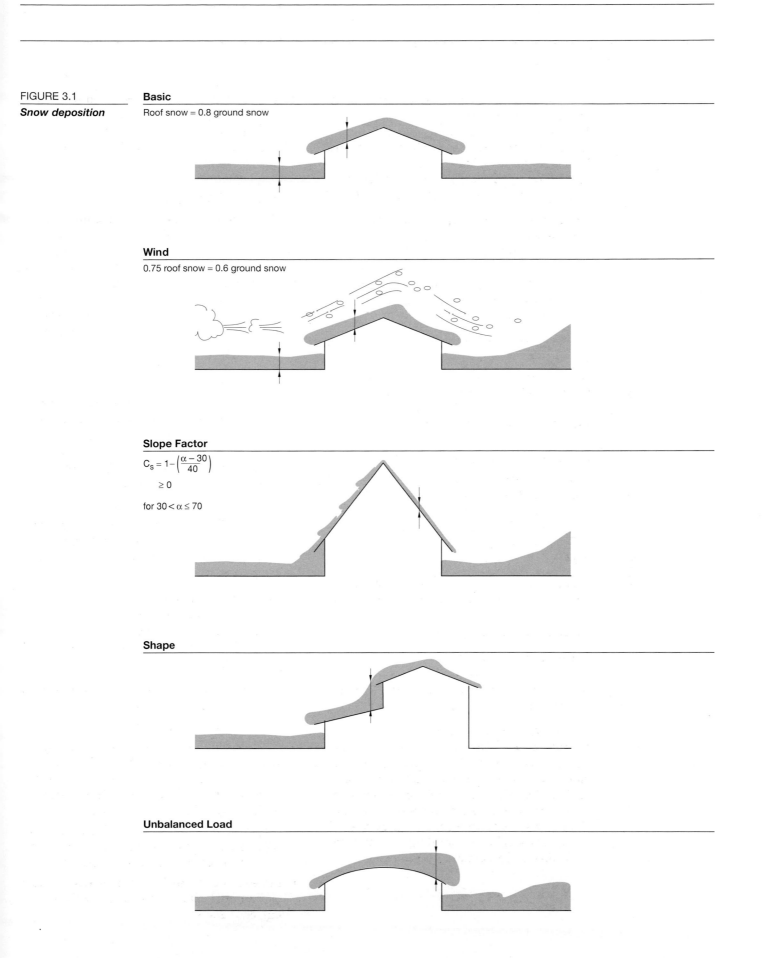

Basic

Roof snow = 0.8 ground snow

Wind

0.75 roof snow = 0.6 ground snow

Slope Factor

$$C_s = 1 - \left(\frac{\alpha - 30}{40} \right)$$

$$\geq 0$$

for $30 < \alpha \leq 70$

Shape

Unbalanced Load

Full and Partial Loading

All roofs must be designed for the full snow load over the entire roof area. In addition, roofs must be designed for combinations of full and partial loading. Flat, shed or gable roofs with slopes 15° or less and arched or curved roofs with rise to run ratios of 1/10 or less must be designed for a combination of full and partial loading. The roof must be designed for full load, with $C_a = 1.0$ on a portion of the roof and half this load on the remainder of the roof. Roof slopes other than these must be designed for partial loadings as described in NBCC-SC. Figure 3.2 describes one of these situations.

Any roof which is able to retain water must be designed for the ponding load that results from a 24 hour rainfall on the horizontal projected area of the roof. This requirement applies whether or not the surface is provided with drainage such as rainwater leaders.

FIGURE 3.2

Snow distributions and loading factors for gable, flat, and shed roofs

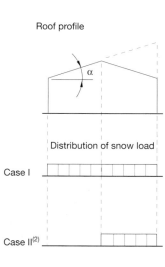

Roof profile

Distribution of snow load

Case I

Case II[2]

| Load case | Roof slope, α | Factors | | |
		C_w	C_s	C_a
I	0° to 90°	1.0[3]	$f(\alpha)$[1]	1.0
II	15° to 20°	1.0	$f(\alpha)$[1]	$0.25 + \alpha/20$
	20° to 90°	1.0	$f(\alpha)$[1]	1.25

Notes:

1. Varies as a function of slope α as defined in the NBCC.

2. Case II loading does not apply to gable roofs with slopes of 15° or less or to single-sloped (shed) roofs or to flat roofs.

3. For Low and Normal Importance category buildings, C_s may be reduced to 0.75 or, in exposed areas north of the treeline, 0.5.

WIND AND EARTHQUAKE LOADS

Both wind and earthquake loads are highly variable, and sound engineering judgement is very important to arrive at a rational design solution. It should also be realized that both are dynamic load conditions.

For large or irregular-shaped structures, dynamic analysis or wind tunnel testing may be required to adequately account for wind and seismic loads. Wood buildings tend to be relatively rigid and not too tall or slender. For these reasons, a simplified approach using equivalent static loads can usually be used.

WIND LOAD

The effect of high winds acting over the large areas of buildings can result in substantial lateral loads (Figure 3.3).

In the NBCC there are three separate approaches for determining design wind loads on buildings.

The Dynamic Procedure is intended for primarily tall buildings and slender structures. The Experimental Procedure consists of wind tunnel testing and other experimental methods. These methods are further discussed in the NBCC Structural Commentaries.

The static procedure is appropriate for use with the majority of wind loadings and types of structures, including the structure and cladding of low-and medium-rise buildings (which are fairly rigid), and the cladding of high-rise buildings.

FIGURE 3.3

Wind effects

External Pressures

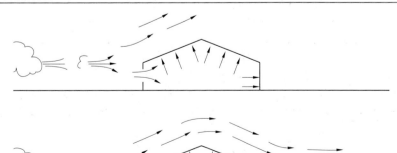

Internal Pressures

The simple procedure uses numerical values for the factors involved, in combination with *Design Data for Selected Locations in Canada* from Appendix C of the NBCC, and pressure coefficients from the NBCC-SC.

Specified External Pressure, P

The specified external pressure or suction due to wind on part, or all, of a surface of a building, is calculated from NBCC 4.1.7.:

$$P = I_w \, q \, C_e \, C_g \, C_p$$

where

    P = specified external pressure acting statically in a direction normal to the surface, either as a pressure directed towards the surface (positive), or as a suction directed away from the surface (negative)

    I_w = importance factor for wind load

    q = reference velocity pressure

    C_e = exposure factor

    C_g = gust effect factor

    C_p = external pressure coefficient averaged over the area of the surface considered

The net wind load for a building as a whole is the difference between the loads on the leeward and windward surfaces.

Coefficients for $C_p \, C_g$ for primary structural actions are shown in Figure 3.4.

Reference Velocity Pressure, q

The reference velocity pressures, q, are listed in *Design Data for Selected Canadian Locations* in Appendix C of the NBCC (see Table 3.5). Values are based on a probability of being exceeded in any one year of 1 in 50.

Exposure Factor, C$_e$

The exposure factor C_e reflects changes in wind speed with height, and the effects of variations caused by the surrounding topography. C_e depends on the reference height for the surface or part of the surface and is calculated as follows:

a) $(h/10)^{0.2}$ but not less than 0.9 for open terrain

b) $0.7(h/12)^{0.3}$ but not less than 0.7 for rough terrain

c) a value intermediate between the two exposures defined in (a) and (b) in cases where the site is less than 1 km or 10 times the building height from a change in terrain conditions, whichever is greater

The reference height applicable to low rise structures for the calculation of external pressures is the mean height of the roof. The eave height may be substituted for the mean height if the roof slope is less than 10°.

For the calculation of internal pressures, the mid-height of the building may be used as the reference height.

Gust Effect Factor, C$_g$

For low-rise and rigid buildings, the gust effect factor is the ratio of the maximum effect of loading to the mean effect of loading resulting from random wind gusts of short duration.

For buildings that are low-rise and relatively rigid, the simple method for determining C_g can be used:

    C_g = 2.0 for the building as a whole and for main structural members

        = 2.5 for small elements including cladding

For information on the gust effect factor for tall, slender, lightweight, flexible, or lightly damped buildings, refer to the NBCC-SC.

External Pressure Coefficient, C_p

The external pressure coefficient is the non-dimensional ratio of wind-induced pressure on a building to the dynamic pressure (velocity pressure) of the wind speed at the reference height.

Pressures on the surfaces of structures vary considerably with the shape, wind direction and the profile of the wind velocity. Pressure coefficients have been established from wind tunnel experiments on small-scale building models, and more recently, from measurements on full-scale buildings.

The products of the external pressure coefficients and gust effect factor ($C_p C_g$) for the design of the cladding and the structure as a whole are given in Figures I-7 to I-14 NBCC-SC for a variety of simple building geometries.

Figure I-7 is reproduced in Figure 3.4. This figure can be used for determining loads on primary structural elements affected by wind loads on more than one surface of a building. In the case of typical wood frame buildings, Figure 3.4 would be used in the design of:

- bracing
- shearwalls
- diaphragms
- pitched roof trusses
- uplift connections for pitched roof trusses and roof rafters

FIGURE 3.4

External peak pressure coefficients $C_p C_g$ (from NBCC-SC Figure I-7)

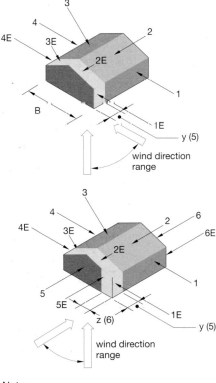

Case A: Winds generally perpendicular to ridge

Roof Slope	Building surfaces							
	1	1E	2	2E	3	3E	4	4E
0 to 5°	0.75	1.15	-1.3	-2.0	-0.7	-1.0	-0.55	-0.8
20°	1.0	1.5	-1.3	-2.0	-0.9	-1.3	-0.8	-1.2
30 to 45°	1.05	1.3	0.4	0.5	-0.8	-1.0	-0.7	-0.9
90°	1.05	1.3	1.05	1.3	-0.7	-0.9	-0.7	-0.9

Case B: Winds generally parallel to ridge

Roof Slope	Building surfaces							
	1	1E	2	2E	3	3E	4	4E
0 to 90°	-0.85	-0.9	-1.3	-2.0	-0.7	-1.0	-0.85	-0.9

	5	5E	6	6E
0 to 90°	0.75	1.15	-0.55	-0.8

Notes:

1. The building must be designed for all wind directions. Each corner must be considered in turn as the windward corner shown in the sketches. For all roof slopes, Load Case A and Load Case B are required as two separate loading conditions to generate the wind actions, including torsion, to be resisted by the structural system.

2. For values of roof slope not shown, the coefficient ($C_p C_g$) may be interpolated linearly.

3. Positive coefficients denote forces toward the surface, whereas negative coefficients denote forces away from the surface.

4. For the design of foundations, exclusive of anchorages to the frame, only 70% of the effective load is to be considered.

5. The reference height, h, for pressure is mid-height of the roof or 6 m, whichever is greater. The eaves height, H, may be substituted for the mean height if the slope of the roof is less than 7°.

6. End zone width y should be the greater of 6 m or 2z, where z is the width of the gable-wall end zone defined for Load Case B below. Alternatively, for buildings with frames, the end zone y may be the distance between the end and the first interior frame.

7. End-zone width z is the lesser of 10% of the least horizontal dimension and 40% of height, H, but not less than 4% of the least horizontal dimension or 1 m.

8. For B/H > 5 in Load Case A, the listed negative coefficients on surfaces 2 and 2E should only be applied on an area of width 2.5H measured from the windward eave. The pressures on the remainder of the windward roof should be reduced to the coefficients specified for the leeward roof (i.e., those for 3 and 3E).

Figures I-8 to I-14 of NBCC Structural Commentaries are used in the design of members only affected by wind loads on one surface of the structure. For wood frame buildings, the appropriate Figure from I-8 to I-14 would be used to determine the loads for:

- sheathing
- studs
- roof joists and rafters
- mono slope or parallel chord roof trusses
- uplift connections for roof joists and mono slope or parallel chord roof trusses

Internal Pressure

The net specified pressure due to wind on part or all of a surface of a building is the difference between the external pressure and the internal pressure. In cases where there is external suction, internal pressure will increase loads on members. The magnitude of the internal pressure or suction depends on the distribution and size of air leakage paths.

If the building is fairly resistant to air flow, in or out, the influence of gusts will be attenuated. If the building has many doors or windows which might be open to strong winds, the effect of gusts will be transmitted to the interior.

The internal pressure, P_i, is determined from

$$P_i = I_w \, q \, C_e \, C_{gi} \, C_{pi}$$

where

C_{gi} = internal gust effect factor

C_{pi} = internal pressure coefficient

Internal Pressure Coefficient, C_{pi}

There are three categories of C_{pi}:

Category 1 is for buildings without large openings and C_{pi} has a value -0.15 to 0.0.

Category 2 is for buildings which have large openings which will routinely be closed during storms. This category applies to most low buildings. The value of C_{pi} is -0.45 to 0.3.

Category 3 is for buildings such as sheds or shipping docks having large openings which cannot be relied upon to be closed during storms. The value of C_{pi} is -0.7 to 0.7.

Internal Gust Effect Factor, C_{gi}

For internal pressures, $C_{gi} = 2.0$

EARTHQUAKE LOAD

The earthquake-resistant design requirements of the NBCC are intended to prevent major failure and loss of life. Structures meeting the NBCC requirements should be able to resist moderate earthquakes without significant damage, and major earthquakes without collapse.

To design an earthquake-resistant structure, there are several variables that need to be ascertained:

- the characteristics and probability of occurrence of the design seismic ground motion
- the characteristics of the structure and the foundation
- the allowable stresses in the material of construction and the foundation soils
- the amount of damage that is tolerable

The structure must have a clearly defined Seismic Force Resisting System (SFRS), designed to resist 100% of seismic loads and their effects.

The design must provide, not only sufficient structural strength to resist the ground motion, but also the proper stiffness to limit lateral deflection and drift.

It is beyond the scope of the NBCC to prescribe earthquake-resistant design for all types of structures. Irregular-shaped buildings and special purpose industrial structures are special cases which may require dynamic analysis. Also, earthquake-related effects such as landslides or soil liquefaction are not covered by the NBCC.

Earthquake loads are generated by acceleration of the mass of a structure and its contents as a result of ground motion. The force resulting from ground motion is based on Newton's Second Law which is expressed as $F = ma$, where F is the force, m the mass, and a the acceleration.

Because the mass of the structure has a bearing on the forces generated, the characteristics of the structure itself have as much of an influence on the forces in the structure as does the magnitude and the nature of the ground motion (Figure 3.5).

The determination of earthquake loads is an iterative procedure since the characteristics of the structure, which is in the process of being designed, need to be known to determine the extent of the earthquake load. The structure must have the strength to limit the damage, and be adequately stiff to limit the lateral deflection or drift.

The design of earthquake resistant structures requires consideration of many structural details. The intent of *Introduction to Wood Design* is not to cover all the details but rather to familiarize the reader with the fundamentals of earthquake loads.

For relatively simple structures, the NBCC prescribes the Equivalent Static Force Procedure. A total base shear force, which depends on several factors including site and structural characteristics is calculated. This force then has to be distributed amongst the respective levels of the structure. The distribution of this force depends on structural characteristics such as mass distribution and stiffness.

Equivalent Static Force Procedure

The minimum lateral earthquake force, V, is calculated using the following formula:

$$V = S(T_a)M_vI_EW/(R_dR_o)$$

Except that V shall not be taken less than

(1) $S(4.0)M_vI_EW/(R_dR_o)$ for walls, coupled walls and wall-frame systems;

(2) $S(2.0)M_vI_EW/(R_dR_o)$ for moment-resisting frames, braced frames, and other systems.

And for buildings located on a site other than Class F and having an SFRS with an R_d equal to or greater than 1.5, V need not be taken greater than $2/3S(0.2)I_EW/(R_dR_o)$.

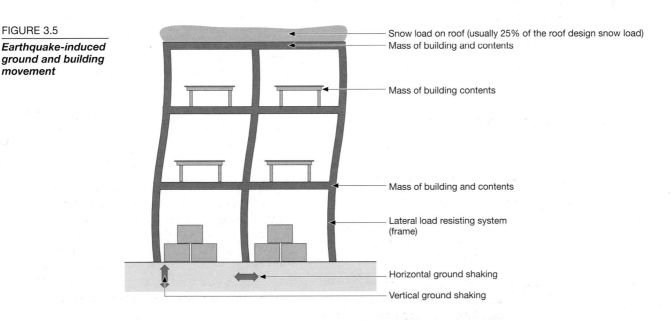

FIGURE 3.5

Earthquake-induced ground and building movement

Snow load on roof (usually 25% of the roof design snow load)
Mass of building and contents
Mass of building contents
Mass of building and contents
Lateral load resisting system (frame)
Horizontal ground shaking
Vertical ground shaking

where

$S(T_a)$ = spectral response acceleration, for the fundamental period T_a

T_a = fundamental lateral period of vibration in seconds

M_v = factor to account for higher mode effect on base shear (NBCC Table 4.1.8.11)

I_E = earthquake importance factor

W = dead load

R_d = ductility related force modification factor

R_o = overstrength related force modification factor

Spectral Response Acceleration, $S(T_a)$

The period of a structure is the most important factor for determining its response to ground motion. A simple model consisting of a series of rods embedded in a wooden board with different masses attached to their tips can be used to demonstrate this phenomenon. By shaking the model with different frequencies, the rods become excited depending on whether the motion corresponds to their fundamental period or not (Figure 3.6). A real structure is of course more complex, and other properties such as damping and soil properties must be considered.

Simplified equations are provided in the NBCC to determine the fundamental period, T_a, of standard buildings. For typical wood buildings, $T_a = 0.05(h_n)^{3/4}$, which is used to determine the design spectral response acceleration, $S(T)$, as follows:

$S(T)$ = $F_a S_a(0.2)$ for $T \leq 0.2s$

= $F_v S_a(0.5)$ or $F_a S_a(0.2)$ whichever is smaller for $T = 0.5s$

= $F_v S_a(1.0)$ for $T = 1.0s$

= $F_v S_a(2.0)$ for $T = 2.0s$

= $F_v S_a(0.2)/2$ for $T \geq 4.0s$

Note: wood buildings will typically have a T of 0.5s or less.

where

F_a and F_v = foundation factors

$S_a(T)$ = 5% damped spectral response acceleration

The peak ground acceleration (PGA), and the 5% damped spectral response acceleration values, $S_a(T)$, for the reference ground condition (Site Class C) for periods T of 0.2s, 0.5s, 1.0s, and 2.0s are provided in Appendix C of the NBCC (See Table 3.5).

FIGURE 3.6

Frequency response of simple cantilever structures

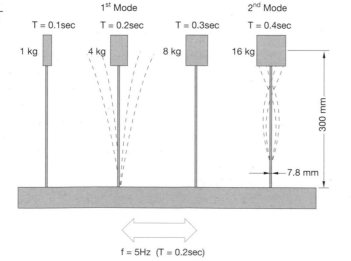

FIGURE 3.6

Frequency response of simple cantilever structures

1st Mode   2nd Mode

T = 0.1sec   T = 0.2sec   T = 0.3sec   T = 0.4sec

1 kg   4 kg   8 kg   16 kg

300 mm

7.8 mm

f = 5Hz (T = 0.2sec)

Foundation Factors

Soil conditions have a large influence on the transmission of seismic waves. It has been determined that deep soft soils often amplify the ground motion or cause a shift in frequency content.

NBCC specifies site classifications reflecting different soil conditions ranging from Site Class A to F. The site classifications are accompanied with descriptive Ground Profile Names, and are ideally determined based on the shear wave average velocity, V_s. Where this value is unknown, site classification may be based on the standard penetration resistance, N_{60}, for sand sites, or the un-drained shear strength, s_u, for clay sites.

The NBCC specifies the acceleration and velocity based site coefficients or foundation factors, F_a and F_v, used to modify the ground motion for the different site classes. Values of F_a and F_v are given for specific values of $S_a(0.2)$ and $S_a(1.0)$ in order to take into account the non-linearity of site response to the intensity of ground motion (See Tables 3.6 and 3.7). Interpolation is used to determine F_a and F_v for intermediate values of $S_a(0.2)$ and $S_a(1.0)$.

Weight of the Structure, W

The weight and thus the mass of the structure is the primary factor that determines the magnitude of the forces exerted. Not only is the magnitude important, but also the distribution of the masses on the various levels.

For design purposes, the weight of the structure is added to 25% of the design roof snow load, 60% of the storage loads and the full weight of the contents of tanks. This represents the probable weight of a structure during an earthquake.

Force Modification Factor, R_d

An earthquake applies a motion rather than a force to the base of a structure and the structure must be able to absorb the energy generated by this motion without failing.

A ductile structure is able to dissipate energy without collapsing. Part of the energy is dissipated by damping. The remaining energy is converted into strain energy which the structural members must be able to absorb.

As the input energy increases, an adequately ductile structure is capable of responding nonlinearly without collapsing. Going into the nonlinear range causes an increase of the fundamental period. This reduces the earthquake induced forces significantly.

The amount of ductility is different for different structural systems and the NBCC assigns a force modification factor R_d for typical systems. For wood structures, the value of R_d usually ranges from 2.0 to 3.0. The relatively ductile systems consisting of shearwalls and diaphragms constructed with structural wood panels are assigned an R_d value of 3. Gypsum wallboard is less ductile than structural wood panels and when it is considered as part of the lateral load resisting system, an R_d value of 2 must be used to determine the base shear.

Force Modification Factor, R_o

Experience has shown that various features of structural systems and their design result in lateral strength considerably larger than that used as the basis of design. The NBCC incorporates the expected overstrength through the overstrength related force modification factor R_o. This factor represents the dependable or minimum overstrength in the structure due to the application of the design and detailing provisions prescribed in CSA O86.

For wood structures, the value of R_o is usually 1.7. In cases where there is a combination of different types of SFRS acting in the same direction in the same storey, R_dR_o is taken as the lowest value of R_dR_o corresponding to these systems. Also Refer to NBCC for restrictions in terms of maximum height.

Load Distribution

Once the base shear has been calculated, it has to be distributed over the height of the building. Since the forces are generated by the acceleration of mass, it is logical to assign each floor (or component) a proportion of the total force according to the product of its mass (or weight) and the acceleration at that level.

Since the first mode dominates the response in most structures, it can be assumed that the floor displacements, and thus also the floor accelerations, are approximately distributed in proportion to the height of each storey from ground level.

One correction is made for relatively tall buildings, which typically experience quite strong second and higher mode vibrations (Figure 3.7). The second and higher modes are similar over the lower portions of a tower and often cancel each other out.

However, at the top they could be cumulative and cause localized high accelerations that could cause failure in the top storeys. Such buildings are thus assigned a larger load portion at the top level to reflect this behaviour.

A force F_t dependent on the fundamental period of the building, is taken from the base shear and applied at the top. The rest of the base shear is distributed as described previously. This would mean that the force applied at a particular level is:

$$F_x = (V - F_t)\frac{W_x h_x}{\sum\limits_{i=1}^{n} W_i h_i}$$

where

$W_{i,x}$ = portion of W at level i or x respectively

$h_{i,x}$ = height to level i or x respectively

These forces are equivalent static forces which are intended to simplify the analysis of structures under earthquake loads. This is acceptable for relatively uncomplicated structures. In reality, however, a structure could behave quite differently in which case a full dynamic analysis would be required. This is typically the case for irregular-shaped buildings that do not meet certain code criteria. There are also additional design restrictions for post-disaster buildings.

FIGURE 3.7

*Mode shapes
and force
distribution*

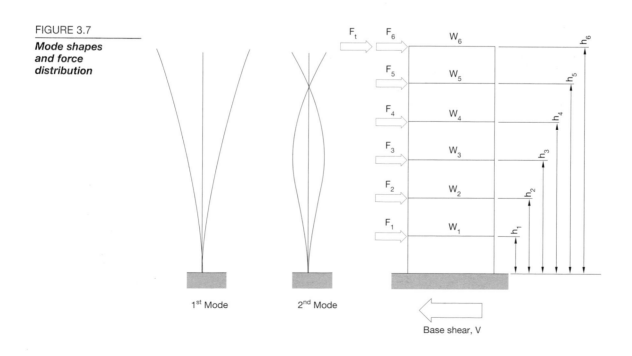

1st Mode   2nd Mode

Base shear, V

Torsion

In addition to the lateral seismic forces experienced by the structure, torsional effects may also be introduced due to eccentricity between the centres of mass and resistance, and due to accidental eccentricities.

For symmetric structures with rigid diaphragms, the torsional moments are applied about a vertical axis at each level based on the following load cases considered separately:

i) $T_x = F_x(e_x + 0.1D_{nx})$

ii) $T_x = F_x(e_x - 0.1D_{nx})$

where

e_x = distance perpendicular to direction of seismic loading between centre of mass and centre of rigidity at Level x

D_{nx} = plan dimension perpendicular to seismic loading at Level x

Guidance on the design of the structures with flexible diaphragms is provided in the NBCC-SC. For these structures, accidental torsion should be taken into account by moving the centre of mass by $\pm 0.05\ D_{nx}$ and using the largest of the seismic loads for the design of each vertical element.

These notes are intended as an introduction to earthquake loads. For guidelines on earthquake-resistant design, see NBCC 4.1.8. and the Structural Commentaries of the NBCC.

OTHER LOADS

The specified load, T, takes into account loads resulting from contraction or expansion caused by temperature changes, shrinkage, moisture changes, creep in component materials, movement due to differential settlement, or of combinations of the above cases. Although there are exceptions, these loads are not usually factors in the design of wood structures due to the characteristics of wood as an engineering material.

Specified load, H, acts on walls such as retaining and basement walls. The lateral earth pressure depends on many factors such as the soil properties, interaction of the soil and structure, and groundwater conditions.

Specified load, P, refers to predetermined stresses that are placed in members to enhance their resistance to service loads, and is generally not applicable to wood members.

Refer to the NBCC for guidance on determining loads due to temperature (T), earth pressure (H), and prestress (P).

EXAMPLE 3.1: LOADS ON A STRUCTURE

The dimensions of a wood framed building are shown in Figure 3.8. The building is a 4 storey multi-residential wood framed apartment building to be constructed in Montreal-est. The foundation for the building is on soft rock.

All exterior walls act as shearwalls and are constructed with 38 × 140 mm studs at 400 mm centres with 9.5 mm thick OSB panels. 15.9 mm thick gypsum wallboard is used as the interior finish and vinyl siding is used on the exterior of the structure. Interior shearwalls in both principal directions are located between dwelling units. Within the dwelling units, there are non-load bearing partition walls.

The roof is to be framed with wood trusses at 600 mm centres. The roof sheathing is 11 mm thick OSB and asphalt shingles are used on the roof. All exterior walls and the roof are insulated.

The floors, which act as diaphragms, are carpet over 15.5 mm thick plywood supported by 300 mm deep wood I-joists spaced at 400 mm centres. The floors are supported on the interior and exterior stud walls. 15.9 mm thick drywall ceilings are used and the building is sprinklered.

Determine the unfactored dead, live, wind and earthquake loads on the structure.

Dead Loads

From Tables 11.25 to 11.27 of the *Wood Design Manual*

		(N/m^2)
Roof		
Shingles	120/cos 18°=	126
Sheathing	(7×11)/cos 18°=	81
Roof trusses		100
Insulation (150 mm)		30
Ceiling		100
Sprinklers		30
Other fixtures		30
		497

Use 0.5 kPa

Floors		
Interior partitions*		1000
Carpets		100
Sheathing	15.5×5=	78
Wood I-joists		150
Ceiling		100
Sprinklers		30
Other fixtures		30
		1488

Use 1.5 kPa

Exterior walls		
Interior finish		100
Studs		70
Insulation		30
Sheathing	9.5×7=	67
Siding		70
Other fixtures		30
		367

Use 0.4 kPa or 1.1 kN/m for each floor

* For earthquake calculations the NBCC allows 0.5 kPa partition load.

FIGURE 3.8

Building dimensions

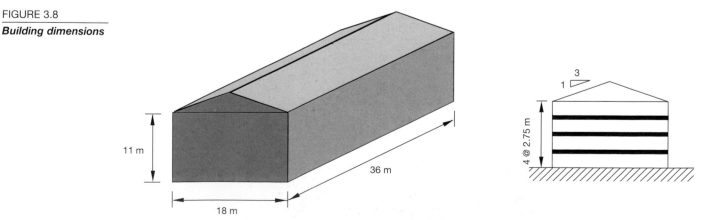

Snow Load

Snow load = $I_s [S_s (C_b C_w C_s C_a) + S_r]$
(From NBCC 4.1.6.2.)

where

I_s = 1.0

S_s = 2.7 kPa (Table 3.5)

C_b = 0.8

C_w = 1.0

C_s = 1.0

C_a = 1.0 for load case I
(See Figure 3.9)

= $0.25 + \alpha/20$ for load case II

= 0.25 + 18/20

= 1.15

S_r = 0.4 (Table 3.5)

Snow load

= 2.6 kPa load case I

= 2.9 kPa load case II

Live Loads

Floors

Use and occupancy

= 1.9 kPa (Table 3.4)

Wind Loads

From NBCC 4.1.7.

Wind loads for shearwalls and diaphragms:

In this case, the internal pressures can be ignored since they are considered to act with equal force and in opposite directions on the opposite sides of the buildings and therefore do not affect the overall lateral loads on the structure.

External pressure

P = $I_w [q C_e C_g C_p]$

I_w = 1.0

q = reference velocity pressure

= 0.42 kPa (Table 3.5)

C_e = exposure factor for a given height h where h is the mid height of the roof

h = [(4 × 2.75 m) + (1/3 × 18 m/4)]

= 12.5 m

C_e = $0.7 (h/12)^{0.3}$
(assuming rough terrain typical of suburban settings)

= $0.7 \left(\dfrac{12.5}{12} \right)^{0.3}$

= 0.71

FIGURE 3.9

Snow load

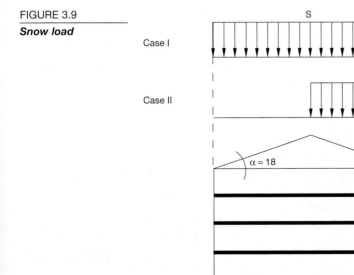

$C_g\,C_p$ = values taken from Figure 3.4

= values shown in Figure 3.10

z   = end zone width of the gable end wall

= lesser of 0.1×18 m or $0.4 \times (4 \times 2.75$ m $+ 1/3 \times 18$ m$/4)$ $\geq 0.04 \times 18$ m or 1 m

= lesser of 1.8 m or 5 m ≥ 0.72 m or 1 m

= 1.8 m

y   = end zone width of the wall parallel to the ridge

= greater of 6 m or 2z

= 6 m

Figure 3.10 shows the resultant wind loads on the building for the design of shear walls and diaphragms. Note that the wind may blow from any side of the building. All corners must be designed for the worst possible wind loads.

Wind loads for individual elements:

The wind loads for individual elements are the sum of the external and internal wind pressures.

FIGURE 3.10

Wind loads for shear walls and diaphragms

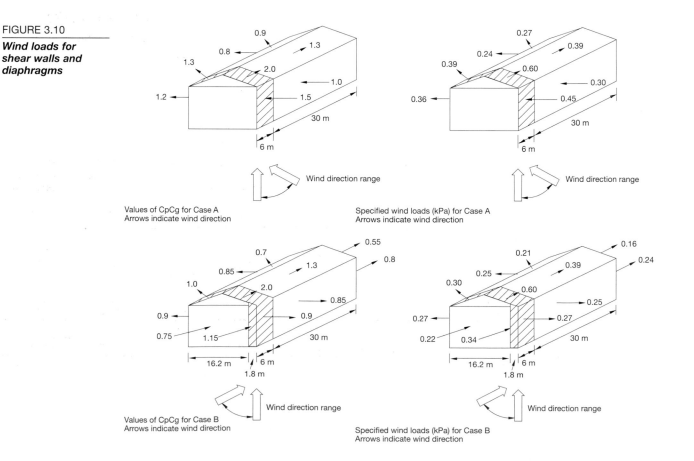

Values of CpCg for Case A
Arrows indicate wind direction

Specified wind loads (kPa) for Case A
Arrows indicate wind direction

Values of CpCg for Case B
Arrows indicate wind direction

Specified wind loads (kPa) for Case B
Arrows indicate wind direction

External wind pressure

$$P = I_w [q \, C_e \, C_g \, C_p]$$

$$q = 0.42 \text{ kPa}$$

$$C_e = 0.71$$

$C_g \, C_p$ = values taken from NBCC Structural Commentaries Figures I-8 to I-14. Values in I-8 to I-14 are based on the design tributary area of the member under consideration.

Internal wind pressure

$$P_i = I_w [q_{1/50} \, C_e \, C_{gi} \, C_{pi}]$$

$$q = 0.42 \text{ kPa}$$

$$C_e = 0.71$$

$$C_{gi} = 2.0$$

C_{pi} = -0.45 to 0.3, whichever produces the most critical effect (assuming category II)

Earthquake Loads

For soft rock foundation,
Site Class = C (NBCC Table 4.1.8.4.A)

$$F_a = 1.0 \text{ (Table 3.6)}$$

$$F_v = 1.0 \text{ (Table 3.6)}$$

$S(T_a)$ is a function of the fundamental period T_a

$$T_a = 0.05 \, (h_n)^{3/4} \text{ (NBCC 4.1.8.11(3)(c))}$$

$$h_n = 12.5 \text{ m}$$

$$\therefore T = 0.05 \times 12.5^{3/4}$$

$$= 0.332$$

From Table 3.5

$$S_a(0.2) = 0.64$$

$$S_a(0.5) = 0.31$$

From NBCC 4.1.8.4(7)

$$S(0.2) = F_a S_a(0.2)$$

$$= 1 \times 0.64 = 0.64$$

$$S(0.5) = \min (F_v S_a(0.5) \text{ or } F_a S_a(0.2))$$

$$= \min (1 \times 0.31 \text{ or } 0.64)$$

$$= 0.31$$

Element	NBCC *Structural Commentary* Reference Diagram	Tributary Area (m²)	External composite pressure-gust coefficients $C_p C_g$	External Pressure P (kPa)	Internal Pressure P_i (kPa)	Net Specified Pressure (kPa)
Trusses 6 m from the end walls						
• Windward slope	Figure I-7	N/A	-2.0	-0.6	0.18	-0.78
• Leeward slope			-1.3	-0.39	0.18	-0.57
Internal trusses						
• Windward slope	Figure I-7	N/A	-1.3	-0.39	0.18	-0.57
• Leeward slope			-0.9	-0.27	0.18	-0.45
Studs 1.8 m from corners	Figure I-8	1.1	-2.1	-0.63	0.18	-0.81
Internal studs	Figure I-8	1.1	-1.8	-0.54	0.18	-0.72

by extrapolation;

$$S(0.332) = 0.495$$

$$V = S(T_a)M_vI_EW/(R_dR_o)$$

$$V_{max} = 2/3[S(0.2)I_EW/(R_dR_o)]$$

$$M_v = 1.0 \text{ (NBCC Table 4.1.8.11)}$$

$$I_E = 1.0 \text{ (Table 3.1)}$$

$$W = \text{dead load} + 25\% \text{ snow load}$$

Weight of levels 2 to 4 = floor dead load
+ dead load of supported walls

$$= (1.0 \text{ kPa} \times 18 \text{ m}) + 2(1.1 \text{ kN/m})$$

$$= 20.2 \text{ kN/m}$$

Weight of roof = roof dead load
+ 25% snow load

$$= (0.5 \text{ kPa} \times 18 \text{ m}) + (2.6 \text{ kPa} \times 18 \text{ m} \times 0.25)$$

$$= 20.7 \text{ kN/m}$$

Total W = (20.2 kN/m × 3 levels)
+ 20.7 kN/m

$$= 81.3 \text{ kN/m (Figure 3.11)}$$

$$R_d = 3.0 \text{ (NBCC Table 4.1.8.9)}$$

$$R_o = 1.7 \text{ (NBCC Table 4.1.8.9)}$$

From NBCC 4.1.8.11.2

$$V = 0.495 \times 1.0 \times 1.0 \times 81.3/(3.0 \times 1.7)$$

$$= 7.89 \text{ kN/m}$$

but need not be greater than:

$$= 2/3 \times 0.64 \times 1.0 \times 81.3/(3.0 \times 1.7)$$

$$= 6.80 \text{ kN/m } (Governs)$$

The loads are distributed to the various
levels as per NBCC 4.1.8.11.(6)

$$F_x = \frac{W_xh_x}{\sum W_ih_i}(V - F_t)$$

Note that when the period T < 0.7 then F_t
is considered to be zero. This results in the
lateral force distribution shown in Figure 3.11.

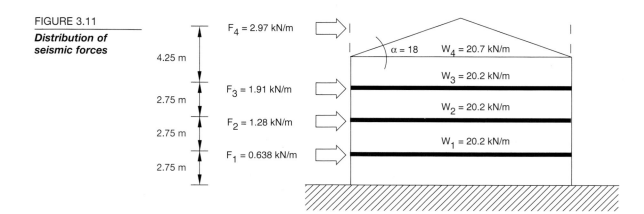

FIGURE 3.11

Distribution of seismic forces

3.3 Tables

TABLE 3.1

Importance factors for Determining S, W, and E loads

Importance category	Importance factors for snow loads, I_S		Importance factors for wind loads, I_W		Importance factors for earthquake loads, I_E	
	Ultimate limit state	Serviceability limit state	Ultimate limit state	Serviceability limit state	Ultimate limit state	Serviceability limit state
Low	0.8	0.9	0.8	0.75	0.8	N/A
Normal	1.0	0.9	1.0	0.75	1.0	N/A
High	1.15	0.9	1.15	0.75	1.3	N/A
Post-disaster	1.25	0.9	1.25	0.75	1.5	N/A

Importance Categories for buildings are based on intended use and occupancy as follows:

- Low – Buildings that represent a low hazard to human life in the event of failure
- Normal – All buildings except those listed as low, high or post-disaster
- High – Buildings that are likely to be used as post-disaster shelters, including schools and community centres
- Post-disaster – Buildings that are essential to provide services in the event of a disaster

TABLE 3.2

Load Combinations for Ultimate Limit States

Case	Principal loads[1]	Companion loads
1	1.4D	
2	(1.25D or 0.9D) + 1.5L[2]	0.5S or 0.4W
3	(1.25D or 0.9D) + 1.5S	0.5L[3] or 0.4W
4	(1.25D or 0.9D) + 1.4W	0.5L[3] or 0.5S
5	1.0D + 1.0E	0.5L[3] + 0.25S

Notes:

1. Refer to the NBCC for;
   - dead load, D, for soil,
   - guidance on combining snow load, S, and live load, L, on exterior areas,
   - loads due to lateral earth pressure, H, prestress, P, and imposed deformation, T.

2. The principal load factor of 1.5 for a live load, L, may be reduced to 1.25 for liquids in tanks.

3. The companion load factor of 0.5 for a live load, L, shall be increased to 1.0 for storage occupancies, equipment areas and service rooms.

TABLE 3.3

Load Combinations for Serviceability Limit States

Case	Principal loads	Companion loads
1	1.0D	
2	1.0D + 1.0L	0.5S[2] or 0.4W
3	1.0D + 1.0S	0.5L[2] or 0.4W
4	1.0D + 1.0W	0.5L or 0.5S

Notes:

1. Dead loads include permanent loads due to lateral earth pressure, H, and prestress, P.

2. Refer to the NBCC for guidance on combining snow load, S, and live load, L, on exterior areas.

TABLE 3.4	Use of area of floor or roof		Minimum specified load, kPa	
Examples of uniformly distributed live loads on an area of floor or roof (from NBCC Table 4.1.5.3.)	Assembly areas	(a) Except for those areas listed under (b) and (c), assembly areas with or without fixed seats including Arenas, Auditoria, Churches, Dance floors, Dining areas, Foyers and entrance halls, Grandstands, reviewing stands and bleachers, Gymnasia, Museums, Promenades, Rinks, Stadia, Stages, Theatres, and other areas with similar use	4.8	(for dining areas, see NBCC)
		(b) Assembly areas with fixed seats that have backs over at least 80% of the assembly area for the following uses: Churches, Lecture halls, Theatres	2.4	
		(c) Classrooms and courtrooms with or without fixed seats	2.4	
	Attics	Accessible by a stairway in residential occupancies only	1.4	
		Having limited accessibility so that there is no storage of equipment or material	0.5	
	Balconies	exterior	4.8	
		interior and mezzanines that could be used for the assembly of people as a viewing area (see NBCC Appendix A)	4.8	
	Equipment areas and service rooms	including Generator rooms, Mechanical equipment exclusive of elevators, Machine rooms, Pump rooms, Transformer vaults, Ventilating or air-conditioning equipment	3.6	(see NBCC)
	Exits and fire escapes		4.8	
	Factories		6.0	(see NBCC)
	Footbridges		4.8	
	Kitchens (other than residential)		4.8	
	Libraries	Stack rooms	7.2	
		Reading and study rooms	2.9	
	Office areas	in office buildings and other buildings (not including record storage and computer rooms) located in basement and first storey	4.8	
		located in floors above first storey	2.4	
	Operating rooms and laboratories		3.6	
	Patients' bedrooms		1.9	
	Recreation areas	that cannot be used for assembly purposes including: Billiard rooms, Bowling alleys, Pool rooms	3.6	
	Residential areas	(within the scope of NBCC Article 1.3.3.2.) Sleeping and living quarters in apartments, hotels, motels, boarding schools and colleges	1.9	
	Residential areas	(within the scope of NBCC Article 1.3.3.3.)	1.9	
	Retail and wholesale areas		4.8	
	Roofs		1.0	(see NBCC)
	Storage areas		4.8	(see NBCC)
	Toilet areas		2.4	
	Warehouses		4.8	(see NBCC)

TABLE 3.5

Design data for major Canadian locations (from Appendix C NBCC)

Location	Ground Snow Load, kPa 1/50		Hourly Wind Pressures, kPa 1/50	Seismic Data				
	S_s	S_r		$S_a(0.2)$	$S_a(0.5)$	$S_a(1.0)$	$S_a(2.0)$	PGA
Halifax	1.9	0.6	0.58	0.23	0.15	0.085	0.027	0.086
Montreal-est	2.7	0.4	0.42	0.64	0.31	0.14	0.047	0.32
Toronto	0.9	0.4	0.44	0.22	0.13	0.067	0.021	0.12
Richmond Hill	1.5	0.4	0.44	0.18	0.11	0.065	0.021	0.063
Winnipeg	1.9	0.2	0.45	0.095	0.057	0.026	0.008	0.036
Calgary	1.1	0.1	0.48	0.15	0.084	0.041	0.023	0.088
Vancouver	1.8	0.2	0.45	0.94	0.64	0.33	0.17	0.46

TABLE 3.6

Values of F_a as a Function of Site Class and $S_a(0.2)$ (from NBCC Table 4.1.8.4.B)

	Values of F_a				
Site Class	$S_a(0.2) \leq 0.25$	$S_a(0.2) = 0.50$	$S_a(0.2) = 0.75$	$S_a(0.2) = 1.00$	$S_a(0.2) = 1.25$
A	0.7	0.7	0.8	0.8	0.8
B	0.8	0.8	0.9	1.0	1.0
C	1.0	1.0	1.0	1.0	1.0
D	1.3	1.2	1.1	1.1	1.0
E	2.1	1.4	1.1	0.9	0.9
F	(1)	(1)	(1)	(1)	(1)

Notes

(1) See NBCC

TABLE 3.7

Values of F_v as a Function of Site Class and $S_a(1.0)$ (from NBCC Table 4.1.8.4.C)

	Values of F_v				
Site Class	$S_a(1.0) \leq 0.1$	$S_a(1.0) = 0.2$	$S_a(1.0) = 0.3$	$S_a(1.0) = 0.4$	$S_a(1.0) \geq 0.5$
A	0.5	0.5	0.5	0.6	0.6
B	0.6	0.7	0.7	0.8	0.8
C	1.0	1.0	1.0	1.0	1.0
D	1.4	1.3	1.2	1.1	1.1
E	2.1	2.0	1.9	1.7	1.7
F	(1)	(1)	(1)	(1)	(1)

Notes

(1) See NBCC

Structural Form

4.1 General Information

Structural form refers to the overall shape of a structure and the arrangement and function of the elements comprising it. There are many structural materials and many ways that structural elements can be arranged. Each material has unique characteristics, and for each basic material type there are a variety of products from which to choose. Each structural arrangement will have an effect on the speed and cost of construction, the appearance, and the ability of the structure to perform during its expected period of service.

In some cases, the choice of a building product will be dictated by building function. For example, a corrosive environment might limit the desirability of selecting steel, and a wet environment might limit the selection of certain wood products. In other cases, the choice of material might be limited by the transportation costs of importing materials from their place of manufacture.

Owing to such factors, there are no fixed rules for selecting structural materials and arrangements. The purpose of this chapter is to describe some basic concepts about structural form that can be used in combination with experience to facilitate the selection of a structural system which will meet all the requirements for a given building.

The following topics are covered with an emphasis on wood products where appropriate:

4.2   Factors Influencing Structural Form

4.3   Wood-Frame Construction

4.4   Post and Beam Construction

4.5   Special Structural Forms

4.6   Lateral Resistance

4.7   Tables

4.2   Factors Influencing Structural Form

INTRODUCTION

In collaborating to develop a successful building design meeting all user requirements, the architect and the engineer must consider many factors. Each project is different and therefore each requires a review to determine the structural form which will meet not only the strength requirements, but also the host of other requirements which may be affected by the choice of structural system.

There are several factors that are common to most projects, as shown in the table below, and others that may be unique. Some factors will be the responsibility of either the engineer or the architect, and some will require the cooperation and involvement of both professions.

Factors in selection of structural form

Cost	cost of design
	cost of materials
	cost of transportation
	cost of installation
	cost of protection and maintenance
Schedule	shop drawings and approvals
	materials acquisition
	construction productivity
Function	clear span
	depth of members and clear height
	location of bearing walls and other supports
	incorporation of mechanical and electrical systems
	thermal insulation
Code requirements	fire protection
	sound transmission
	structural capacity
	durability
Appearance	appearance of materials
	appearance of the finished systems
	architectural blend of form and function
Environmental issues	environmental impact of harvesting, mining, quarrying, and manufacture
	energy required to manufacture, transport, and install materials
	thermal efficiency of building systems
	disposal, recycle, or reuse at end of life cycle

ARRANGEMENT OF MEMBERS — VERTICAL DEAD AND LIVE LOADS

Horizontal spanning members are used to carry gravity loads to the vertical supports. Decks, joists, beams and trusses span between supports that can be either horizontal members or a structural wall or column.

In a one-way system, members span one direction. A deck panel is an example of a one way system. One way systems may have load transfer through a structural system which is direct, as in the case of a system with one level spanning, or there may be several levels of members transferring loads in a hierarchical system (Figure 4.1).

In a two-way system, members act as plates transferring loads in two directions. A reinforced concrete slab is an example of a two-way system.

Two-way systems have practical limits to spanning capability because of the ever increasing effect of the assembly's own dead weight as spans increase.

RELATION BETWEEN LOADING TYPE AND STRUCTURE TYPE

The nature of the loading, whether uniform or concentrated, symmetric or unsymmetric, is an important consideration in the selection of a structural system.

The assemblies for light, uniformly distributed floor or roof loads are typically surface-forming in nature and are usually made up of a series of closely spaced similar elements. Wood joist and open web steel joist systems, long-span precast concrete planks, precast channels, and reinforced concrete flat plates are examples of systems used for this type of loading.

FIGURE 4.1

*Levels of members
for transferring loads*

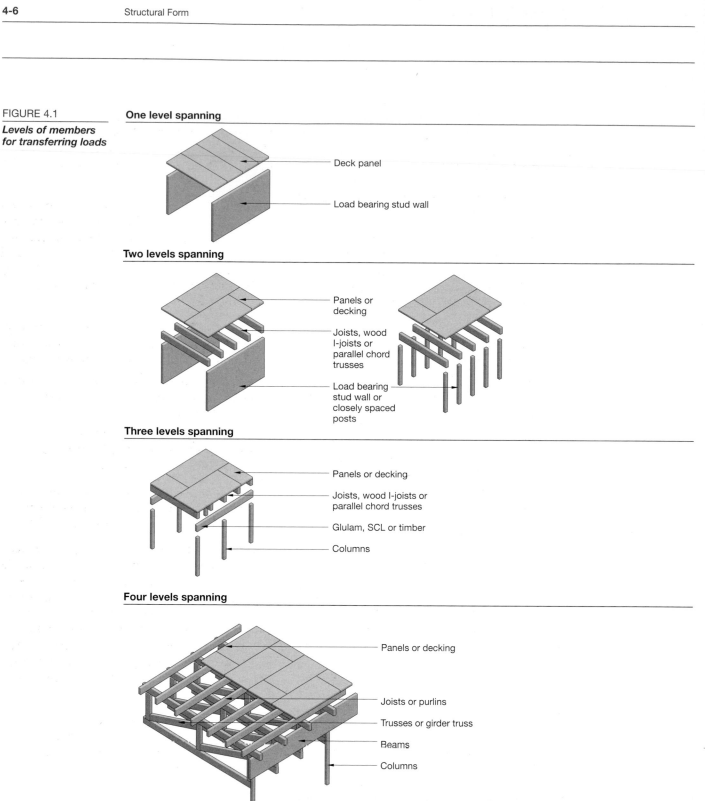

One level spanning

Deck panel

Load bearing stud wall

Two levels spanning

Panels or
decking

Joists, wood
I-joists or
parallel chord
trusses

Load bearing
stud wall or
closely spaced
posts

Three levels spanning

Panels or decking

Joists, wood I-joists or
parallel chord trusses

Glulam, SCL or timber

Columns

Four levels spanning

Panels or decking

Joists or purlins

Trusses or girder truss

Beams

Columns

The structural level in closest proximity to the loads should be designed first. For this reason, the spacing of more specially designed members supporting these surface elements such as purlins or beams is often based on the most efficient arrangement of the smaller elements above.

For example, the wood joist spacing for a floor should be based first of all on the optimum spacing for the structural capability of the sheathing. And the design of joists, purlins, beams, and columns would follow sequentially.

However, each group of members in the structural hierarchy will have limits which place practical limitations on what is possible. For example, dimension lumber joists have a maximum available length of about 7 m. If this limitation causes the rest of the hierarchy of purlins and beams to be too expensive or constrains the layout of the building, wood I-joists or parallel chord trusses, for example, might be considered in place of the wood joists to increase the spans.

For structural assemblies exposed to large concentrated loads, surface-forming elements or systems require adjustment. Thus, supplemental members must be added to carry concentrated loads. For example, a wood joist roof to which a heavy roof-mounted air handling unit is added would likely benefit from the addition of a member or members to carry this point load, rather than designing the entire roof system for such a unique, localized load.

The designer must ascertain whether, for example, it is more efficient to carry a given load with one large column or with two or more smaller ones. As indicated at the beginning of this section, such determinations must assess the cost impact on labour and material.

In addition, building function will often limit the options available. For example, if large clear room openings are required, the use of smaller and more numerous columns will not be an option.

Table 4.1 describes some typical wood assemblies for light and medium duty applications. However, designers must develop a feel for structural arrangements which are practical because there are no fixed rules for selecting a structural system. This is due to the following reasons:

- Labour and material costs are constantly changing in response to market conditions and vary from one location to the next.
- Due to climatic factors, loading conditions for wind, snow and earthquake vary by location.
- Each project is different in terms of budget, user requirements, size, and appearance requirements.

Before the structural system can support external dead and live loads, it must first be capable of supporting its own weight.

Because wood has a high strength to weight ratio, dead load is a smaller component of the total load factor than for heavier materials. Figure 4.2 shows the usual span capabilities of a number of structural systems in wood, steel, and concrete. Wood is not only an ideal material for residential construction, but can also be used for high load and large span applications where its low weight is an advantage.

Usually, the lightest or least involved construction type appropriate for a combination of span, and loads, is the most preferable.

FIGURE 4.2

Approximate span ranges for structural systems

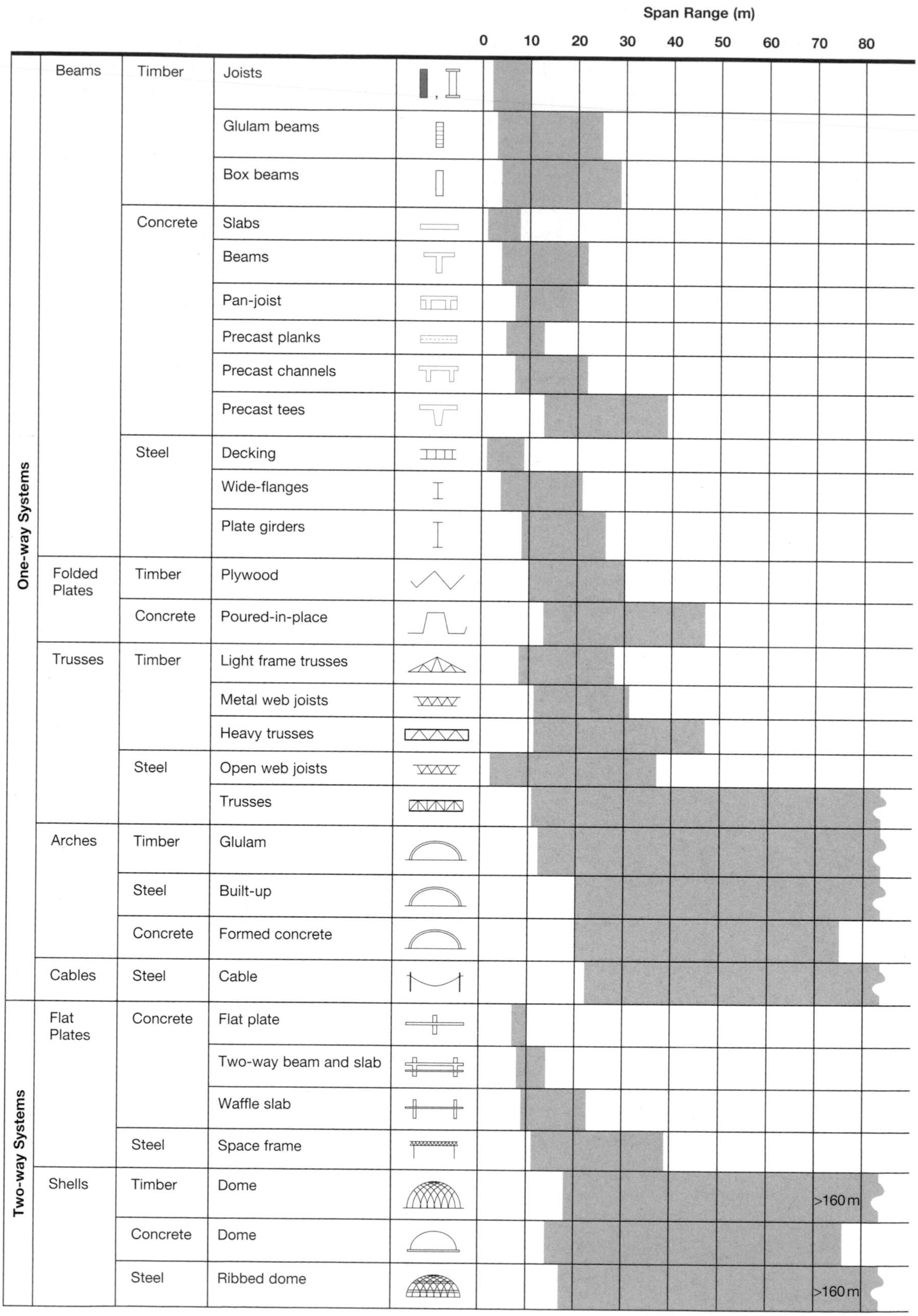

Span Range (m)

0 10 20 30 40 50 60 70 80

System	Category	Material	Type
One-way Systems	Beams	Timber	Joists
			Glulam beams
			Box beams
		Concrete	Slabs
			Beams
			Pan-joist
			Precast planks
			Precast channels
			Precast tees
		Steel	Decking
			Wide-flanges
			Plate girders
	Folded Plates	Timber	Plywood
		Concrete	Poured-in-place
	Trusses	Timber	Light frame trusses
			Metal web joists
			Heavy trusses
		Steel	Open web joists
			Trusses
	Arches	Timber	Glulam
		Steel	Built-up
		Concrete	Formed concrete
	Cables	Steel	Cable
Two-way Systems	Flat Plates	Concrete	Flat plate
			Two-way beam and slab
			Waffle slab
		Steel	Space frame
	Shells	Timber	Dome (>160 m)
		Concrete	Dome
		Steel	Ribbed dome (>160 m)

LENGTH OF SPAN

Span length is crucial in selecting a structural system for a given situation. Some structural systems are quite appropriate for certain span ranges and not for others.

For the span ranges normally encountered in most buildings, it is evident that a number of systems and materials are suitable (Figure 4.2).

Horizontal members are sensitive to shear, bending moment, deflection, and vibration. For short, heavily loaded spans, shear often governs, and for long uniformly loaded spans, deflection or vibration is particularly critical.

Bending moments for uniformly distributed loads are proportional to the square of the length of the span, whereas deflections are proportional to the 4th order of the span.

This means that doubling a span length increases the moment by a factor of 4; and the deflection by a factor of 16. Therefore, bending member sizes are determined to a large extent by the span length.

The depths of simple beams have practical limits brought on by manufacturing limitations or member dead weight. For this reason, increases can only be accommodated to a certain point beyond which it is necessary to go to a more complex structural solution such as a truss.

Figure 4.3 shows the common wood elements used for horizontal load-bearing applications. Note how the depth to length ratio changes for spans which are beyond the capability of simple members.

Appropriate structural systems for long-span applications typically include shaped trusses, arches, cable or air supported structures, and domes, but can also include flat trusses or space frames (Section 4.5).

The versatility of the truss in terms of shapes available and structural efficiency make it one of the few structural elements useful for the full range of short, intermediate, and long spans.

Specific characteristics and geometries of trusses for different span ranges vary. For short and intermediate spans, light frame trusses are typically used closely spaced. Long-span trusses are usually specially made and placed relatively far apart (Section 4.5).

ROOF SHAPE

Roof systems usually have fewer constraints in terms of depth and shape relative to floors.

Many roof shapes have been used in building construction. Generally, the flat or pitched shape, regardless of the type of building, offers economy due to the simplicity of connections. However, there are many instances where more elaborate roof shapes (Figure 4.4) are desired for architectural reasons.

For flat or pitched roofs and for floors, there are several different arrangements of sheathing or decking and primary structural members that can be used. In wood construction, the sheathing or decking serves a structural role of distributing gravity loads to the framing. In addition, the sheathing or decking is often the prime source of resistance to lateral loads through the provision of shearwall and diaphragm effect (Chapter 12).

A change in the profile of a roof usually requires a change of some sort in the framing system. The profile change often necessitates the introduction of a vertical support line such as a bearing wall, columns, or a beam or girder truss.

FIGURE 4.3

Spanning capabilities of wood members

Decking, joists, and beams	Typical spans, m	Approximate span to depth ratio (ℓ/d)
Wood decking	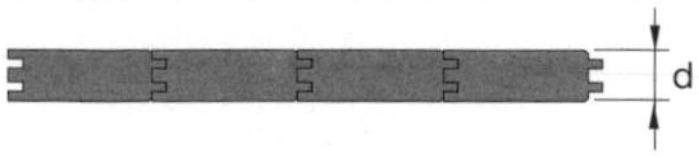 1 to 2.5	25 to 35
Panels	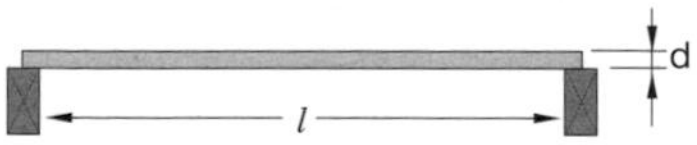 0.3 to 0.6	20 to 40
Dimension lumber	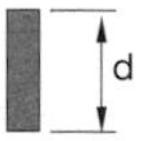 3 to 7	15 to 25
Wood I-joists	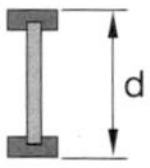 6 to 10	20 to 25
Stressed-skin panels	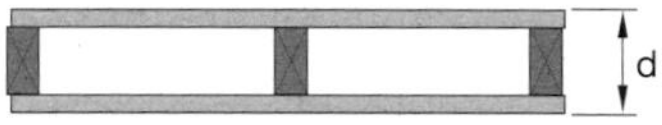 3 to 7	24 to 30
Plywood box beams	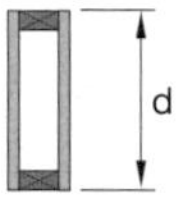 4 to 9	18 to 20
Parallel strand lumber	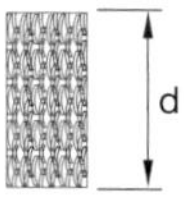 4 to 18	18 to 20
Laminated veneer lumber	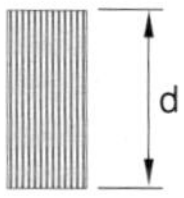 4 to 18	18 to 20
Glulam	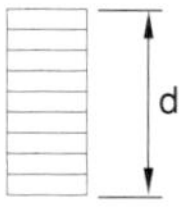 4 to 25	18 to 20

Trusses and Arches		
Pitched trusses	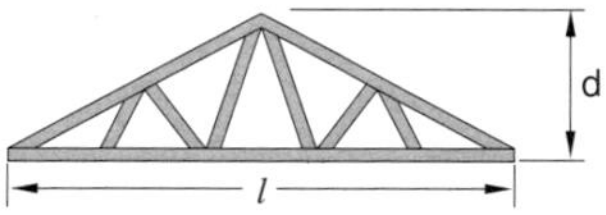 6 to 30	2 to 5
Parallel chord trusses	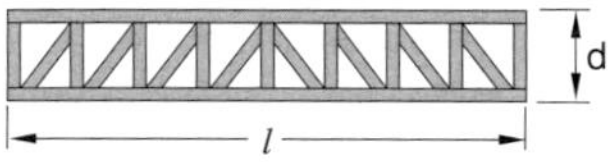 6 to 30	10 to 15
Bowstring trusses	 20 to 50	5 to 10

FIGURE 4.4

*Structural forms
for roofs*

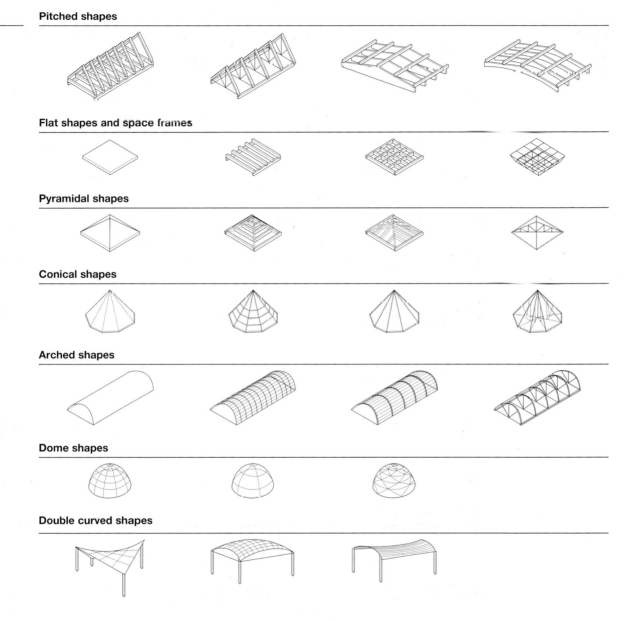

Pitched shapes

Flat shapes and space frames

Pyramidal shapes

Conical shapes

Arched shapes

Dome shapes

Double curved shapes

LATERAL LOAD RESISTANCE

The size and arrangement of structural systems is determined primarily by the imposed vertical gravity loads. However lateral loads due to wind and earthquake (Chapter 3) must also be distributed to the building foundations. Beams, trusses, space frames and simple columns resist mainly vertical loads and therefore an additional lateral load resisting system may be required. This could be in the form of bracing or shearwalls (Section 4.3).

Some structural forms are able to resist lateral load without additional bracing or lateral support. Portal frames and arches possess lateral load resistance in the plane of the frame and some shell structures have load capacity in all directions. Wood frame construction using repetitive wood members with structural sheathing provides an efficient and economical system for resisting lateral loads.

For specific information on lateral load resisting systems, refer to Chapter 12.

FIRE SAFETY

Wood is a combustible material. For this reason, fire safety is often a concern raised when wood construction is proposed. In Canada, the fire safety requirements for buildings are set by the *National Building Code of Canada* (NBCC).

The NBCC bases fire safety primarily on the need to evacuate occupants from a building during a fire situation. The construction must be able to remain in place long enough to allow safe evacuation for the type and size of fire that may occur. Building occupancy type, area and size are the main factors in determining whether wood construction is permitted.

In the majority of fires, the contents of the building are the items first ignited.

Consequently, the smoke and heat generated by the burning contents poses the greatest danger to the occupants. The combustibility of the structure is not usually a factor in the safety of the building. Each type of construction must meet the fire resistance requirements set out by the NBCC.

The "acceptable solution" portion of the NBCC, Division B, has set four storeys as the maximum height for buildings whose supporting structure is of combustible construction. Various occupancies have different limitations on the heights and areas permitted to be of wood construction (Table 4.2).

In some jurisdictions, wood construction is permitted to be used in buildings up to 6 storeys in height.

FIGURE 4.5

Effect of access and sprinklers on building height and area[1, 2]

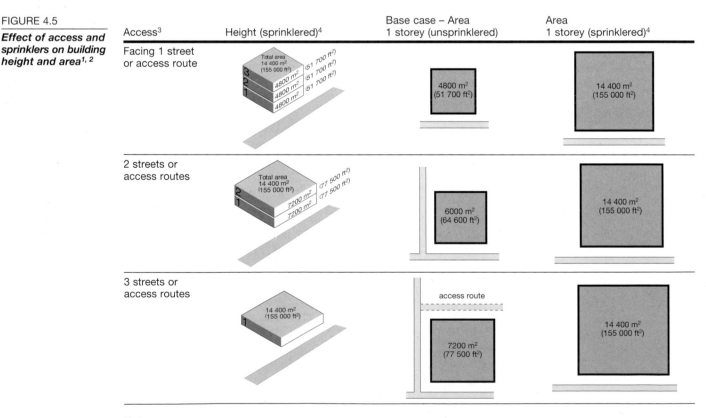

Notes:

1. Comparison based on wood-frame (45 min. fire–resistance rating), Noncombustible (unprotected), or Heavy Timber construction.

2. For a building occupancy classified as Group D, Business and Personal Services.

3. Minimum street width is 9m (30'). Minimum access route width is 6m (20').

4. For sprinklered options, access is required on one side only.

Construction statistics show that 60% of all commercial floor space constructed in North America is contained in buildings of four storeys or less. The majority of residential and commercial projects meet the height and area limitations in the NBCC, which makes wood construction an attractive option.

Wood construction can resist the effects of fire in two ways. In light frame construction, gypsum board attached to the wood framing members can result in building assemblies with the required fire resistance. In laboratory testing, these assemblies have been shown to resist the passage of flame, heat and smoke for the prescribed times of 45 minutes, one hour or up to two hours, depending on the construction.

Secondly, for post and beam construction, larger wood members are used without any gypsum wallboard protection. In a fire, wood burns slowly, approximately 0.6 mm/minute. The char, which is formed on the members, has an insulating effect, protecting the remaining cross-section of wood. For these reasons, heavy timber construction can stay in place and support its load for a long duration in a fire.

In the NBCC, wood members that meet minimum size requirements qualify as Heavy Timber and are allowed an equivalency to a 45-minute fire-resistance rating. The NBCC also permits the use of heavy timber roof assemblies in many large non-combustible buildings. The NBCC also has a calculation method for glued-laminated beams and columns that can assign fire resistance up to 90 minutes to large members.

The addition of sprinklers to any type of building can significantly increase the fire safety. This is recognized by the model building codes in North America. In the NBCC, sprinklers are mandatory for most large buildings and for all high rises. In addition, the permitted heights and areas of buildings of combustible construction are significantly increased if the building is sprinklered (Figure 4.5).

Fire-fighter access to the building is not as critical when a building is sprinklered because the sprinklers can control or contain the fire. For this reason, there is no distinction in the heights and areas allowed for sprinklered buildings of the same occupancy type when facing one or more streets.

The building code requires fire separations between different occupancies or suites to limit the area of a compartment. These fire separations are designed to separate the building into compartments to prevent or at least inhibit the spread of fire from one area to another.

In many cases, particularly in low- to medium-rise buildings, the load-bearing walls are designed to coincide with the location for the required fire divisions so that the same walls serve both functions.

There have been many disastrous fires in non-combustible buildings, which historically have always been considered safe and "fire proof". The contents of a building, which are difficult to control through building codes, have a large effect on the safety of buildings. For this reason, building codes in North America are moving towards setting performance criteria for building materials and assemblies in fire conditions rather than basing requirements on the crude classification of combustibility and non-combustibility of the construction.

Additional information on the fire safety of wood construction can be found through CWC publications and other tools at CWC's web site, www.cwc.ca.

COST

Cost is always, to varying degrees, a factor in the design selection. Wood is a material which is suited to the whole range of architectural requirements for buildings from those where economy alone drives the project to those where cost is given a secondary role relative to appearance.

Cost analysis should include all construction costs including manufacture and purchase, transportation, installation, and finishing. The selection of a final design should also consider maintenance costs during the expected service life of the structure.

For an industrial building, cost and function may dominate design, whereas a public building would likely have a budget which would allow a greater emphasis to be placed on appearance. The degree to which these factors dominate will influence the selection of trial structural forms.

The cost of construction will vary from one location to another as a result of varying transportation costs, labour costs and productivity. Several publications, such as *Means Yardsticks for Costing*, give information which the designer can use to supplement experience in determining cost effective assemblies.

Wood products are cost competitive building materials, and in many situations, offer substantial savings. They may be used in applications where low cost is the main project requirement, and can also be used for upscale construction where appearance carries a high degree of importance.

Transportation

There are practical limits to the length and width of structural members that can be transported by road or rail. For wood frame construction, transportation is not a constraint. However, it may be a limitation for long span trusses or beams made of glulam, parallel strand lumber (PSL), or laminated veneer lumber (LVL).

Up to a certain length (about 20 m depending on provincial highway regulations), over-length transportation permits can be acquired. In other cases, long members may be spliced together on site.

Width may also be a factor for curved members or for wall or floor units which are factory manufactured. However, the usual maximum width limitation of 4.8 m is one which is easily incorporated into most designs.

The size of the tree of origin is a limitation to the maximum member size that can be manufactured by sawing alone. The use of adhesives allows the production of wood structural members that have longer span and greater load-carrying capability than sawn members.

Glulam, PSL, LVL, and trusses are wood structural materials which can be laminated or assembled to a size limited only by transportation regulations.

Longer trusses or laminated beams may require permits or need to be transported outside peak traffic hours. Curved or prefabricated members such as portals or arches are often site joined at the apex, which reduces the sizes of the members to be transported.

The light weight of wood often gives it a cost advantage in northern Canada where the cost of importing building materials by air is so crucial.

Erection

Due to their strength to weight ratio, wood assemblies are relatively light in comparison, for example, to concrete. As a result, components can be factory built or site built and be lifted into place by hand or by using relatively light lifting equipment.

In some cases, roof trusses have been assembled on the ground and lifted into place in sections. This results in time and cost savings because safer working conditions on the ground result in more productivity and better quality.

The erection of modules for wall, floor, or roof assemblies requires of course, that the components are adequately linked together.

Member Profile

In addition to determining the type of framing system used, each member selected should have an effective shape.

For example, a bending member that is deep and narrow is generally more efficient in the use of material than, for example, a square member (Chapter 7).

However, bending members that are too deep and too narrow are more prone to lateral buckling in the transverse direction. To provide the lateral stability, lateral bracing may be required which again increases the material and labour costs. The most effective beam for a given application requires the comparison of several different profiles to determine the one which will result in the lowest material and labour cost.

Similarly, a member loaded only in compression should be symmetrical about both axes so that the member has the same strength in both directions. A rectangular column will have an overcapacity about one axis which does nothing to increase the resistance of the member overall.

Specialty suppliers such as glulam and truss manufacturers will often make suggestions that can reduce costs without affecting strength. For example, it may be economical to alter a beam layout by using slightly larger beams at a greater spacing with the possibility of reducing the number of beams required.

4.3 Wood-Frame Construction

INTRODUCTION

Wood-frame construction is the construction technique of choice for millions of housing units in North America. The technique, using small members spaced closely together in load sharing arrangements, offers economy, strength, and flexibility that can also be applied to large commercial buildings when provision is made for longer spans and larger loads. Strength is derived from the combined action of the main structural members (the framing) and secondary structural materials (sheathing or decking).

Wood-frame construction is economical because roof, floor and wall assemblies, comprised of main load bearing members such as wall studs and roof rafters, in combination with sheathing and decking materials, serve a number of functions.

The combination of sheathing and framing provides rigidity for the resistance of lateral loads (Chapter 12), a space for the installation of insulation, and robust surfaces for the application of exterior and interior finish materials.

The building technique is efficient because members are easy to handle, load sharing with adjacent members results in strong but light-weight assemblies, and because lumber is economical to produce with modern production methods.

Wood-frame construction is sometimes referred to as planar construction because the main and secondary structural members (framing and sheathing) are in the same plane space that is shared by structure, envelope, and insulation. This is in contrast to wood post and beam or typical steel construction where the frame and the building skin overlay each other, and the skin is not usually the primary contributor to the lateral strength of a wall or roof.

All wood frame-construction is classified as light frame construction by the NBCC. This terminology is not meant to infer that wood framing is light in terms of being suited only for light duty applications. It means that the members used are small in cross-section and that special fire protection characteristics afforded Heavy Timber construction are not applicable. Therefore, other measures such as the use of fire-resistant gypsum wallboard are required to ensure that wood frame-construction meets the degree of fire safety required by the building code for some types of construction.

Part 9 of the NBCC applies to buildings of certain size, the design of which is based upon satisfactory past performance and does not require specific engineering input.

Part 9 of the NBCC provides prescriptive design solutions for wood frame buildings 3 stories or less in height and 600 m² or less in area. The *Engineering Guide for Wood Frame Construction* published by the CWC provides structural design solutions for wood frame buildings that meet Part 9 size criteria, but are beyond the scope of the Part 9 prescriptive solutions.

Buildings that exceed the size or other criteria for Part 9 buildings must be designed according to Part 4 of the NBCC, and the structural elements of such buildings must be engineered.

Part 4 buildings usually have larger span and load requirements, and wood-frame members for commercial buildings must be sized to account for these needs.

Structural performance is achieved in such buildings in several ways. In the case of load bearing partitions, the 38 × 89 mm walls common to residential construction may have to be increased to 38 × 140 or 184 mm to accommodate larger loads and increased ceiling heights.

For joists, it may be necessary to reduce spacing, use deeper dimension lumber joists, or use wood I-joists. Similarly, dimension lumber headers and lintels may have to be replaced with parallel strand lumber (PSL) or laminated veneer lumber (LVL) to increase capacity. Refer to Chapter 6 for a description of the types of wood products available and their applications.

The FPInnovation (formerly Forintek) building in Vancouver is a good example of how residential wood-frame techniques can be augmented and applied to commercial applications. The Western Research Facility is a 10 000 m^2 (100 000 ft^2) wood products research facility. Half the building, the office/laboratory portion, is wood-frame construction. The industrial side of the building is a mixture of wood-frame and post and beam construction.

Wherever possible, planar construction was used rather than hierarchical beam and column construction. This approach made use of exterior walls and interior partitions as load bearing structural elements.

The walls, which are required for enclosure or for separating interior spaces, also support vertical loads thereby eliminating the need for beams and columns. And when sheathed in accordance with engineering standards, they provide shearwall stiffening thereby eliminating the need for cross-bracing within the wall cavity.

In this way, the economy of wood-frame construction can be applied to a commercial building with high serviceability requirements such as those resulting from the precise laboratory work which is undertaken at FPInnovations.

The CWC website contains several case studies demonstrating how Canadian building designers have found exciting ways to use wood products in commercial buildings.

PLATFORM FRAMING

Platform framing is more commonly used for modern structures due to its simplicity and ease of erection. Its main advantage is that the floor assembly is built separately from the walls; therefore, the preceding floor provides a working surface on which to assemble and erect the walls and partitions. Generally, the wall framing is assembled and fastened together on the floor, then raised by hand into place. However, wall components can also be prefabricated off-site and then be erected in sections, thereby reducing on-site labour.

In platform framing, all of the walls are one story high and consist of a top plate (double or single), studs and a bottom plate (Figure 4.6). The plates provide a nailing surface for sheathing and interior finishes. They also act as firestops that resist the spread of fire from one floor to another in the wall cavity.

Balloon framing is another style of framing. The main difference between this method and platform framing is that the studs for the exterior walls and some of the interior walls are continuous between floors below the roof framing.

FIGURE 4.6
Platform frame construction

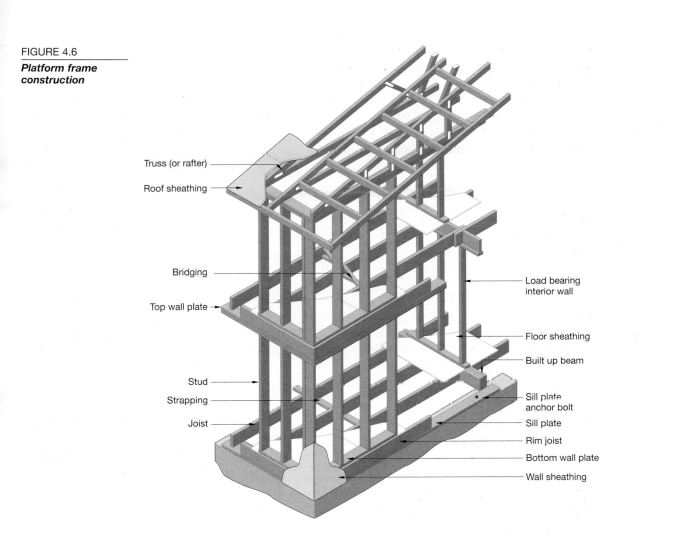

Truss (or rafter)
Roof sheathing
Bridging
Top wall plate
Stud
Strapping
Joist
Load bearing interior wall
Floor sheathing
Built up beam
Sill plate anchor bolt
Sill plate
Rim joist
Bottom wall plate
Wall sheathing

4.4   Post and Beam Construction

INTRODUCTION

Post and beam construction is a method of construction that makes use of large members spaced far apart in non load-sharing arrangements. This method is often used for large spans or loadings, or where the structure of the building is left exposed to make use of the aesthetic qualities of the wood members.

The North American model building codes have recognized the ability of large wood members to remain structurally intact for a certain period of time when exposed to fire. For this reason, the model codes, such as the *National Building Code of Canada* (NBCC), afford large wood members meeting certain minimum size requirements, special fire resistance ratings. When post and beam members meet these minimum size requirements, the members qualify as Heavy Timber construction as defined by the NBCC (refer to NBCC and *Fire Safety Design in Buildings* for further information).

In post and beam construction (Figure 4.7), the roof and floors are comprised of decking supported by purlins. The purlins frame into beams that in turn are connected to columns. It is a construction method that is similar in arrangement to structural steel building construction.

The large wood members are connected together with bolted steel connections or some other type of high capacity connection.

Usually the structural members are left exposed in the completed building as an architectural feature.

Sawn timber, glulam, parallel strand lumber (PSL), and heavy timber trusses are typically used for the main members (Chapter 6).

FIGURE 4.7

Post and beam construction

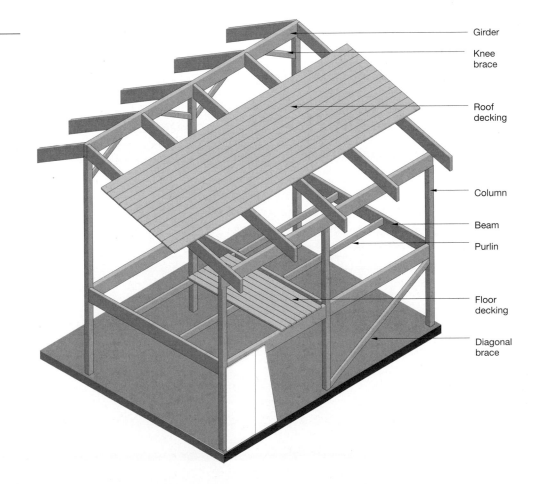

Girder

Knee brace

Roof decking

Column

Beam

Purlin

Floor decking

Diagonal brace

BENDING MEMBERS

Bending members are the basic elements that support roofs or floors of buildings. Horizontal members such as purlins, rafters, lintels, and joists can be generally categorized as bending members (Chapter 7).

They must be strong enough to carry the loads safely and be stiff enough to prevent sagging or undesireable movement as dictated by the strength and serviceability limit states.

Bending members must meet minimum size requirements in order to meet the Heavy Timber construction requirements defined by the NBCC.

Beams can also be propped or braced from columns to reduce bending moments in members, or to increase spans where the length of available material is limited. Propping can also provide lateral bracing to a post and beam structure.

COLUMNS

Columns (or posts) are used to support roof and floor elements such as beams, arches, and trusses, and to transfer the loads from these members down to the foundations.

In addition to compressive stresses, columns in some applications may also be subjected to bending and shear. See Chapter 8 for the design of compression members.

The most efficient section shape for a column is circular or square because, being symmetrical, the column has the same capacity about both axes. Slender columns may require intermediate bracing to prevent buckling.

SHEATHING AND DECKING

The decking used in conjunction with post and beam construction is usually tongue and groove plank deck, although in older industrial buildings vertically nail laminated 38×89 mm ($2" \times 4"$ nom.) decks were often used.

Decking should always be dried to a moisture content of 15% (maximum 19%) before installation so that the tongue and groove joint does not become loose after drying in service.

BRACING AND ANCHORAGES

Unlike wood-frame construction that derives its resistance to lateral loads from the interaction of the sheathing and the framing members, post and beam construction requires additional framing members or bracing to provide this lateral resistance.

Wind acting on a building also causes uplift on the roof. For this reason, it is important that the roof members and the supporting beams and columns be tied together to resist these uplift forces.

The columns must be securely anchored to the foundation to hold the building in place and to prevent wind from lifting the building away from the foundation. This anchorage is particularly critical at the diagonal brace locations since the bracing pulls or pushes on the column base when wind acts on the building.

CONNECTIONS

The large loads usually carried by post and beam members require connections using large fasteners such as bolts, lag screws, shear plates and split rings, often in combination with wood or steel side plates (Chapter 11). Timber rivets, in combination with steel side plates, are used for glued-laminated and timber members, and for parallel strand lumber (PSL).

WALLS AND PARTITIONS

Exterior walls and partitions may be constructed using conventional stud wall framing between columns. The walls may be only envelope forming, or they may be structural by contributing to the lateral resistance of the post and beam structure.

Commercially available composite panels may also be used to enclose the building. These panels have a rigid insulation core with a gypsum wallboard face on the interior side and a panel sheathing face on the exterior side. The panels are generally connected together with tongue and groove joints and are fastened with nails to the exterior surface of the timber framework.

POST AND BEAM COMBINED WITH WOOD-FRAME CONSTRUCTION

Post and beam construction is often combined with conventional wood-frame construction (Figure 4.8) in the following ways depending on fire safety considerations:

- Conventional framing or light trusses and panel sheathing are used in the roof while the remaining above grade structure is post and beam construction.

- The structural frame is post and beam construction but joist or rafter framing and panel sheathing is used in place of plank decking.

- Interior loadbearing walls are used instead of columns.

Combined post and beam construction and wood-frame construction offers a number of practical advantages including the following:

- Concealment of Services
  With post and beam construction, extra planning is required for the concealment of electrical conduits, plumbing, and heating ducts. The layout of these services must be carefully planned to achieve a practical, convenient and aesthetic solution. When wood-frame floor, roof, or walls are used, it may be possible to run most of these services between the framing and therefore hide them from view.

- Insulation and Finishes
  Combining post and beam construction with light frame construction gives the designer flexibility in the choice of building materials such as insulation and interior finishes. Wood-frame construction roofs and walls may be insulated with flexible batt insulation in the space between members rather than with rigid insulation on top of the roof deck, which would normally be used for a post and beam plank roof. Conventional finishes such as gypsum wallboard may be used with wood-frame floors and roofs to provide contrast with the exposed timber members.

FIGURE 4.8

Post and beam construction with wood-frame construction

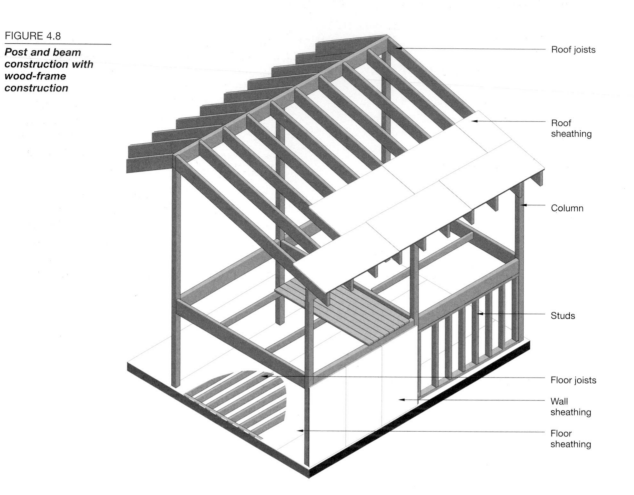

Roof joists

Roof sheathing

Column

Studs

Floor joists

Wall sheathing

Floor sheathing

4.5 Special Structural Forms

INTRODUCTION

In addition to the most common wood construction methods of frame construction and post and beam construction, there are several construction techniques used for special applications.

POLE CONSTRUCTION

Pole construction is a simple form of construction used mainly for agricultural buildings. The columns are treated poles embedded in the ground which also provide a degree of lateral load resistance due to the moment resisting effect at ground level.

HEAVY TRUSSES

Heavy trusses can be manufactured from timber, glulam, PSL, or LVL. See Chapter 11 for more information on bolts and timber connector joints.

While closely spaced light frame trusses can achieve long spans, heavy trusses usually achieve long spans spaced further apart, and are thus used where a particular architectural effect is desired. The trusses may be supported on timber columns or masonry walls and can span up to 50 m depending on the type of truss. Truss spacing is typically between 3 and 6 m on centre.

Heavy trusses can be pitched, flat, or bowed. Glulam is conventionally used for bow string trusses due to the curvatures possible with this product, but there are also examples of using glued laminations of PSL to create curved members for use in bow string trusses.

FIGURE 4.9

Portal frames

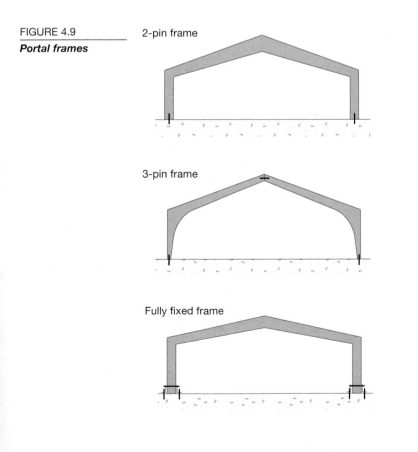

2-pin frame

3-pin frame

Fully fixed frame

PORTAL FRAME BUILDINGS

Portal frames are often used for single storey industrial and recreational buildings. Wood frames are usually made in one curved piece. The curvature possible with glulam makes it suited for this type of portal frame, and provides an alternative to steel portal frames (Figure 4.9).

The frames may also be made from straight sections in which case a moment resisting connection is required at the knee of the frame. New proprietary methods of creating a moment connection using epoxy embedded rods have been developed, which make the knee-jointed portal frame more effective.

Curved portals eliminate the need for a moment-resisting joint. Usually, the additional cost of using curved members of small laminations (see Glulam in Chapter 6) is cheaper than using straight sections and a costly moment-resisting joint.

The encroachment into the building space of the curved knee is not usually a problem but can be reduced by using a smaller radius of curvature which requires thinner and more expensive laminations.

ARCHES

The curved arch is an efficient structural form for the resistance of vertical loads over a large span. The profile of an arch can be shaped to reduce bending moments to the extent that for a uniformly distributed load on a parabolic arch, pure compression is induced with no bending.

However, unbalanced live loads, snow loads or wind loads induce bending moments which must be allowed for in design. The size of the arch will generally be determined by bending resulting from unbalanced loads.

Curved shapes are easy to fabricate with glulam, and large spans of 120 m have been achieved.

Arch structures produce large horizontal reactions which are best resisted at ground level (Figure 4.10), but a simple arch springing from the ground may result in a low clearance, or in a portion of the arches being outside the building and exposed to the weather.

The exposure of wood structural members to the elements was a popular architectural style of the 1960s. However, lack of maintenance led to problems in many cases, and present wisdom suggests that the members be inside, or be pressure treated or flashed if left exposed.

If the arches are raised above ground level, larger foundations are required to resist the thrust, which would increase the cost.

A tension member can also be used to resist thrust as long as the intrusion of the tie into the ceiling space is acceptable, and provisions are made to accommodate wind uplift forces (Chapter 3).

Where seating will be provided as in a recreational building, the seating structure can be employed to resist thrust.

Arches are usually fabricated from glulam. A variety of shapes are possible including circular, straight (A-frame) or tudor.

The arch is usually built in two sections and connected at the peak. If a hinge is formed at the crest, it is called a three-hinged arch, which is a statically determinate structure. Besides the fact that it is much easier to analyse, member forces are not sensitive to foundation settlements. A two-hinged arch is continuous from one pier support to the other and typically experiences smaller member forces and deflections. However, small movements in the foundations can cause significant force redistributions.

Arches are usually spaced from 1.2 to 5 m apart and may be used for any building where a large clear span is required, such as swimming pools, churches, arenas, solariums, agricultural buildings, and commercial buildings.

FIGURE 4.10

Arches and domes

Arches supported at grade level

Arches supported above grade level

Thrust taken by tension member

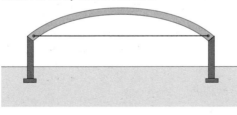

Thrust taken by vertical anchors

Dome distributes weight to circumference

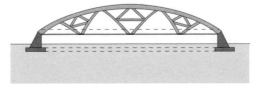

SPACE FRAMES

Space frames are three-dimensional trusses that can be almost any size or shape. They have particular advantages where large clear spans are desired with a minimum of supporting columns. The major disadvantage is that space frames require special jointing systems to be effective. Some of these can be quite simple, others can be complex and expensive both in the manufacture of jointing hardware and assembly.

Roof or floor spans can range from 8 to 60 metres, with overall depth about 1/8 to 1/16 of the distance between supporting columns.

They can be fabricated from a network of trusses at right angles to each other, or as tetrahedral shaped three-dimensional components.

In North America, such structures are usually made of steel. Wood is seldom used because of the meticulous workmanship required to make the complex joints. However, in Europe, there are many stunning examples of space frames that have been made entirely of wood, or with wood used in combination with steel ties.

FLAT PLATES

Flat plates or stressed-skin panels consist of lumber webs covered on one or both sides with a panel material. The panel material is glued to the lumber to ensure that the whole assembly functions as a structural unit. These panels are efficient use of material because of the composite action between the plywood face layers and the wood web.

DOMES

Domes are structures that carry loads to a circumferential foundation (Figure 4.10). The lateral thrust forces are typically absorbed by a relatively stiff ring beam, sometimes in combination with buttresses. Numerous wood dome structures have been constructed in North America. The best known is the Tacoma Dome in the State of Washington which spans 160 m and houses a sports arena. The wood dome was the low cost option when tendered against steel and concrete designs.

The members for such domes are made of glulam. Because of the way that the loads are distributed, the members can be relatively small. The members in the Tacoma Dome, for example, are 800 mm deep and it is estimated that a traditional steel truss system would be 3 m in depth to span this distance.

4.6   Lateral Resistance

INTRODUCTION

All structures must be able to resist the lateral loads imposed on them by earthquakes and/or wind. In conventional wood homes, lateral design is often ignored since the form of the building is inherently resistant to lateral forces. Expanding the conventional form of wood construction to buildings other than housing and using other forms of wood structures means that lateral loads must be accounted for in the conception and design of the building. Generally there are three types of lateral load resisting systems for wood structures that are used alone or in combination:

- shearwalls and diaphragms
- bracing
- parallel to span lateral resistance of main frames such as heavy trusses, portal frames and arches

SHEARWALLS AND DIAPHRAGMS

In conventional wood-frame construction, sheathed roofs and floors act as diaphragms and the sheathed stud walls act as shearwalls (Figure 4.11). This system is efficient since members used to resist vertical loads can be used to resist lateral loads as well.

In large structures or in locations with high wind or earthquake forces, the conventional construction techniques can be easily and cheaply adapted to resist the higher forces. In shearwall and diaphragm construction, it is important to consider the location of openings (doors and windows) at the conception stage.

Shearwalls and diaphragms may also be used in combinations with other forms of lateral bracing. Roof diaphragms may transfer loads into a perimeter member which in turn is resisted by bracing. Shear walls may be used in combination with bracing in some larger structures.

Considering seismic loads, the NBCC assigns values for ductility related force modification factor, R_d, and overstrength related force modification factor, R_o, for the various lateral load resisting systems in a structure (refer to Chapter 3). These values are meant to reflect the structure's reaction to earthquake loads, which differs based on the type of structural system selected.

FIGURE 4.11

Shearwall and diaphragm action

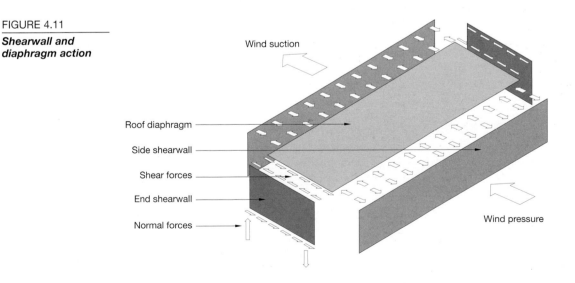

Wind suction

Roof diaphragm

Side shearwall

Shear forces

End shearwall

Normal forces

Wind pressure

BRACING

Bracing is more commonly used with post and beam construction or special structural forms. Diagonal bracing may be used in the plane of the roof and in the plane of the walls. The bracing in the plane of the roof (horizontal bracing) transfers lateral forces to bracing in the plane of the walls (vertical bracing) which in turn transfers the loads to the foundations (Figure 4.12).

Horizontal bracing is usually made of steel rods but lumber or timbers may also be used. The vertical bracing must be provided between columns at regular intervals. Knee braces have traditionally been used to provide wind resistance.

FRAMES

In some structures such as arenas, swimming pools or churches, frames, arches or trusses are used to provide large clear spans. Vertical bracing cannot be used where it will interrupt the clear span of the structure. Therefore, it becomes necessary to design the frames, arches or trusses to resist the lateral forces parallel to their span (Figure 4.13). Perpendicular to the span of the frames, horizontal bracing or roof diaphragms are used to transfer the lateral loads to the side walls where the forces are resisted by bracing or shear walls.

FIGURE 4.12

Diagonal bracing

FIGURE 4.13

Lateral resistance of frames

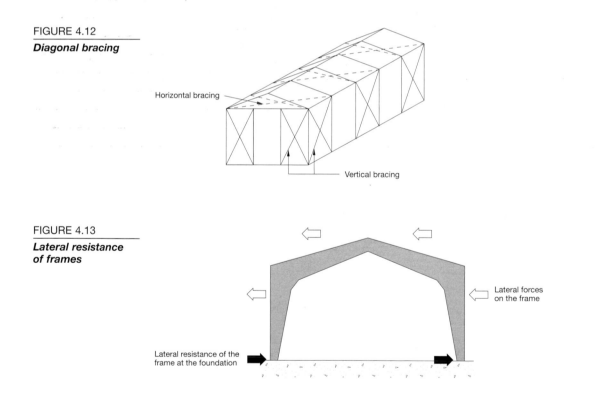

4.7 Tables

TABLE 4.1

Typical wood assemblies

Residential (Part 9)

Floors	Plywood or OSB sheathing 12.5 to 20.5 mm thick spanning 300 to 600 mm.	
	Lumber joists 38 × 140 mm to 38 × 286 mm spaced 300 to 600 mm spanning up to 5 m.	
	Wood I-joists 140 to 286 mm deep spaced 300 to 495 mm spanning up to 10 m.	
	Parallel Chord Trusses 225 to 300 mm deep spaced 400 to 600 mm spanning up to 10 m.	
Walls	Plywood or OSB sheathing 9.5 to 15.5 mm thick spanning 400 to 600 mm.	
	Lumber Studs 38 × 89 mm or 38 × 140 mm spaced 400 to 600 mm, 3.8 m in length.	
Roofs	Plywood or OSB sheathing 9.5 to 15.5 mm thick spanning 400 to 600 mm.	
	Rafters 38 × 140 mm to 38 × 286 mm spaced 400 to 600 mm spanning up to 4 m.	
	Pitched trusses spaced at 600 mm and spanning up to 10 m or more.	

Commercial (Part 4)

Floors	Plywood or OSB sheathing 12.5 to 20.5 mm thick spanning 300 to 600 mm.	
	Concrete topping 38 mm thick optional.	
	Wood I-joists 235 to 406 mm deep spanning up to 12 m.	
	Parallel chord trusses 235 to 508 mm deep spanning up to 20 m.	
	Joists or trusses supported by bearing walls or by PSL and LVL beams for spans up to 5 m and by glulam beams for spans up to 15 m.	
Roofs	Plywood or OSB sheathing 12.5 to 20.5 mm thick spanning 400 to 600 mm.	
	Wood I-joists 235 to 406 mm deep spanning up to 12 m.	
	Pitched or parallel chord trusses at 600 mm spanning up to 30 m.	
Walls	Plywood or OSB sheathing 9.5 to 15.5 mm thick spanning 400 to 600 mm.	
	Wood studs 38 × 140 mm or 38 × 235 mm spaced 400 to 600 mm.	
	Close spaced nailing 75 to 300 mm centres for shearwall applications.	
	Tie downs as required for uplift.	

TABLE 4.2

Examples of maximum building area per floor[1]

Major occupancy		Building height in storeys	Maximum building areas $m^2 \times 10^3$
A	**Assembly**		
Div 1	Performing arts[2]	1	unlimited
Div 2	Other (schools, restaurants)	2	0.8 / 1.0 / 1.2 / 2.4
		1	1.6 / 2.0 / 2.4 / 4.8
Div 3	Arenas	1	2.4 / 3.0 / 3.6 / 7.2[3]
Div 4	Outdoor viewing (no FRR)[4]	–	unlimited[5]
B	**Detention, Treatment and Care**		
Div 2	Hospitals	2	1.6
		1	2.4
Div 3	Assisted living facilities, group homes	3	1.8[6]
		2	1.6
		1	2.4
C	**Residential** Apartments, hotels, motels	3	0.6 / 0.75 / 0.9 / 1.8
		2	0.9 / 1.125 / 1.35 / 2.7
		1	1.8 / 2.25 / 2.7 / 5.4
C	**Residential (1 hour FRR)** Apartments, hotels, motels	4	1.8
		3	0.8 / 1.0 / 1.2 / 2.4
		2	1.2 / 1.5 / 1.8 / 3.6
		1	2.4 / 3.0 / 3.6 / 7.2

Scale markings for Maximum building areas: 0, 5, 10, 15

Legend:
- facing one street, unsprinklered
- facing two streets, unsprinklered
- facing three streets, unsprinklered
- sprinklered[7]

Notes:
1. In general, buildings described are required to have 45-minute fire-resistance rating (FRR), or to be of Heavy Timber construction (exceptions noted).
2. Occupant load limited to 300 persons.
3. Building requires no fire-resistance rating.
4. Occupant load limited to 1500 persons.
5. Building requires a limiting distance of not less than 6 m.
6. Building requires 1-hour fire-resistance rating.
7. For sprinklered options, access is required on one side only.

TABLE 4.2
(continued)

Maximum building area per floor (sprinklered)[1]

Major occupancy		Building height in storeys	Maximum building areas $m^2 \times 10^3$				
				0	5	10	15
D	**Business and personal** Services (Offices)	4[2]	3.6				
		3	1.6 2.0 2.4 4.8				
		1	4.8 6.0 7.2 14.4				
E	**Mercantile** (Stores, supermarkets)	4[2]	1.8				
		3	0.8 1.0 1.5 2.4				
		1	1.5 1.5 1.5 7.2				
F Div 1	**Industrial** High hazard	2	1.2				
		1	0.8[3] 0.8[3] 0.8[3] 2.4				
Div 2	Medium hazard	4	2.4				
		1	1.5 1.5 1.5 9.6				
Div 3	Low hazard	4	1.2 1.5 1.8 3.6				
		1	4.8 6.0 7.2 14.4				

facing one street, unsprinklered
facing two streets, unsprinklered
facing three streets, unsprinklered
sprinklered[4]

Notes:
1. In general, buildings described are required to have 45-minute fire-resistance rating (FRR), or to be of Heavy Timber construction (exceptions noted).
2. Building requires 1-hour fire-resistance rating.
3. Building requires no fire-resistance rating.
4. For sprinklered options, access is required on one side only.

Design Properties of Wood

Design Properties of Wood

5.1 General Information

Because wood is a naturally occurring material, there is variability in wood properties due to factors such as rate of growth, growing conditions, species, and moisture content. A basic understanding of the unique properties of wood, as explained in this chapter, is necessary so that wood products can be used by the designer to maximum potential.

Like all building materials, wood has unique properties. By understanding the nature of wood, designers are able to optimize design details.

For example, hygroscopicity (the ability to absorb moisture) is a major property of wood that needs to be understood so that it can be accounted for in material selection and design.

Wood will gain or lose moisture depending on the environmental conditions to which the wood is subjected.

Moisture affects wood products in two ways. First, change in moisture content causes dimensional change (shrinkage and swelling). Secondly, when combined with other necessary conditions, moisture leads to deterioration of wood by decay.

This chapter reviews general information about wood properties, and factors which are used in design to account for these properties, and is organized as follows:

5.2   Basic Properties

5.3   Modification Factors

5.4   Tables

5.2 Basic Properties

INTRODUCTION

For many applications, wood properties such as acoustic performance and fire resistance must be considered in design. However, this section will focus on the properties which are considered in structural design, including strength properties and hygroscopicity.

STRENGTH PROPERTIES

Grain Direction

As a tree grows, a layer of wood cells is added each year directly below the bark. This layer is known as an annual ring (Figure 5.1).

Due to growth patterns, wood has different strength properties in different grain directions (Figure 5.2) and is therefore categorized as an anisotropic material. CSA O86 provides values of specified strengths for various wood products, in which separate (and very different) values are given for parallel to grain resistance and perpendicular to grain resistance.

For example, the 24f-E stress grade of Douglas Fir-Larch glulam has the following specified strengths listed in CSA O86 (Table 6.3).

Tension parallel to grain (at net section)
= 20.4 MPa

Tension perpendicular to grain
= 0.83 MPa

Compression parallel to grain
= 30.2 MPa

Compression perpendicular to grain
= 7.0 MPa

Density

The density of wood varies by species, and there are variations within species groups depending on growing conditions (Table 5.1). The density of wood is a general indicator of strength properties (Figure 5.3). Density is usually related to strength, and affects design parameters such as fastener strength.

FIGURE 5.1

Microscopic wood structure

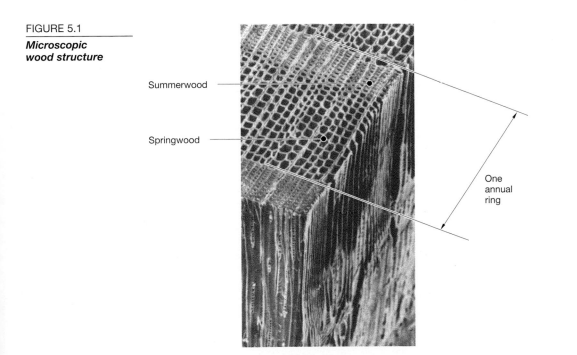

Summerwood

Springwood

One annual ring

FIGURE 5.2

Strength properties and grain directions

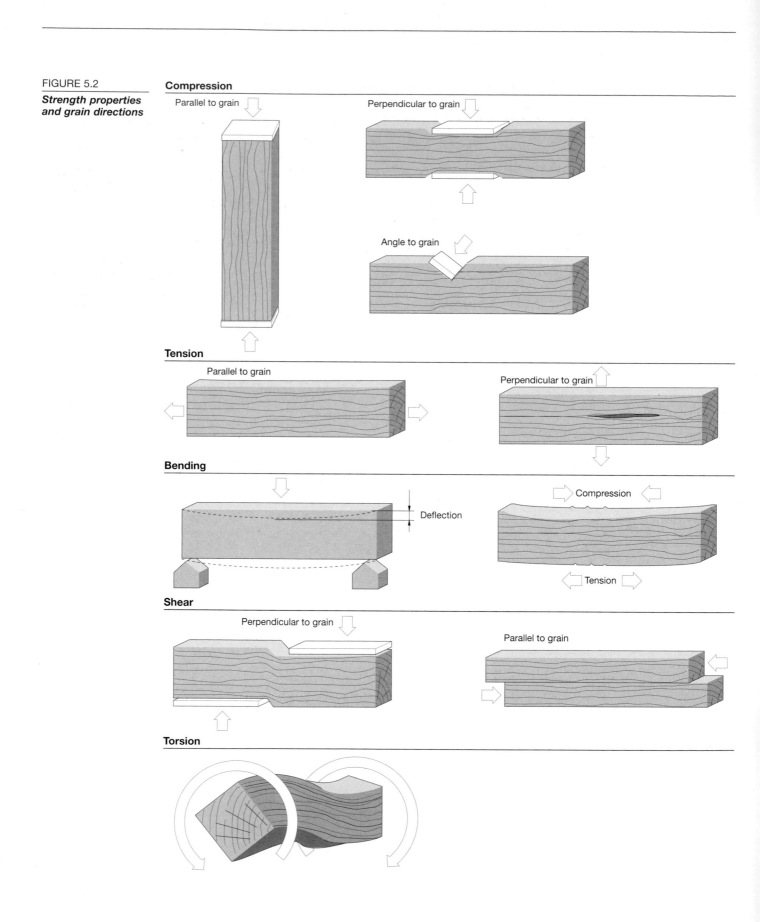

Compression

Parallel to grain

Perpendicular to grain

Angle to grain

Tension

Parallel to grain

Perpendicular to grain

Bending

Deflection

Compression

Tension

Shear

Perpendicular to grain

Parallel to grain

Torsion

Density is also a general indicator of hardness. Hardness is not usually a design parameter except where impact or abrasion need to be considered.

EFFECTS OF MOISTURE

Wood is a hygroscopic material. It gains and loses moisture depending on the environmental conditions to which it is exposed. The loss and gain of moisture affects dimensional stability and strength, and the presence of water in combination with other conditions can cause decay.

Strength

Below the fibre-saturation point (at approximately 28% moisture content), strength increases as moisture content decreases. But not all strength properties are affected to the same degree (Figure 5.4). (As explained in Section 5.3, a service condition factor, K_S, is used in design to account for this.)

Dimensional Change

Wood shrinks when it dries and swells when it gains moisture. The extent to which dimensional changes occurs depends upon the species and the orientation of the wood fibres (Table 5.2).

FIGURE 5.3

Strength variation relative to density

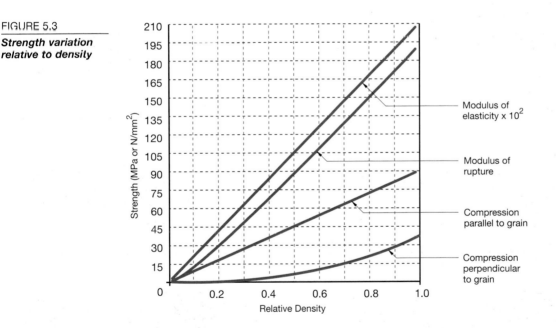

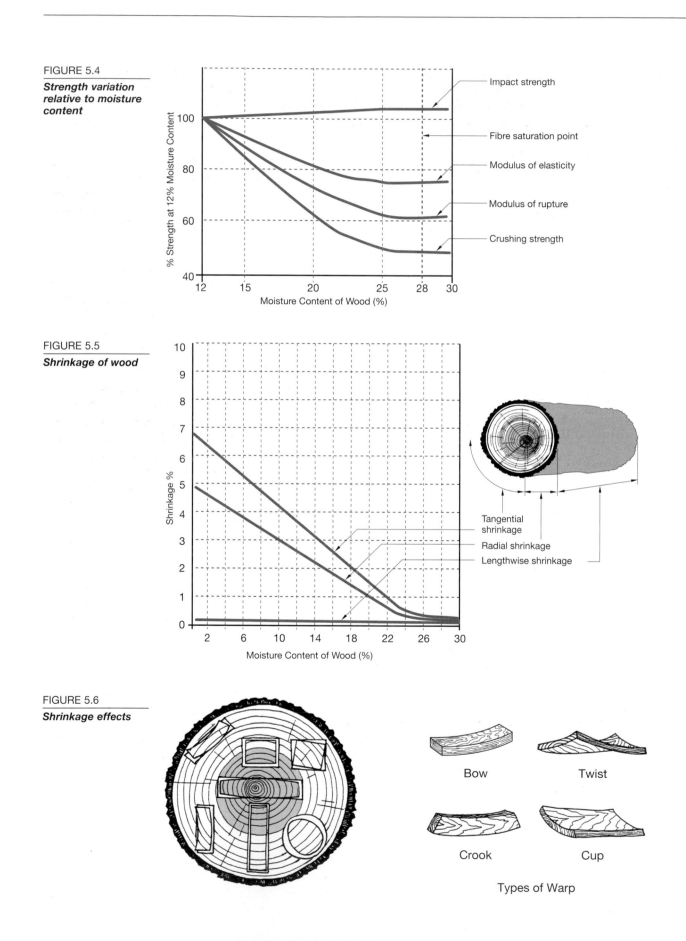

FIGURE 5.4

Strength variation relative to moisture content

FIGURE 5.5

Shrinkage of wood

FIGURE 5.6

Shrinkage effects

Impact strength

Fibre saturation point

Modulus of elasticity

Modulus of rupture

Crushing strength

% Strength at 12% Moisture Content

Moisture Content of Wood (%)

Shrinkage %

Moisture Content of Wood (%)

Tangential shrinkage

Radial shrinkage

Lengthwise shrinkage

Bow

Twist

Crook

Cup

Types of Warp

When wood dries from its green condition, little or no shrinkage occurs until the moisture content falls below the fibre saturation level (Figure 5.5). At this level, all free moisture has been released from the cell cavities, leaving only the cell walls saturated. The moisture content at which this condition is reached varies, but averages 28% (based on the ratio of the weight of water to the oven-dried weight of wood) for Canadian softwoods. As the cell walls continue to release moisture, the wood shrinks almost in direct proportion to its moisture loss. That is, for each percentage drop in moisture content, the wood shrinks by about 1/30 of its total potential shrinkage.

The moisture level of the wood will eventually reach equilibrium, and will continue to adjust to changing conditions by gaining or losing moisture.

Lumber which has been air dried or kiln dried to lumber grading standards will have a moisture content of 19% or less. Using dried lumber reduces the potential for shrinkage because the moisture of the lumber will be closer to the equilibrium moisture content in service.

At moisture contents less than about 28%, wood shrinks when it loses moisture and expands when it gains moisture. However, due to the cellular structure of wood, it does not shrink or expand equally in each direction. Generally, wood shrinks very little along the grain (longitudinally), while the shrinkage across the grain can be quite large. In addition, shrinkage along the growth rings (tangentially) is generally larger than the shrinkage across the growth rings (radially) (Figure 5.6).

While engineered products such as glulam and plywood behave somewhat differently because of laminations and gluelines, they nevertheless gain and lose moisture (Figure 5.7).

The difference in shrinkage between the radial and tangential directions can cause lumber to warp. Badly warped pieces of lumber are unsuitable for use as framing members.

Warping may occur as lumber dries during storage. The use of S-Dry lumber will reduce warpage since it has been surfaced after drying to a moisture content of 19% or less. Warping can also be reduced by restraining the wood while drying takes place.

Checking occurs when lumber is rapidly dried. The surface dries quickly, while the core remains at a higher moisture content for some time. As a result, the surface attempts to shrink but is restrained by the core. This restraint causes tensile stresses at the surface, which if large enough, can pull the fibres apart thereby creating a check.

Splits are through checks that generally occur at the end of wood members. When a wood member dries, moisture is lost very rapidly from the end of the member. At mid-length, however, the wood is still at a higher moisture content. This difference in moisture content creates tensile stresses at the end of the member. When the stresses exceed the strength of the wood, a split is formed.

A number of growth and manufacturing characteristics are shown in Figure 5.8.

Sawn timbers are susceptible to checking and splitting since they are always dressed green (S-Grn). Furthermore, due to their large size, the core dries slowly and the tensile stresses at the surface and at the ends can be large.

Minor checks confined to the surface areas of a wood member very rarely have any effect on the strength of the member. Deep checks could be significant if they occur at a point of high shear stress. Checks in columns are not of structural importance, unless the check

FIGURE 5.7
_____

*Moisture content
and shrinkage*

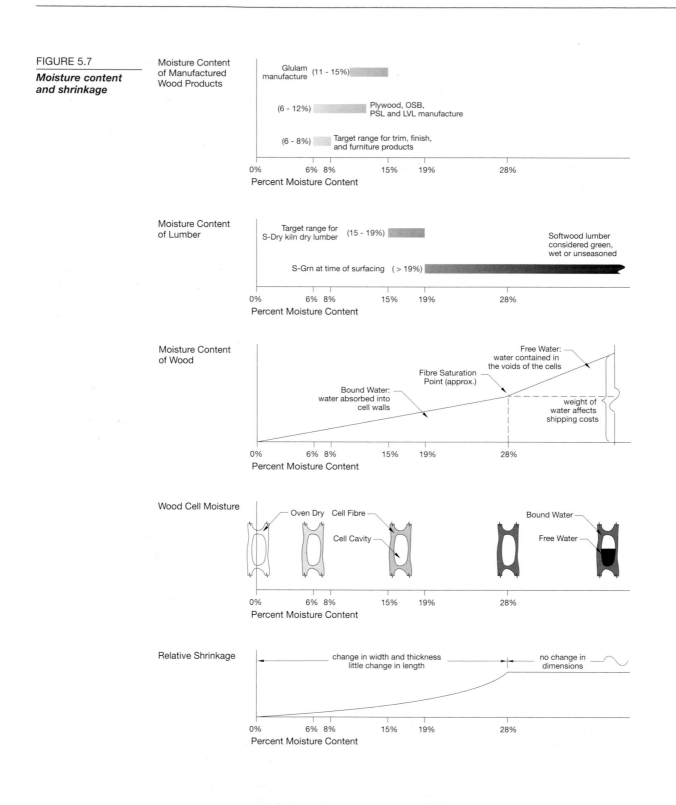

Moisture Content
of Manufactured
Wood Products

Glulam manufacture (11 - 15%)

(6 - 12%) Plywood, OSB, PSL and LVL manufacture

(6 - 8%) Target range for trim, finish, and furniture products

0%   6% 8%   15%   19%   28%
Percent Moisture Content

Moisture Content
of Lumber

Target range for S-Dry kiln dry lumber (15 - 19%)

Softwood lumber considered green, wet or unseasoned

S-Grn at time of surfacing (> 19%)

0%   6% 8%   15%   19%   28%
Percent Moisture Content

Moisture Content
of Wood

Free Water:
water contained in
the voids of the cells

Fibre Saturation
Point (approx.)

Bound Water:
water absorbed into
cell walls

weight of
water affects
shipping costs

0%   6% 8%   15%   19%   28%
Percent Moisture Content

Wood Cell Moisture

Oven Dry   Cell Fibre

Cell Cavity

Bound Water

Free Water

0%   6% 8%   15%   19%   28%
Percent Moisture Content

Relative Shrinkage

change in width and thickness
little change in length

no change in
dimensions

0%   6% 8%   15%   19%   28%
Percent Moisture Content

develops into a through split that will increase the slenderness ratio of the column. The specified shear strengths of sawn lumber and timbers have been developed to consider the maximum amount of checking or splitting permitted by the applicable grading rule.

The possibility and severity of splitting and checking can be reduced by controlling the rate at which drying occurs. This may be done by keeping wood out of direct sunlight and away from any artificial heat sources. Furthermore, the ends may be coated with an end sealer to retard moisture loss.

Other actions which will minimize dimension change and the possibility of checking or splitting are:

- specifying wood products that are as close as possible in moisture content to the expected equilibrium moisture content of the end use

- ensuring that the investment made in purchasing dry wood products is protected by proper storage and handling

Equilibrium Moisture Content (EMC)

Moisture affects strength and stiffness, and dimension (Section 5.3). Seasonal climatic variation may cause finish work such as doors to fit differently between humid and dry times of year. Usually, seasonal variations are not extreme enough to affect strength.

Table 5.3 gives some typical Canadian conditions and the equilibrium moisture contents that result. Once wood has been seasoned, it adjusts slowly to changing humidity levels (Figure 5.9). This is an important feature because it shows that, barring immersion, wood can serve in very high relative humidities without reaching an equilibrium moisture content that will initiate decay.

Wood is considered to be in a dry service condition when the average equilibrium moisture content (EMC) over a year is 15% or less and does not exceed 19%. The EMC of wood in the interior of most buildings in Canada rarely exceeds 12%.

FIGURE 5.8

Growth and manufacturing characteristics

Edge-grain

Flat-grain

Cross-grain

Loose knot

Spiral-grain

Diagonal-grain

Spike knot

Sound tight knot

Check

Shake

Wane

Pitch pocket

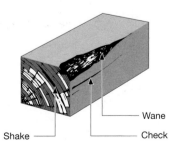
Shake — Wane — Check

Therefore, dry service conditions usually apply, but strengths and stiffnesses for wood will need to be modified by a service condition factor, K_S, if the material will be used in a wet environment such as a swimming pool enclosure (an application which wood serves well).

Moisture Content Determination

The moisture content of lumber may be determined by oven drying samples in a laboratory, or by measuring with electrical meters.

With the oven drying method, the wood samples to be assessed for moisture content are weighed and then dried in an oven until all moisture has been driven off. After drying, the samples are weighed again, and the moisture content, MC, is calculated as follows:

$$MC\% = \frac{\text{initial weight} - \text{oven dry weight}}{\text{oven dry weight}} \times 100$$

(The procedures and details for this method are outlined in American Society for Testing and Materials [ASTM] Standard D4442-07).

In many instances, the oven dry method is impractical due to the time required to complete the testing. For this reason, several types of electrical meters have been developed. Although less precise than the oven drying method, moisture meters provide instantaneous readings, are easy to use, and are not destructive. This makes them well suited to industrial and field applications. ASTM standard D7438-08 addresses standard practice for field calibration and application of hand-held moisture meters.

Several different types of meters are available that measure the electrical resistance, dielectric, or radio-frequency power-loss properties of wood. Those which measure the relationship between moisture content and electrical resistance (resistance type) are most common. They consist of a meter and an electrode with pins. Two pin electrodes are usually used, but four or eight pins are available for special applications such as measuring the moisture content of thin veneer. Pins can be purchased in a variety of lengths and they can be insulated or uninsulated.

FIGURE 5.9

EMC variation with relative humidity

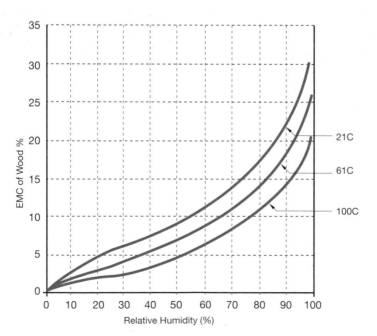

Uninsulated pins record the highest moisture content along the depth of penetration of the electrodes, whereas insulated pins measure the moisture content present in the wood at the tip (uninsulated portion) of the electrodes.

ASTM D7438 requires that, for dimension lumber and decking, the pins be driven into the board to a depth equal to 1/5 to 1/4 of the thickness. Since the resistivity of wood differs with the grain orientation, the pins must be driven so as to measure electrical resistivity parallel to the grain. The reading area must be at least 500 mm from the board ends, near mid width, and be free of defects such as knots, splits, resin pockets and decay.

The electrical resistance of wood varies with both temperature and species. Resistivity decreases directly with increasing temperature, and is affected by the presence of electrolytes and moisture gradients over the depth penetrated by the electrodes. If temperature or species differs from the factory calibration of the instrument, correction factors must be applied to the meter reading.

Most of the newer meters have the species correction applied automatically when the appropriate species group setting is chosen on the meter, while some meters can automatically correct for both species and temperature. Where correction factors are required, tables supplied by the manufacturer should be used. It is important to note that resistance type meters are only reliable between 6% and 30% moisture content.

Effects of Wood Shrinkage in Buildings

Wood shrinks (or swells) tangentially, radially, and longitudinally. Tangential shrinkage (concentric to the growth rings) is approximately twice the radial shrinkage (perpendicular to the growth rings). Shrinkage values for individual specimens of the same species can vary considerably, and therefore values based on averages may be somewhat misleading.

For example, the average tangential shrinkage of spruce from the fibre saturation level (28%) to the oven-dried state (0%) is 7 to 8%, while the average radial shrinkage is about 4%. The longitudinal shrinkage for most species over this moisture range is only 0.1 to 0.2%.

This small longitudinal shrinkage is usually ignored in design. Greater longitudinal shrinkage can occur if the wood is badly cross-grained or contains juvenile (coming from the central core of trees) or compression wood (wood subjected to unusual compression stresses during its growth).

Plywood has shrinkage characteristics similar to that of lumber in the longitudinal direction. This stability is due to the much higher modulus of elasticity of wood parallel to grain than perpendicular to grain. Alternating the direction of the grain in adjacent plies, therefore, stabilizes the plywood in both directions.

This stabilizing effect of different grain directions also applies to oriented strand-board (OSB).

FIGURE 5.10

*Detailing to account
for shrinkage*

Unequal shrinkage at ends of joists may cause an uneven floor

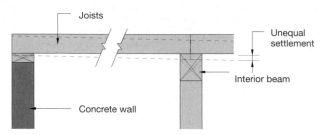

Providing a sill beam to equalize shrinkage is recommended

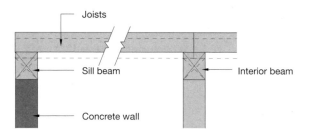

Bolt near top of hanger will cause a split

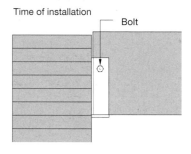
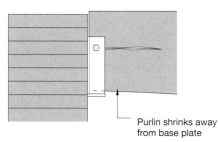

Locating bolt near bottom of hanger recommended

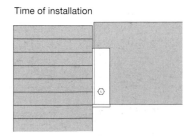
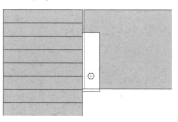

Equilibrium moisture contents for wood stored under cover during the summer in most inland areas of Canada vary from 11 to 12%, while in the coastal areas they range from 14 to 16%. At these levels about half to two-thirds of the total potential shrinkage will have occurred.

If lumber is installed in a building before the equilibrium level is reached, not all of its potential shrinkage will have taken place, and the risk of shrinkage-related problems is increased.

For this reason, the *National Building Code of Canada* and most provincial building codes specify that the moisture content of framing lumber must not exceed 19% at the time of installation so that some dimensional change will have already taken place.

In addition, there are detailing practices that should be used to negate the effect of shrinkage should it occur (Figure 5.10).

Wood in heated buildings can be subjected to a wide range of humidity levels over an annual cycle. Winter humidity levels of 20 to 30% are common in houses, and may be even lower in other occupancies that generate little or no moisture such as offices. During the summer, outdoor humidity levels average 60 to 70% in most inland areas. These differences cause the equilibrium moisture content of wood to vary from 6% in winter to 12% in summer, assuming steady-state conditions are reached.

Shrinkage in Multistorey Wood-frame Buildings

For some types of occupancies, wood frame buildings up to four storeys in height are permitted in Canada. In B.C. wood construction is allowed in buildings up to six storeys. For high wood buildings, shrinkage of the wood frame may be an important consideration in the design of the structures, particularly if brick veneer is used.

In such cases, it is important to evaluate the shrinkage of a building's wood frame in four major areas:

- where nonuniform shrinkage may occur
- where metal connections are used to support large solid sawn timber or glued-laminated timber
- where shrinkage could cause distress in the finish material
- where shrinkage could cause distress in plumbing, electrical and mechanical systems

Calculating Wood Shrinkage

The shrinkage of a wood member can be estimated using the equation

$$S = D \times M \times c$$

where

S = shrinkage (mm)

D = actual dressed dimension (mm) (thickness or width)

M = percent of moisture change below the fibre saturation point

c = shrinkage coefficient

The total shrinkage of the wood frame in a high wood-frame building can be calculated by summing the shrinkage of the wood members making up the wall, plates, and joists.

Shrinkage coefficients for both radial (across the growth rings) and tangential (parallel to the growth rings) directions have been determined for individual species (Table 5.2). Because lumber is often sold as a mixture of species and grain orientations, an approximation is recommended whereby a shrinkage coefficient of 0.002 per 1% change in moisture content for multistorey wood frame shrinkage calculations can be assumed.

To determine the percent moisture change, assumptions must be made regarding the initial and final moisture contents of the lumber. The initial moisture content depends largely on what type of lumber is specified. For the purpose of the shrinkage calculation, an initial moisture content of 19% is used based on the NBCC requirement for lumber to be 19% moisture content or less at the time of installation. The final in-service moisture content of protected framing members is usually between 8 and 12% in most structures.

The main shrinkage, because of grain orientation, occurs in the plates and header joists. For a four-storey wall using S-Dry lumber and consisting of three 38×235 mm header joists and twelve 38×89 mm plates (three per floor), and a predicted final moisture content of 10%, shrinkage is calculated as follows:

$$S = D \times M \times c$$

$$= ([3 \times 235] + [12 \times 38]) \times (19 - 10) \times 0.002$$

$$= 20.9 \text{ mm}$$

Shrinkage of the wall studs is generally neglected because of its smaller effect (using a c value of 0.00005 for shrinkage longitudinally for 3 m high walls, $S = 9 \times 12000 \times 0.00005 = 5.4$ mm).

The Canadian Wood Council's web site www.cwc.ca contains Δ DimensionCalc. This tool makes it easier for designers to estimate and account for dimensional changes in new building construction.

Effect of Shrinkage on Fasteners

Any shrinkage of the wood along the embedded length of metal fasteners causes their heads to rise above the wood surface while forcing the tips slightly deeper into the wood. The initial and final moisture contents of the wood, and the depth of fastener penetration, are the principal factors in determining the amount of outward moment, but subsequent seasonal cycles of moisture content changes can add to the initial movement.

Wood shrinkage can cause nail popping in gypsum wallboard finishes. As the fasteners are eased out of the wood, a space is created between the gypsum wallboard and its supports. Subsequent pressure on the gypsum wallboard causes the fastener heads to push through the gypsum wallboard finish.

Shrinkage produces similar effects when fasteners in subflooring or underlayment are covered by thin materials such as vinyl. The raised fastener heads may show on the finished floor as a pattern of tiny bumps. This problem can be reduced by recessing the fastener heads into the wood before the flooring is laid.

Other Shrinkage Effects

Since greater shrinkage occurs across the grain, wood-strip flooring is particularly vulnerable to the effects of shrinkage and swelling.

Thus when flooring is installed, its moisture content should be as close as possible to the level it will attain in service. To avoid buckling, the flooring should be stored in a location that will allow it to reach the *in-situ* equilibrium moisture level before it is laid. A clearance of 10 to 15 mm around the floor perimeter should be provided to allow for swelling.

Although conventional wood framing is reasonably tolerant of the effects of shrinkage, using unseasoned lumber can invite problems, particularly if construction proceeds rapidly and the lumber is enclosed before much of the potential shrinkage has occurred. This prevents corrective action being taken, such as using shims to compensate for the shrinkage effects. Differential shrinkage commonly occurs around windows and doors where the lintels shrink away from the supporting jack studs. It also occurs where metal joist hangers support unseasoned wood joists around floor openings.

The manufacturing process for plywood and OSB results in a final moisture content of about 4%, which is considerably below its moisture content in use. A 2 mm gap should be left between the plywood or OSB sheets to reduce the possibility of buckling due to expansion.

Detailing for Shrinkage

Shrinkage should be taken into consideration where wood framing is combined with materials not subject to dimensional change as in the case of a masonry block elevator shaft in a wood frame building. If the floor joists are supported by a wood frame wall on one end and by the masonry block on the other, differential movement between ends of the joists may occur.

This condition may require framing the wood floor so it is entirely independent of the block wall, or framing the joists to the block wall after the wood framed walls and joists reach equilibrium.

The detailing of metal connections to prevent stresses due to wood shrinkage is most critical in large wood member connections such as heavy timber framing or glue-laminated timber framing. Improperly designed connections can restrain shrinkage and cause splitting. An example is the beam to column connection. The preferred method of connecting these members is a seat or saddle connection rather than a metal angle with a column of bolts.

To avoid problems in finish materials such as gypsum wallboard, siding, and sheathing, avoid continuous vertical runs which can result in buckling at each floor level. Expansion joints or slip-type architectural details are typically used at each floor level.

In multistorey buildings, detailing to accommodate the differential movement between the wood (shrinkage due to drying) and exterior brick veneer (expansion due to wetting) is required. Procedures exist for calculating the differential movement between wood framing and exterior brick veneer. Realistic shrinkage and expansion must be considered and architectural detailing is required to accommodate this movement.

NATURAL HAZARDS

Deterioration

Wood is an organic material and is subject to deterioration by decay. Decay is a naturally occurring process in the forest whereby fallen wood is broken down into organic matter which in turn nourishes new growth. It is, of course, a process which must be avoided when wood is used as a building material.

For decay to proceed, four conditions must all exist. Elimination of any one arrests decay and the decay cannot become active until all four conditions are once again satisfied. The conditions are as follows:

- Fungi must have oxygen to flourish. For buildings, the exclusion of oxygen is not controllable, and therefore the control of decay comes from controlling the other conditions.

- Temperatures in the 20 to 30°C range are optimum for fungi. At low temperature, fungi activity slows or stops. This means that fungi activity for exposed applications reduces in winter. However, summer temperatures offer ample opportunity for fungi activity, as do the normal temperatures for indoor applications. For this reason, temperature control, like oxygen control, is not usually feasible.

- Enough moisture must be present for fungi to be active. Fungi cannot infest or be active when the moisture content in wood is below 20%. Therefore construction details should keep wood products from direct exposure to water where intermittent drying is not possible.

- The wood food supply must be available. The food supply can be made unavailable by pressure treating with chemicals which are not conducive to fungi, or by using species such as cedar which have some natural resistance to decay.

Detailing to Prevent Deterioration

There are three common sources of moisture in wood buildings:

- Ground moisture
- Moisture from precipitation
- Moisture from condensation

Wood will not deteriorate if the moisture content is below 20%. If moisture is prevented from accumulating on the wood members, deterioration is avoided. Following are some details commonly used to prevent decay.

To prevent deterioration from ground moisture:

- Unless the bottom of a wood member is more than 150 mm above grade, untreated wood members supported on concrete in contact with the ground or fill must be separated from the concrete by at least a 0.05 mm polyethylene film or Type S roll roofing.
- Untreated wood members framing into concrete or masonry at or below the ground line shall be provided with a 12 mm air space at the ends and sides of the members.
- Soil in crawl spaces should be covered with polyethylene or other moisture-impervious soil cover.
- Crawl spaces should be well vented.

To prevent deterioration of roof and wall members from precipitation:

- Use steep roofs where possible.
- Ensure roofs are properly insulated and vented thus preventing water damage as a result of ice damming.
- Protect members projecting beyond the eaves with flashing or covers.
- In areas of frequent and heavy rainfall, provisions in the design should be made to deflect most of the rain from the surface of the building, for example, by building longer eaves.
- Where water may be able to infiltrate the wall envelope cavity, leave a space between the outside envelope and the frame that allows the excess water to exit the cavity.
- Design the wall envelope with sufficient ventilation of the cavity.

To prevent deterioration of the basement and first floor members from precipitation:

- Provide good drainage around buildings including sloping of grade away from the building and providing for drainage through weeping tiles, sumps etc.
- Waterproof foundation walls to limit seepage into the basement.

To prevent deterioration of exterior wood members:

- Space decking boards (6 mm or more) to allow drainage and air circulation on porches, patios, etc.
- Protect exposed wood joints which can't drain with capping, flashing or caulking.
- Prevent wood absorption in exposed ends of posts or poles by capping the top or cutting it at a slope to force water to run off.
- Prevent water from building up around arch or column bases by raising the wood member or sloping the footing to allow drainage.
- Use preservative treated wood in locations where deterioration is likely to occur.

To prevent deterioration from condensation:

- Provide properly constructed well sealed air and vapour barriers.
- Provide power exhaust fans, vented to the outside of the structure, in bathrooms, laundry rooms, kitchens and other areas that produce large volumes of moisture.
- Provide adequate venting in the attic.

Insects

Termites, carpenter ants and powder post beetles are insects that use wood for either food or shelter and can cause significant damage when they infest wood buildings. The Formosan termite is particularly notorious for damaging wood members. They inhabit the ground beside or below the foundation and build mud tunnels along the foundation wall to safely reach the wood above. Although termite related issues are concentrated in the southern US, there is some termite activity in Southern B.C., Manitoba and Ontario.

To prevent deterioration from termite attacks:

- Carefully clean and prepare the site and ensure that wood debris is removed rather than buried to discourage colonisation near the structure.
- Grade the site to avoid collecting water near the foundation.
- Ensure that there is proper clearance between the soil and the wood structure.
- Use sand or stone barriers of a proper granularity that will act as a soil barrier under the foundation slabs
- Build visible foundations and install metal sheet barriers that will ease the detection of termite shelter tubes
- Use treated wood in high-risk areas.

PRESERVATIVE TREATMENT

In applications where wood is subject to biological deterioration due to the action of fungi or insects, the decay and insect resistance of wood must be considered. Chemically treating wood under pressure is the most common method for ensuring long service life in harsh environments. Properly preservative-treated wood can have 5 to 10 times the service life of untreated wood in severe exposure conditions.

Pressure treatment is the most effective way to treat wood products. Penetration and retention of preservative is achieved by driving the preservative into the wood cells with pressure under controlled conditions. In Canada, the CSA O80 series of Standards specifies the requirements for preservative treatment of a broad range of wood products used in different applications.

Each type of preservative has distinct advantages and the preservative used should be determined by the end use of the material. Information on wood preservatives may be obtained from the Wood Preservation Canada at www.woodpreservation.ca. Health Canada's Pest Management Regulatory Agency is responsible for the registration of pesticides in Canada. Since the regulatory status of wood preservatives is being constantly reviewed, one may contact the Agency or the local authorities if the use of a particular preservative for a specific application is in question.

Preservation treatment does not usually affect the mechanical performance of the member. However, for hard to treat species such as spruce, the treatment may involve incising the wood locally to increase penetration, which in turn may decrease the mechanical properties of the lumber. CSA O86 includes a treatment factor, K_T, that accounts for this condition.

5.3   Modification Factors

INTRODUCTION

Due to the unique properties of wood described in the previous section, design codes and standards provide several modification factors to be used to tailor a design for a specific application. Such factors are used for member and for connection design.

The design of wood structures is in accordance with the latest edition of CSA O86 *Engineering Design in Wood*. It uses the load factors required by the *National Building Code of Canada* (NBCC) as presented in Chapter 2.

Because wood exhibits different material behaviour compared to other materials, the design approach for wood requires the use of factors specific to the structural behaviour of wood. These modification factors are used to adjust the specified strengths and capacities in CSA O86 to account for material characteristics specific to wood.

The reliability of lumber is based on test results. Bending, compression and tension tests were conducted on many thousands of specimens. From the lumber test data, statistical inferences were made so that the specified strength values in CSA O86 are reliable to a high degree.

Reliability analyses were conducted and led to the values used for the resistance factor, ϕ, as follows:

ϕ = 0.90 for bending, shear and tension

= 0.80 for compression both parallel and perpendicular to grain

The specified strength data for timbers was reviewed and modified as a result of the lumber test program so that values for specified strengths and performance factors represent the behaviour of structural timber sizes.

Testing of full size beams, reliability analysis, and modelling used to establish reliability factors for glulam support the use of the resistance factor ϕ = 0.90 for glulam.

For plywood, CSA O86 gives specified strength capacities only for standard constructions of regular grades of unsanded Douglas fir plywood (DFP) and Canadian softwood plywood (CSP). Specified strength properties are also provided for construction sheathing OSB. Reliability analyses result in a resistance factor ϕ = 0.95 for all strength calculations.

The following sections describe the modification factors commonly required for the design of dimension lumber members.

DURATION OF LOAD, K_D

Wood has the ability to carry short-term loads of a higher magnitude than those it will support for a long time. This dependence on the duration of applied load is well documented from studies of load duration effects for Canadian dimension lumber and on conceptual models (Figure 5.11).

The tabulated specified strengths in CSA O86 for lumber and glulam are for standard duration of load such as snow loads and live loads on the floors of most assembly, residential, institutional and commercial occupancies.

The use of K_D accounts for the influence of the expected duration of the specified loads, and maintains a uniform margin of safety for all duration of loading conditions.

For loads applied for a longer or shorter duration than standard, the load duration factor, K_D, is used to modify the specified strengths CSA O86 Table 4.3.2.2.

The three classes of load duration used in CSA O86 are:

- Short Term
- Standard Term
- Long Term

Short Term

Short term loads ($K_D = 1.15$) include wind and earthquake loads, falsework and formwork loads, and impact loads.

Standard Term

The load duration factor, K_D, for standard term load duration is 1.00 because the specified strength data from short term tests have been adjusted to give the values used in CSA O86.

FIGURE 5.11

Duration of load effect for dimension lumber

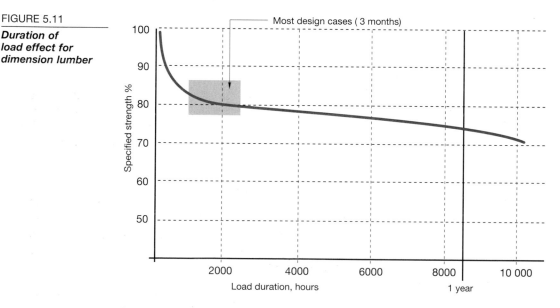

Notes:

1. Specified strengths in CSA O86 have incorporated a factor of 0.8 to account for load duration.

2. This curve is derived assuming the wood members are fully stressed to their short term resistance for the cumulative period shown.

Standard term loads include snow loads, live loads due to use and occupancy, wheel loads on bridges, and dead loads in combination with the foregoing.

For standard term loads where long-term load exceeds live load, a load duration factor of $K_D = 0.65$ for long-term loads may be used. Alternatively, a less conservative value for K_D may be calculated as follows:

$$K_D = 1.0 - 0.50 \log \left(\frac{P_L}{P_s} \right) \geq 0.65$$

where

P_L = specified long-term load

P_S = specified standard-term load based on S and L loads acting alone or in combination

= S, L, S + 0.5L, or 0.5S + L, where S is determined using $I_S = 1.0$.

In designing for combinations of loads, the load which acts for the shortest duration determines the K_D factor.

Long-term

The third case of duration of load is permanent loading ($K_D = 0.65$) and includes loads due to bulk materials in tanks or bins, earth pressure on retaining walls, floor loads in storage structures where the loads may be continuously applied, or loads from machinery fixed in place.

SYSTEM FACTOR, K_H

Many wood construction systems are arranged so that loads are distributed over several adjacent framing members. The effect of repetitive members all acting together to support applied loads reduces the effect of any one member being weaker because loads can be transferred to adjacent members. The K_H factors in Table 5.4.4 of CSA O86 were developed based on reliability analyses of wood systems.

For an assembly to behave as a system, there must be three or more essentially parallel members spaced not more than 610 mm apart. For such an assembly, the Case 1 system factors listed in CSA O86 apply.

If in addition, a minimum thickness of plywood, OSB, or lumber is attached to the members as specified in CSA O86, the more liberal Case 2 system factors can be used.

For lumber construction systems defined as Case 1 systems, designers may modify specified strength by a K_H factor of 1.1; for Case 2 systems, with certain combinations of sheathing and fastening, larger values of K_H (as large as 1.4) may be used.

The Case 2 system factors apply to traditional solid lumber joist, rafter or stud systems with basic sheathing and fastenings. The K_H for Case 2 systems is intended to reflect both composite action and load-sharing effects. For systems of trusses or other types of construction, Case 2 factors may not be applied. However, Case 1 factors may apply, depending on the configuration of framing, sheathing and fastenings.

Specified strengths for glulam (except tension) may be modified by K_H values of 1.1 for systems consisting of 3 or more essentially parallel members not more than 610 mm apart and so arranged that they mutually support the applied load.

SERVICE CONDITION FACTOR, K_S

Wood is hygroscopic, which means it is able to gain and lose moisture. Because wood strength varies with moisture content, the equilibrium moisture content of wood in service must be predicted.

The specified strengths of wood structural elements are based on test results for dry service conditions, which is defined as a condition in which the average equilibrium moisture content over a year is 15% or less and does not exceed 19%.

When dry service conditions are not expected, a modification factor K_S is used to account for lower expected strengths. The values for K_S for wet service conditions are different for different specified strengths and depend on member size as shown in CSA O86 Table 5.4.2.

The values for K_S can differ for different properties and wood products. Subscripts are used to denote the particular service condition factors as: K_{Sb} for bending, K_{Sv} for shear, K_{Sc} for compression (with a further designation of K_{Scp} for compression perpendicular to grain), K_{St} for tension and K_{SE} for modulus of elasticity. Values for K_S are given for lumber, glulam, plywood and fastenings in CSA O86.

In wet service conditions, K_S for lumber in thicknesses of 89 mm or less ranges from $K_{Scp} = 0.67$ for compression perpendicular to grain to $K_{Sv} = 0.96$ for longitudinal shear.

The specified strengths for lumber in sizes larger than 89 mm (which is less likely to be dry when installed) are values appropriate for material that is not dry and, except for compression, values of K_S are 1.00.

SIZE FACTOR, K_Z

The effect of size on strength is taken into account by using a size factor, K_Z, which depends on the property under consideration and on the larger dimension of the member cross section (CSA O86 Table 5.4.5). For compression parallel to grain strength of lumber, the K_{Zc} factor also varies with length. K_{Zb}, K_{Zv}, and K_{Zt} are for bending , shear and tension respectively and allow for modifying specified strength values by as much as 70%.

For glulam, size effects on strength are recognized for tension perpendicular to grain (factor K_{Ztp}), for bending (factor K_{Zbg}), for compression (factor K_{Zcg}), for bearing (factor K_{Zcp}), and shear (by incorporating beam volume in the calculation of shear resistance).

Therefore, larger (deeper) members tend to be weaker than smaller members. The size factor is used to account for this effect in dimension lumber and timber.

TREATMENT FACTOR, K_T

The influence of chemicals and pressure treatment processes on wood strength properties and capacities is taken into account by use of a factor K_T for preservative and fire-retardant treatment (CSA O86 Table 5.4.3). In the case of fire-retardant treatment, it is recommended that information about the effect on strength values be obtained from the manufacturer of the treating chemical. Some formulations of fire-retardants have significant effects on wood properties. The documented strength reduction factors should be based on tests that take into account the effects of time, temperature and moisture content.

5.4   Tables

TABLE 5.1

*Density and
hardness
of Canadian
softwoods*

Species	Subgroup	Relative density based on volume air-dry and mass oven-dry[2]	Hardness (N)[1]	
			Side	End
Cedar	Eastern White	0.30	1360	2380
	Western Red	0.34	1470	3000
	Yellow	0.43	2510	3960
Douglas fir		0.49	2990	4020
Fir	Amabilis	0.39	1970	3710
	Balsam	0.35	1820	3170
Hemlock	Eastern	0.43	2380	3670
	Western	0.43	2740	4410
Tamarack		0.51	3220	3760
Larch	Western	0.58	4210	5670
Pine	Jack	0.44	2560	3200
	Lodgepole	0.41	2190	2990
	Red	0.40	2120	2540
	Western White	0.37	1700	2280
	Ponderosa	0.46	2640	3360
	Eastern White	0.37	1650	2140
Spruce	Black	0.43	2430	3210
	Engelmann	0.40	2020	2660
	Red	0.40	2280	3130
	Sitka	0.39	2200	3090
	White	0.37	1880	2470
Aspen	Trembling	0.41	2140	2820
	Largetooth	0.40	1850	2520
Poplar	Balsam	0.42	1840	2740
Cottonwood	Eastern	0.39	1880	2830
	Black	0.32	1350	2000

Notes:

1. Load required to imbed 11.3 mm. sphere to half diameter (N).

2. Volume air-dry, mass oven-dry means that the specimen dimensions were measured at about 12% MC, and the mass was measured after drying to 0% MC.

3. Source: Forintek Canada Corp. (Eastern Forest Products Laboratory).

TABLE 5.2

Shrinkage for Canadian softwoods

Species	Direction of shrinkage	Shrinkage (% of green wood) to:			
		19%	15%	12%	6%
Cedar, Western Red	Radial	0.9	1.2	1.4	1.9
	Tangential	1.8	2.5	3.0	4.0
Douglas Fir, Coast	Radial	1.8	2.4	2.9	3.8
	Tangential	2.8	3.8	4.6	6.1
Douglas Fir, Interior	Radial	1.4	1.9	2.3	3.0
	Tangential	2.5	3.4	4.1	5.5
Hemlock, Western	Radial	1.5	2.1	2.5	3.4
	Tangential	2.9	3.9	4.7	6.2
Larch, Western	Radial	1.7	2.2	2.7	3.6
	Tangential	3.3	4.6	5.5	7.3
Pine, Eastern White	Radial	0.8	1.0	1.3	1.7
	Tangential	2.2	3.0	3.7	4.9
Pine, Red	Radial	1.4	1.9	2.3	3.0
	Tangential	2.6	3.6	4.3	5.8
Pine, Western White	Radial	1.5	2.0	2.5	3.3
	Tangential	2.7	3.7	4.4	5.9
Spruce, Eastern	Radial	1.5	2.0	2.4	3.2
	Tangential	2.5	3.6	4.4	5.8
Spruce, Engelmann	Radial	1.4	1.9	2.3	3.0
	Tangential	2.6	3.6	4.3	5.7

Notes:

1. Tangential shrinkage applies to the width of the flat-grain face. Radial shrinkage applies to the width of the edge-grain face.

2. To calculate expected shrinkage, determine the average equilibrium moisture content of wood for end use conditions.

TABLE 5.3

Equilibrium Moisture Content (EMC)

Location		Average EMC %	Winter EMC %	Summer EMC %
West coast	indoors	10 to 11	8	12
	outdoors	15 to 16	18	13
Prairies	indoors	6 to 7	5	8
	outdoors	11 to 12	12	10
Central Canada	indoors	7 to 8	5	10
	outdoors	13 to 14	17	10
East coast	indoors	8 to 9	7	10
	outdoors	14 to 15	19	12

Notes:

1. Lumber used in the indicated locations would eventually stabilize at or near the average EMC. Finishes and protection from elements limit seasonal moisture change. Designers should expect some shrinkage or swelling, however, until the average moisture content is reached.

Wood Products

6.1   General Information

In addition to dimension lumber and timber, the traditional wood building materials, a host of composite wood products are available to the designer. These engineered wood products have been made possible by advances in adhesive chemistry and have been driven by a demand for increased strength and spanning capabilities.

Engineered wood products offer several advantages. Because they are made from small pieces, undesirable growth features such as knots can be removed, resulting in an end product having greater strength and less variability than the wood from which it originated.

The structural improvement that comes from gluing makes underutilized species such as poplar or aspen suitable for structural applications such as oriented strandboard (OSB). Manufacturing advances have made it possible to reconstitute production waste such as sawdust into a useful product such as particleboard.

A variety of wood products are used for building construction. Wood beams, joists and columns are used as main structural members. Wood products are also commonly used as sheathing and decking.

The products for main structural members range from the standard sawn wood products such as dimension lumber, to enhanced sawn wood products such as machine stress-rated (MSR) lumber, to composite wood products such as laminated veneer lumber (LVL). For secondary structural elements, plank decking, board sheathing, plywood and oriented strandboard (OSB) are available.

Whether a wood product is solid lumber or manufactured from a gluing process, the properties described in Chapter 5, such as moisture movement, apply and should be understood to make effective use of the material.

This chapter describes the characteristics of common wood products used for structural applications, and is organized as follows:

6.2   Main Structural Members

- Dimension lumber, fingerjoined lumber, machine stress-rated (MSR) lumber and machine evaluated lumber (MEL)
- Timber
- Glulam
- Structural Composite Lumber (SCL)
- Light frame trusses
- Wood I-joists

6.3   Sheathing and Decking

- Plywood
- OSB and waferboard
- Plank decking

6.4   Tables

6.2 Main Structural Members

INTRODUCTION

This section provides information on the types of wood products available which are commonly used for main structural members such as beams, columns, joists, rafters and studs.

DIMENSION LUMBER

Dimension lumber is solid sawn wood that is less than 89 mm thick. Canadian lumber is manufactured in accordance with CSA O141 *Softwood Lumber* and marketed under four species combinations (Table 6.1). While it is possible to obtain any species combination, the S-P-F group is by far the most widely used in Canada.

The manufacturing process includes sawing, sorting, drying, planing and grading, as illustrated in Figure 6.1.

Table 6.2 shows typical sizes and grades of lumber used for studs, joists, rafters and purlins. Other sizes and grades are available, but are less common. Typically, stud grade is used for wall framing and No.2 and better for joists, rafters and purlins. The maximum length of lumber that may be obtained is about 7 m and varies from province to province.

Lumber is graded by a visual examination of the material in accordance with the National Lumber Grades Authority (NLGA) *Standard Grading Rules for Canadian Lumber*. These rules provide a list of the permitted characteristics within each grade. Some of the characteristics that affect the strength and stiffness of lumber are:

- size and location of knots
- slope of grain
- amount of wane
- size of shakes, splits and checks

FIGURE 6.1

Manufacture of sawn lumber

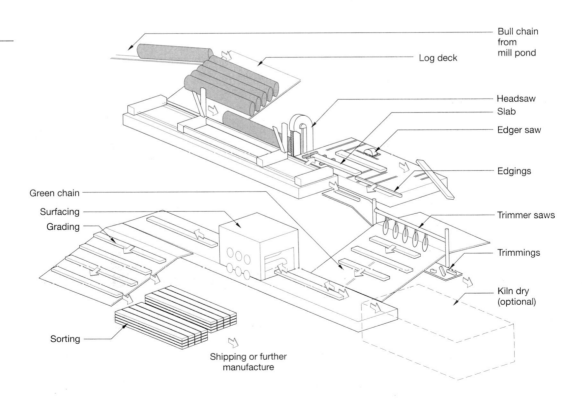

Other characteristics are limited by the grading rules for appearance reasons. Some of these include sap and heart stain, torn grain and planer skips.

A sample NLGA grade description used by a mill lumber grader in appraising lumber is as provided below.

No.2 – Structural Light Framing

This grade is recommended for most general construction uses where moderately high design values are required.

Characteristics permitted and limiting provisions

Checks	Seasoning checks not limited. Through checks at ends are limited as splits.
Knots	Well spaced knots of any quality are permitted in sizes not to exceed the following or equivalent displacement:

Nominal Dimension	At edge width	wide face	Centreline wide face	Holes (any cause)
2"	5/8"	5/8"	5/8"	one hole or equivalent smaller holes per 2 lin. ft.
3"	7/8"	7/8"	7/8"	
4"	1-1/4"	2"	1-1/4"	

Manufacture	Standard "F" (para. 722 f).
Pitch and pitch streaks	Pitch or bark – not limited
Rate of growth	Limited to medium grain in Douglas fir and western larch only (para 350 a).
Shake	If through at ends, limited as splits. Away from ends through heart shakes up to 2' long, well separated. If not through, single shakes may be 3' long or up to 1/4 the length, whichever is greater.
Skips	Hit and miss, and in addition 5% of the pieces may be hit or miss or heavy skip not longer than 2' (para. 720 e, f, and g).
Slope of grain	1 in 8.
Splits	Equal in length to 1 1/2 times the width of the piece.
Stain	Stained sapwood. Firm heart stain or firm red heart. Not limited.
Unsound wood	Not permitted in thicknesses over 2". In 2" thick lumber, small spots or streaks of firm honeycomb or peck equal to 1/6 the width are permitted. Any other unsound wood is limited to a spot 1/12 the width and 2" in length or equivalent smaller.
Wane	1/3 thickness and 1/3 the width full length, or equivalent on each face, provided that wane not exceed 2/3 the thickness or 1/2 the width for up to 1/4 the length (para. 750).
Warp	Light (para. 752).
White speck	1/3 the face or equivalent.

FIGURE 6.2

Typical Canadian lumber grade stamp

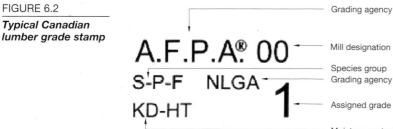

Grading agency

Mill designation

Species group
Grading agency

Assigned grade

Moisture content

Once a piece of lumber has been evaluated, a grade stamp is applied to one face (Figure 6.2). This stamp contains the following information about the piece of lumber:

- grading agency identification
- mill identification number
- grading rule used where applicable
- grade
- species or species group
- moisture content at time of surfacing

To ensure the quality of lumber, Canadian mills are required to have each piece of lumber graded by lumber graders who are approved by a grading agency. Grading agencies are accredited by the Canadian Lumber Standards Accreditation Board.

Air-dried or kiln dried lumber is readily available in the 38 mm thickness. Dimension lumber that has been air or kiln dried to a moisture content of 19% before surfacing (planing or dressing) is classified as S-Dry (surfaced dry) or KD (kiln dried). Lumber that is surfaced at a higher moisture content is referred to as S-Grn (surfaced green). Generally, 64 and 89 mm thick lumber is readily available as S-Grn only. Heat-Treatment (HT) refers to lumber that has been heated, with or without moisture content reduction.

Part 9 of the NBCC requires that all framing lumber be marked with a grade stamp and be dried to a moisture content of 19% or less prior to installation. The use of dry material is a requirement because it reduces the incidence of nail pops and floor squeaks that might occur when green lumber is used.

Lumber may be referred to by its nominal size in inches, which means the actual size rounded up to the nearest inch, or by its actual size in millimeters. For instance, 38×89 mm (1-1/2" $\times$ 3-1/2") material is referred to as 2×4 lumber (Table 6.3). S-Grn lumber is produced slightly larger

than S-Dry lumber to allow for shrinkage as it dries. Thus after drying, S-Grn lumber should be the same size as S-Dry material.

Lumber Properties

As related in Chapter 2, the reliability of lumber design data was improved during the 1980s by shifting from test values for small clear samples to test values from full size members.

The Lumber Properties Program was conducted across North America with the goal of verifying lumber grading correlation from mill to mill, from region to region, and between Canada and the United States.

The scientific data resulting from the program showed:

- close correlation in the strength properties of visually graded No.1 and No.2 dimension lumber
- good correlation in the application of grading rules from mill to mill and from region to region
- a decrease in relative strength as size increases (i.e. size effect) – for example the unit bending strength for a 38×89 mm member is greater than for a 38×114 mm member.

Both CSA O86 and the NBCC have adopted the results from the Lumber Properties Program.

Dimension Lumber

Principal Applications	Studs, Joists, Rafters Purlins, Light Frame Trusses
Applicable Manufacturing Standards	CSA O141 *Softwood Lumber* NLGA *Standard Grading Rules for Canadian Lumber*
Applicable Service Conditions	Dry or Wet
Treatability With Wood Preservatives	Treatable but species dependent
Applicable Fastenings	Nails, Bolts, Truss Plates, Joist Hangers, Framing Anchors

MACHINE STRESS RATED (MSR) LUMBER

Machine Stress Rated (MSR) lumber is dimensional lumber that has been graded by mechanical stress rating equipment and manufactured in conformance with the NLGA *Special Product Standard 2* (SPS-2). Under this evaluation method, each piece of lumber is visually inspected prior to testing. Then it is passed through mechanical evaluation equipment and the stiffness is measured and recorded every 150 mm along the member. Since stiffness is correlated to strength, the lumber can be grouped into stress grades that have higher strength and stiffness than visual graded lumber.

As with visual grading, MSR evaluation is a continuous process. In a mill operation, the evaluation equipment can process up to 365 m of lumber per minute. This includes evaluating the stiffness and applying a grade stamp to the lumber.

The grade stamp on MSR lumber (Figure 6.3) is similar to that found on visually graded lumber. The grade stamp identifies the material as machine rated along with the stress grade, the grading agency, the mill of origin, the species group and an indication of moisture content.

MSR lumber is commonly used in long span prefabricated trusses and for chords of wood I-joists. It is generally available in 38 × 89 mm to 38 × 184 mm lumber only.

The grade designations for MSR were developed for working stress design and refer to the allowable bending stress and modulus of elasticity of the material. For instance, 1650f - 1.5E means that the allowable bending stress was 1650 psi and the modulus of elasticity was 1.5 million psi. For Limit States Design (LSD), the corresponding values are 24.0 MPa and 10300 MPa, respectively.

FIGURE 6.3

MSR grade stamp and manufacture

Sample MSR grademark

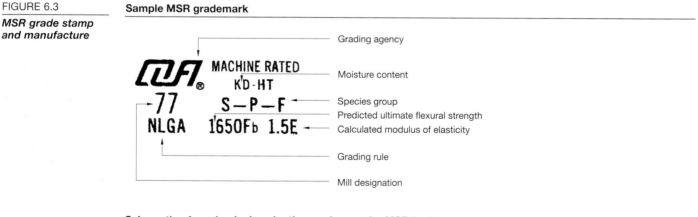

Schematic of mechanical evaluating equipment for MSR lumber

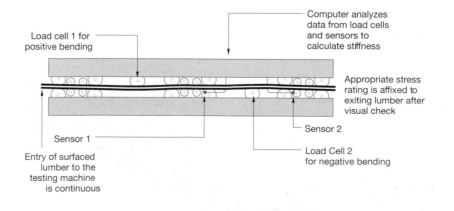

Machine Stress Rated (MSR) Lumber

Principal Applications	Joists, Light Frame Trusses, Wood I-Joists
Applicable Manufacturing Standards	NLGA *Special Product Standard 2* (SPS-2)
Applicable Service Conditions	Dry or Wet
Treatability With Wood Preservatives	Treatable but species dependent
Applicable Fastenings	Nails, Bolts, Truss Plates, Joist Hangers, Framing Anchors

MACHINE EVALUATED LUMBER (MEL)

MEL and MSR lumber are basically interchangeable except that the minimum (5th percentile) modulus of elasticity (MOE) for MSR lumber is limited to 0.82 times the grade mean value, whereas for MEL lumber it is limited to 0.75 times the grade mean. This results in slightly different compressive capacities for the two products.

MEL is also manufactured in conformance with the NLGA *Special Product Standard 2* (SPS-2). MEL grades are designated from M-10 to M-26, where M-26 is the strongest grade.

Machine Evaluated Lumber (MEL)

Principal Applications	Joists, Light Frame Trusses, Wood I-Joists
Applicable Manufacturing Standards	NLGA *Special Product Standard 2* (SPS-2)
Applicable Service Conditions	Dry or Wet
Treatability With Wood Preservatives	Treatable but species dependent
Applicable Fastenings	Nails, Bolts, Truss Plates, Joist Hangers, Framing Anchors

FINGERJOINED LUMBER

Fingerjoined lumber is made by gluing together short pieces of lumber into the ends of which finger profiles have been machined (Figure 6.4). This process can result in the production of joists and rafters in lengths of 12 m or more.

Canadian fingerjoined lumber is manufactured in conformance with the NLGA *Special Product Standard 1* (SPS-1) or *Special Product Standard 3* (SPS-3).

Fingerjoined lumber manufactured to the requirements of SPS 1 is interchangeable with non-fingerjoined lumber of the same species, grade and length, and can be used for joists, rafters and other applications. Fingerjoined lumber manufactured according to SPS 3 can only be used as vertical end-loaded members in compression (i.e. wall studs), where bending or tension loading components do not exceed short term duration, and where the equilibrium moisture content of the wood will not exceed 19% and the temperature will not exceed 50 °C for an extended period of time. SPS 3 lumber is manufactured in sizes up to 38 × 140 mm, in lengths up to 3.66 m.

There are several different types of adhesives used in the manufacture of fingerjoined lumber. The NLGA Special Product Standards outline what types of adhesives can be used in SPS 1 and SPS 3 fingerjoined lumber as well as the test standards that those adhesives must meet. Adhesives used in fingerjoined lumber are designated as either a Heat Resistant Adhesive (HRA) or Non-Heat Resistant Adhesive (Non-HRA). Qualification

FIGURE 6.4

Fingerjoined lumber

Vertical or horizontal use

A.F.P.A.® 00
S-P-F NLGA SPS 1
       CERT FGR JNT
S-DRY HRA   2

Vertical use only

A.F.P.A.® 00
S-P-F NLGA SPS 3
S-DRY HRA STUD
       CERT FGR JNT
VERT STUD USE ONLY

as an HRA adhesive requires an adhesive to be exposed to elevated temperatures during a standard fire resistance test of a loadbearing fingerjoined stud wall assembly loaded to 100 percent of the wall's allowable design load. All SPS 1 products must be manufactured using an HRA adhesive. SPS 3 products may be manufactured with either HRA or non-HRA adhesives. The fire-resistance ratings in Table A-9.10.3.1.A of the 2010 National Building Code of Canada are only applicable to constructions using fingerjoined lumber that has been manufactured with a Heat Resistant Adhesive (HRA).

SAWN TIMBER

Sawn timber refers to posts and beams with a minimum thickness of 140 mm. Timbers are manufactured in accordance with CSA O141 *Softwood Lumber*, and marketed under four species combinations. Large timbers are generally available in the D.Fir-L and Hem-Fir combinations with smaller sizes available in all four species groupings (Table 6.4).

Sizes up to 394 × 394 mm may be obtained for D.Fir-L and Hem-Fir species combinations; however, S-P-F and Northern species are generally available in sizes up to 241 × 241 mm only. Timbers can be obtained in lengths up to 9.1 m but availability of large sizes and long lengths should always be checked with suppliers before specifying.

Grading is based on visual examination of the timber in accordance with the NLGA *Standard Grading Rules for Canadian Lumber*. The most readily available grades are No.1 and No.2, but Select Structural may be ordered.

Materials available from lumber yard stock are usually sawn to order from large timbers and should be regraded after cutting. In addition, the original grade stamp is often removed during resawing and cutting. Therefore, verification of the grade should be obtained in writing from the supplier, or a qualified grading agency should be retained to check the supplied material.

There are two categories of timber:

- beams and stringers (depth more than 51 mm greater than width)
- posts and timbers (depth less than 51 mm greater than width)

The *National Building Code of Canada* (NBCC) recognizes the use of solid timbers for inherent fire-safety performance.

Species

Because of the log sizes required to obtain large timbers, the larger timbers most often come from the west.

Timber availability	Species
More common	Douglas Fir-Larch
	Hem-Fir
Less common	Western cedars
	Western white pine
	Eastern white pine
	Red pine

Grades

There are three stress grades for both the Beam and Stringer and the Post and Timber grade categories of timbers:

- Select Structural
- No.1 grade
- No.2 grade

In addition, there are two non-stress grades – Standard and Utility. Designers often specify No.1 or No.2 grade, which are the most commonly available timber grades. No.1 grade may contain varying amounts of Select Structural, depending on the sawmill of origin. Select Structural grade can be ordered when the highest strength and the highest quality appearance are desired.

Standard and Utility grades have no assigned strength properties so timbers of these grades are permitted for use in some specific applications where strength is not important.

In the Beam and Stringer category, cross cutting may affect the grade of timber. This is due to the variability of allowable knot size along the length of the piece, with longer knots being allowed near the ends. Thus, timbers in the Beam and Stinger category must be regraded if cut to length after grading.

Moisture Content

Sawn timbers are generally surfaced green since their large size makes air or kiln drying impractical. As a result, sawn timbers will shrink as they dry after installation. Checking and splitting may also occur; however, these defects are cause for concern only if they exceed the limits set out in the NLGA grading rules. Standard sizes of sawn timber are shown in Table 6.5.

Sawn Timber

Principal Applications	Beams, Columns, Bracing, Crib work, Retaining Walls
Applicable Manufacturing Standards	CAN/CSA O141-05 *Softwood Lumber* NLGA *Standard Grading Rules for Canadian Lumber*
Applicable Service Conditions	Dry or Wet
Treatability With Wood Preservatives	Treatable but species dependent
Applicable Fastenings	Bolts, Drift Pins, Lag Screws, Timber Rivets, Shear Plates and Split Rings, Heavy Duty Hangers

GLULAM

Glued-laminated timber (glulam) is an engineered wood product manufactured by gluing together lumber laminations with a waterproof adhesive (Figures 6.5 and 6.6). Glulam is manufactured to meet CSA O122 *Structural Glued-Laminated Timber*, and the manufacturers of glulam must be certified in accordance with CSA O177 *Qualification Code for Manufacturers of Structural Glued-Laminated Timber*.

Glulam is commonly used in post and beam structures. It can also be curved and tapered to create pitched tapered beams and a variety of arch shapes and trusses. Glulam beams may also be cambered, which means that they may be produced with a slight upward bow so that the amount of deflection under service loads is reduced. A typical camber is 2 to 4 mm per metre of length.

In the manufacture of glulam, lumber laminations are visually and mechanically sorted for strength and stiffness into lamstock grades. The lamstock must be dried to a moisture content of between 7 and 15% before laminating to maximize adhesion and minimize shrinkage in service.

The laminations are glued under pressure using an adhesive that is fully waterproof.

Glulam is primarily produced in Canada from two species groups: Douglas fir-Larch and Spruce-Pine (Table 6.6). Hem-Fir species are also used occasionally.

FIGURE 6.5

Typical glulam timber beam

Typical glulam timber beam

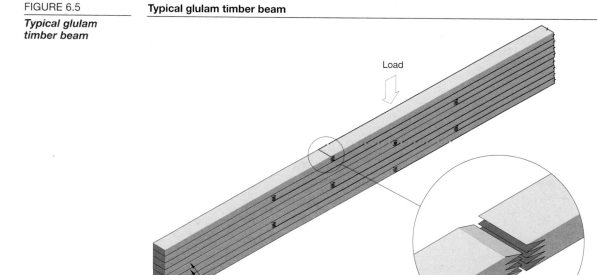

Load

Gluelines and
lumber laminations

The standard widths and depths of glulam are shown in Table 6.7. The depth of glulam is a function of the number of laminations multiplied by the lamination thickness. For economy, 38 mm laminations are used wherever possible, and 19 mm laminations are used where greater degrees of curvature are required.

Grades

There are two classifications or grade categories for glulam:

- stress grade
- appearance grade

Stress grades define the strength of the material. Glulam is available in a number of stress grades depending on the type of member required (Table 6.6). Stress grades are developed by locating higher quality lamstock in high stress areas. For continuous beams, the high strength laminations are placed near the top and bottom to provide the greatest strength and stiffness. For columns and tension members, the stronger laminations are more equally distributed.

The stress grade designations were developed for working stress design and refer to the allowable stress of the material. For instance, 20f means an allowable bending stress of 2000 psi. The letter E indicates that mechanical sorting or E-rating has been used to grade the laminations. The lower case letters indicate the use of the grade as follows: f is for flexural (bending) members, c is for compression members, and t is for tension members.

The difference between the f-E grade and the f-EX grade is that the f-E grade has high strength laminations on the bottom only, while the f-EX has them on both faces. Therefore, the f-E grade is used for single span beams where little reverse bending can occur. The EX grade is used for continuous beams or cantilevered beams that experience reverse bending and require high strength material on both faces. The top sides of f-E beams are marked to show proper orientation.

FIGURE 6.6

Glulam manufacture

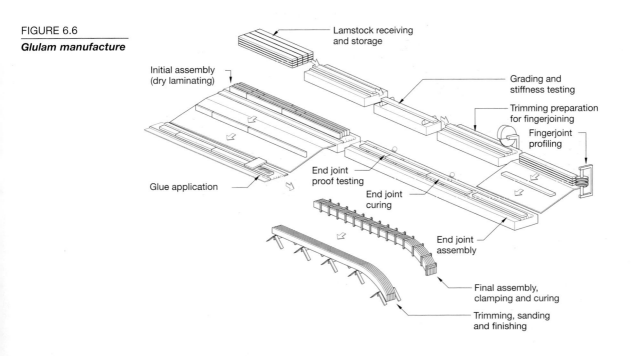

Appearance Grades

Glulam is available in the following appearance grades:

- Industrial
- Commercial
- Quality

The appearance grade defines the amount of patching and finishing work done to the exposed surfaces after laminating (Table 6.8) and has no strength implications. Quality grade provides the greatest degree of finishing and is intended for applications where appearance is important. Industrial grade has the least amount of finishing.

Shapes

Because glulam is manufactured from laminations, many shapes, including curved members can be manufactured (Figure 6.7 and 6.8).

Standard 38 mm laminations are limited to a maximum 8.4 m radius of curvature for members having tangent ends such as pitched beams, and 10.8 m for wholly curved members.

Standard 19 mm laminations are limited to a 2.8 m radius for members having tangent ends, and 3.8 m for wholly curved members. A lesser radius of curvature can be specified, but must be made from non-standard stock that is less than 19 mm, which increases the cost.

FIGURE 6.7

Glulam shapes for large buildings

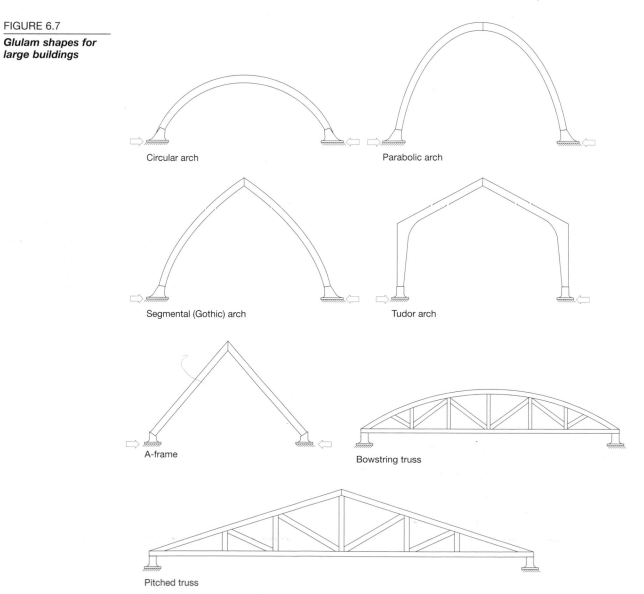

Circular arch

Parabolic arch

Segmental (Gothic) arch

Tudor arch

A-frame

Bowstring truss

Pitched truss

FIGURE 6.8

Glulam columns and beams

Type & shape	Typical sizes			Common applications

Columns

Rectangular	L_e (m)	b × d (mm)		Columns in all types of industrial, commercial, recreational, institutional, religious and residential buildings; vertical members in exterior structures such as towers and bridges.
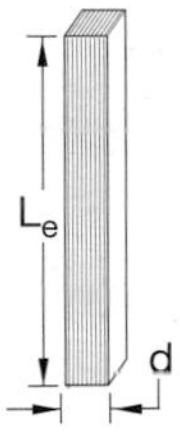	≤ 6	≤ 175 × 266		
	≤ 12	≤ 215 × 342		
	≤ 15	≤ 365 × 418		

Straight beams	L (m)	b (mm)	d (mm)	
Single 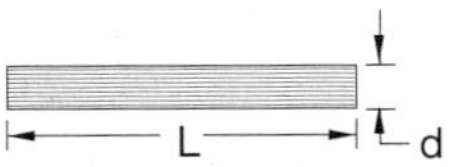	≤ 12	80	≤ 608	Beams and girders for floors and roofs in all types of industrial, commercial, recreational, institutional, religious and residential buildings; oblique purlins for roofs; bending members in exterior structures such as bridges, ramps and wharves.
Continuous 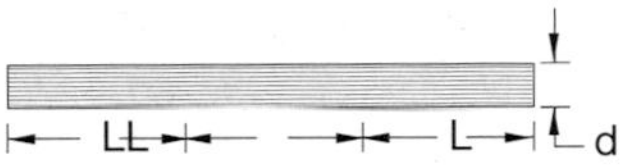	≤ 18	130	≤ 1026	
Cantilevered 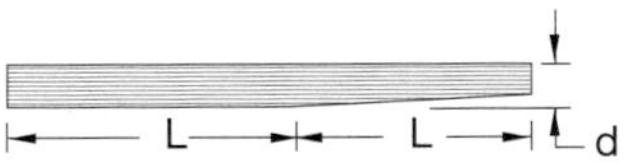	≤ 24	175	≤ 1406	
Single-tapered 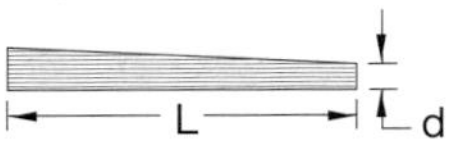	≤ 27	215	≤ 1786	
Double-tapered 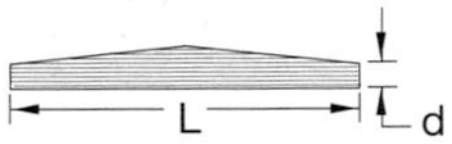	> 27	265 315 365	≤ 2128	

Curved and pitched beams

Curved	Standard widths up to 315 mm and depths up to about 1216 mm can span up to about 21 m, depending on R, α and other factors.	Roof beams or girders for all types of commercial, recreational, institutional, religious and residential buildings; upper surface curved or sloped for roof drainage; bottom surface curved for architectural effect.
Double-tapered curved 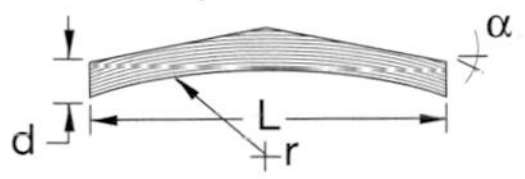 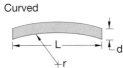		
Pitched 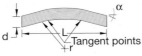		
Double-tapered pitched 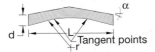		

Protection

Untreated glulam can be used in humid environments such as swimming pools, curling rinks, or industrial buildings that use water in their manufacturing process. The alkyd sealer applied to glulam members in the factory provides adequate protection for most high-humidity applications.

Fire Resistance

Glulam is most often used in sizes which qualify it as Heavy Timber construction which assigns the members a 3/4-hour fire resistance.

Cost

For the best economy when ordering glulam members, specifiers should:

- Select the section with the smallest cross-sectional area or the least weight required for the job. For bending members, this is usually the section with the greatest depth and least width, however the depth to width ratio must be appropriate for the design.

- Use 38 mm laminations and the standard sizes whenever possible.

- Limit the size of glulam members to those which can be economically and legally shipped. This applies to both lengths and curves, since shipping height limitations (usually about 4 to 6 m depending on the province) may restrict arch sizes.

- Use the appropriate appearance grade.

- Consider using larger than necessary members where this will simplify connection details and result in better overall economy.

- Minimize the number of concealed or semi-concealed connections which require costly shop fabrication.

Glulam	
Principal Applications	Beams, Columns, Arches, Frames, Heavy Trusses, Curved and Pitched Beams
Applicable Manufacturing Standards	CAN/CSA O122-06 *Structural Glued-Laminated Timbers* CAN/CSA O177-06 *Qualification Code for Manufacturers of Structural Glued-Laminated Timber*
Applicable Service Conditions	Dry or Wet
Treatability With Wood Preservatives	Treatable but species dependent
Applicable Fastenings	Bolts, Lag Screws, Glulam Rivets, Shear Plates and Split Rings, Heavy Duty Hangers

STRUCTURAL COMPOSITE LUMBER (SCL)

Structural composite lumber (SCL) is a term used to encompass laminated veneer lumber (LVL) and parallel strand lumber (PSL), which are engineered products having similar structural capabilities. Typically, SCL has three times the bending strength of a similar size piece of lumber and is about 30% stiffer.

Laminated veneer lumber is manufactured by gluing veneers together to produce a lumber product (Figure 6.9). The grain direction of each veneer is oriented parallel to the length of the piece (Figure 6.11). Typical sizes for LVL are shown in Table 6.9.

Parallel strand lumber consists of strands of veneers that are glued together with the strands oriented along the length of the piece (Figure 6.10). Typical sizes for PSL are shown in Table 6.10. Both products are manufactured using exterior waterproof adhesives.

FIGURE 6.9
LVL manufacture

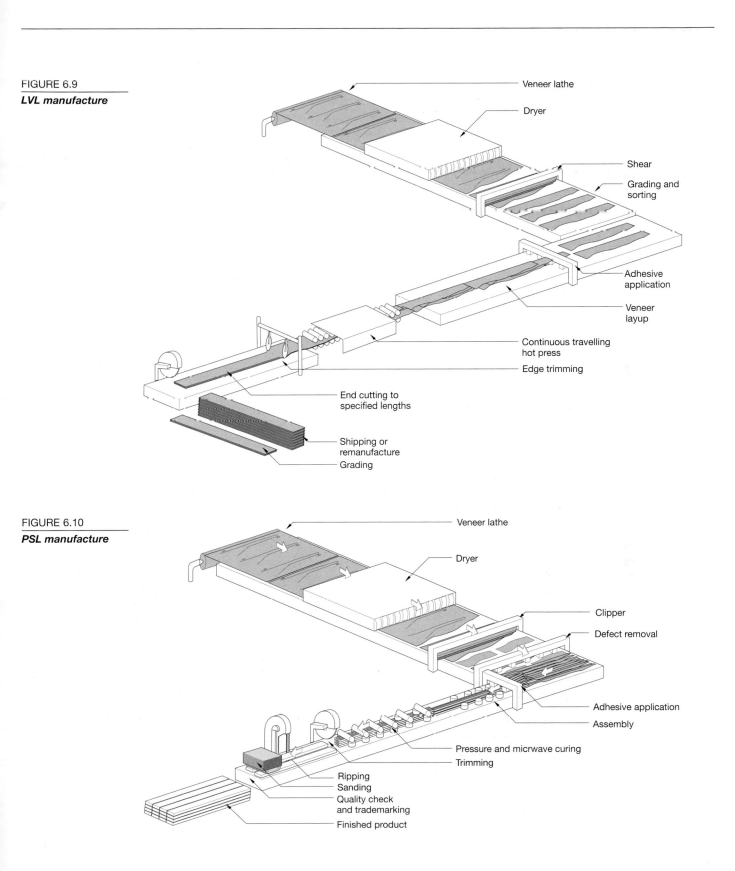

Veneer lathe

Dryer

Shear

Grading and sorting

Adhesive application

Veneer layup

Continuous travelling hot press

Edge trimming

End cutting to specified lengths

Shipping or remanufacture

Grading

FIGURE 6.10
PSL manufacture

Veneer lathe

Dryer

Clipper

Defect removal

Adhesive application

Assembly

Pressure and micrwave curing

Trimming

Ripping

Sanding

Quality check and trademarking

Finished product

SCL is produced at a low moisture content so that very little shrinkage will occur after installation. SCL will also be free of checks or splits.

Unlike sawn lumber, timber and glulam, SCL products are proprietary which means that each manufacturer publishes unique design values for their products. Thus, SCL products do not have a common standard of production and common design values. Design values are derived from test results analysed in accordance with Clauses 13 and 14 of CSA O86. In Canada, design values are reviewed and approved by the Canadian Centre for Materials in Construction (CCMC). SCL design values are published and available from the manufacturer, and designers and installers should follow the design, use and installation guidelines given by the manufacturer. Sample specified strengths for SCL suitable for preliminary sizing are shown in Table 6.11.

SCL is produced in a number of standard sizes (Tables 6.9 and 6.10). Some products are available in a number of thicknesses while others are available in the 45 mm thickness only. The 45 mm laminations may be nailed or bolted together to form built-up beams. Generally, SCL is available in lengths up to about 20 m. The manufacturers name or product identification and the stress grade is marked on the material at various intervals, but due to end cutting it may not be present on every piece.

FIGURE 6.11

Ply orientation
of LVL

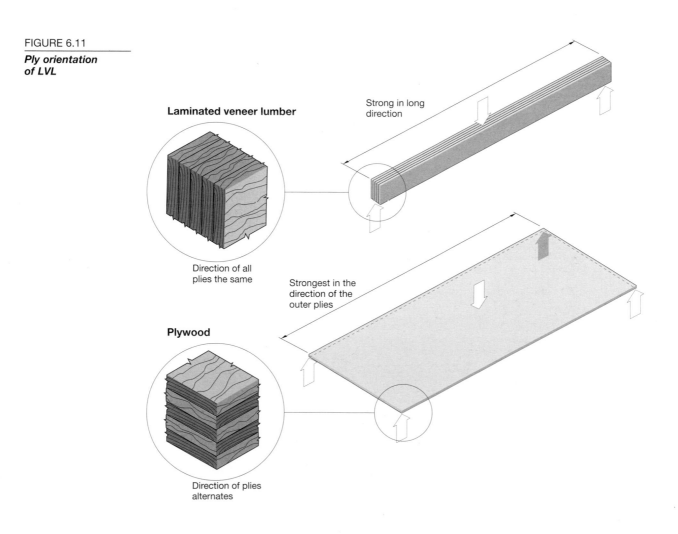

Laminated veneer lumber

Strong in long direction

Direction of all plies the same

Strongest in the direction of the outer plies

Plywood

Direction of plies alternates

Structural Composite Lumber (SCL)

Principal Applications	Beams, Columns, Joists
Applicable Manufacturing Standards	Proprietary products — Check with the manufacturer
Applicable Service Conditions	Dry or Wet — Check with the manufacturer
Treatability With Wood Preservatives	Some products are treatable — Check with the manufacturer
Applicable Fastenings	Nails, Bolts, Joist Hangers, Framing Anchors, Heavy Duty Hangers

LIGHT FRAME TRUSSES

Light frame trusses are prefabricated by connecting 38 mm dimension lumber together with metal truss plates which are produced by punching light gauge galvanized steel so that teeth protrude from one side (Figure 6.12). The teeth are pressed into the faces of the truss members at each joint to connect the truss framework (Figure 6.13).

FIGURE 6.12

Truss composition

Pitched (triangular) truss

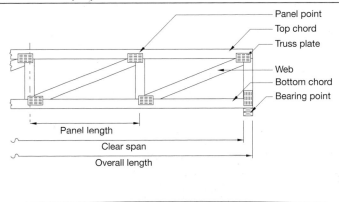

Parallel chord (flat) truss

Truss plates must conform to the requirements of CSA O86 and must be approved by the Canadian Centre for Materials in Construction (CCMC). To obtain approval, the plates are tested in accordance with CSA S347 *Method of Test for Evaluation of Truss Plates Used in Lumber Joints.*

Trusses are generally engineered by the truss plate manufacturer on behalf of the truss fabricator. The design procedures are based on the criteria in the Truss Plate Institute of Canada publication titled *Truss Design Procedures and Specifications for Light Metal Plate Connected Wood Trusses.*

Applications

Light frame trusses connected with truss plates are used in numerous applications where a safe and economical structure is required. Economy, ease of fabrication, fast delivery and simplified erection procedures make wood trusses competitive in many roof and floor applications. Their long span capability often eliminates the need for interior load bearing walls, offering the designer flexibility in floor layouts. Roof trusses offer a variety of pitched roof and sloped ceiling shapes, giving designers greater scope for both interior and exterior visual effects. If a flat roof configuration is needed, however, it can be easily achieved with wood trusses,

FIGURE 6.13

Manufacture of light frame trusses

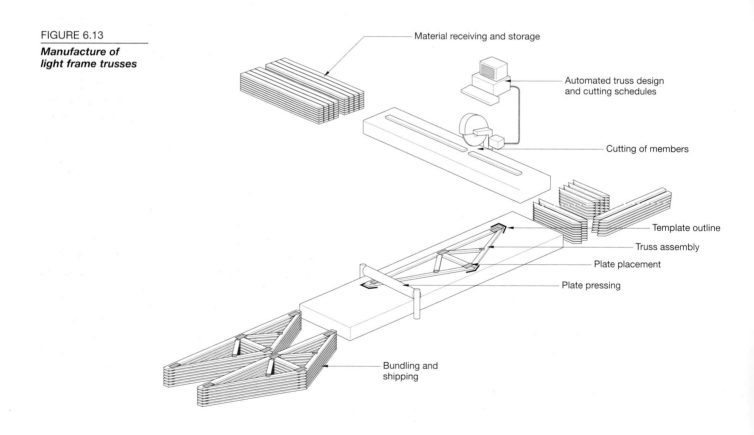

Material receiving and storage

Automated truss design and cutting schedules

Cutting of members

Template outline

Truss assembly

Plate placement

Plate pressing

Bundling and shipping

while providing ample space for insulation and ventilation. Since most trusses are custom designed, unusual shapes or loading conditions present no problem. Typical structures include:

- residential roofs
- residential floors
- commercial or industrial roofs with clear spans up to 20 m or more
- commercial or industrial floors with clear spans up to 15 m or more
- roofs and floors for agricultural buildings

Light frame trusses may be manufactured to suit any roof profile. Truss shape and size is limited only by manufacturing capabilities, shipping limitations, and handling considerations. Many of the shapes which can be fabricated are shown in Figure 6.15. The arrangement of the webs is generally determined by the fabricator at the detailed design stage and is not included in the figure.

For each project, the truss fabricator will provide a layout drawing and design drawings for each truss (Figure 6.14).

The Role of the Designer

The design of light frame trusses in general and truss plate connections in particular does not follow the traditional design procedure used for the design and construction of many wood structures. In the traditional design role, the designer provides details of all wood member sizes and wood connections to be used in the structure. With light frame trusses, the design of the members and connections is generally the responsibility of the truss plate manufacturer.

Most manufacturers are equipped with computer software that can rapidly design trusses of any configuration. In order to do the design, they must be provided with the following information:

- the type of structure
- design loads: special loading such as snow drift loads must be specified

- truss spans
- truss shape required including depth and clearance limitations
- bearing details
- overhang details

The truss plate manufacturer provides structural drawings that include such information as: the loads on which the design is based; truss spacing; points of support; species, grade and size of lumber required for the chords and webs; type, size and location and orientation of truss plates; lateral bracing requirements; bearing size; and other general notes.

When inspecting trusses *in situ*, it is important to carefully examine the truss plate connections. The plates must be properly installed and of the size specified in the drawings. A minor shift in the location of the truss plate can severely weaken the connection, so it is important to ensure that the plates are installed in the locations specified on the truss plate manufacturer's drawing.

The building designer is typically responsible for the structure that supports the trusses including the support of the truss bracing system. Bearing walls and lintels must be designed for the truss loads, including the point loads from girders. The building designer should also ensure that all connections between the trusses and support framing, such as hangers and uplift anchors are adequate. Truss drawings often call for bracing of long web members loaded in compression. It is typically the responsibility of the building designer to design the system for supporting the web bracing and to ensure that the bracing is properly installed.

FIGURE 6.14

Typical truss shop drawing

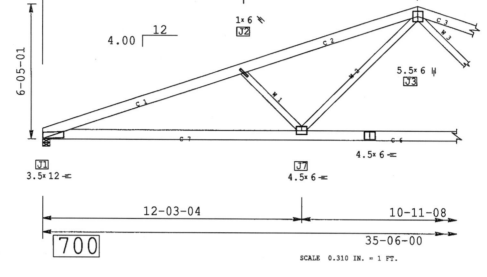

SCALE 0.310 IN. = 1 FT.

```
JOB         1/ 1  TYPE-  700       TOP SLP   4.00/12   TCLL-  40.00 PSF    TPIC & NBCC 1985   21-JUN-88
SCARF = 1-03-12   SPAN- 35-06-00   BUTT CUT - 0-00-04  TCDL-   5.00 PSF    LOAD SHARING SYSTEM  V44.852
O/A HT- 6-05-01   SPCG- 2-00-00                        BCLL-   0.00 PSF    TRUSS SYM ABOUT CL      CMAN
TTS SYSTEMS                                            BCDL-  10.00 PSF    INCR:PL-1.15 LM-1.15    L2.0
                                                       TOTL-  55.00 PSF

PANEL LENGTH    SLOPE CHORD FORCE MOMENT WEB  FORCE    PANEL LENGTH    SLOPE CHORD FORCE MOMENT WEB  FORCE
        FT-IN-SX  /12        [LBS]  IN-LB    [LBS]             FT-IN-SX  /12        [LBS]  IN-LB    [LBS]
P 1- 9-06-06    4.00  C 1-   -4430  7295 W 1-  -819    P 6- 10-11-08   0.00  C 6-   2878   3946
P 2- 8-02-10    4.00  C 2-   -3866  7295 W 2-  1162    P 7- 12-03-04   0.00  C 7-   4202   3946
```

```
--------LUMBER DESIGN SUMMARY---------(DESIGNED IN ACCORDANCE WITH TPIC & CAN3-086-M84)-----------------
                          COMBINED
                          STRS RATIO- AXIAL + BEND   FB   FT   FC
TOP CHD  2X 6 SEL STR S-P-F   0.895  = 0.465 + 0.430 1697  989 1001
BOT CHD  2X 6 NO. 2 S-P-F     0.999  = 0.677 + 0.322 1226  654  754

ALL WEBS  2X 4 NO. 2 S-P-F        JOINT   REACT(LB) MIN BRG(IN)    TOTL LOAD DEF AT J 7- 0.427 IN.
                                  [J 1, 5]  -1952      4.3         L/DEF- 998 L-35.50FT CAMB 0 1/8
```

```
--------------------------------------CONNECTOR PLATE SELECTION------------------------------------------

JOINT   CONNECTOR    SLOT        LOCATION   JOINT   JOINT   CONNECTOR    SLOT        LOCATION   JOINT
        PLATE SIZE   DIRECTION   X (IN) Y   TYPE            PLATE SIZE   DIRECTION   X (IN) Y   TYPE

[J 1, 5] 3.5 X 12    ROT NRM     CENTERED    1      [J 3]   5.5 X 6      VERT        5 1/2  3     3
[J 2, 4] 1 X 6       PARA-WB     CENTERED    4      [J 7, 6] 4.5 X 6     PARA-CD     6           2
```

```
-CHD SPLICES-SLOTS PARA TO CHD(20FT. MAX LUMBER)-     --------------(PLATE RATINGS PER PAIR)--------------
[C 6]    4.5 X  6                                     PT20 (20 GA.  GRIP = 250 PSI NET)    CMHC NO. 8219
                                                           (SHEAR = 376. PLI, TENSILE = 886. PLI)
```

```
SPECIAL NOTES:
1.  ALL PLATES ARE PT20 TYPE FROM TTS SYSTEMS UNLESS OTHERWISE INDICATED.
2.  LUMBER CONDITION:   SEASONED AT TIME OF FABRICATION.
3.  DRY SERVICE CONDITION. TREATMENT FACTORS: LUMBER- 1.00 PLATE- 1.00.
```

FIGURE 6.14
(continued)

**Typical truss
shop drawing**

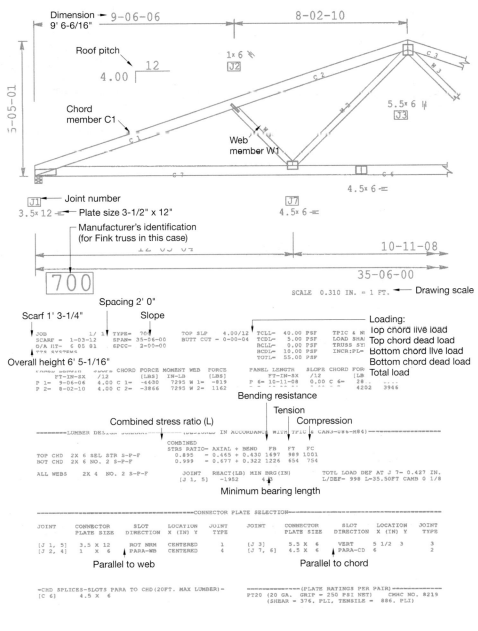

FIGURE 6.15

Truss shapes

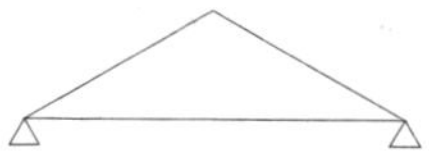	Triangular	These trusses may be simple span, multiple bearing, or cantilevered. Where the truss height exceeds approximately 3m (10'), a piggyback system (see below) may be needed due to transportation restrictions.
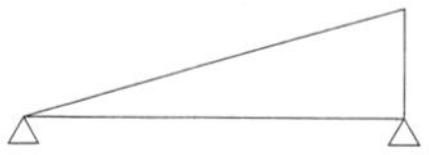	Mono	This shape may be simple span, multiple span, or cantilevered. Top chord bearing is possible.
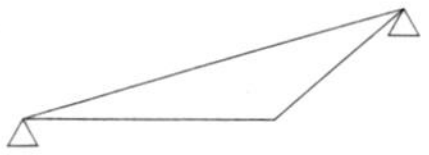	Inverted	The inverted truss is used to provide a vaulted ceiling along a portion of the span.
	Cut-off (Bobtail, Stubend)	This shape may be used where a triangular truss will not fit.
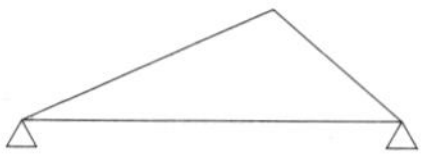	Dual Slope	This truss provides an asymmetric roof slope.
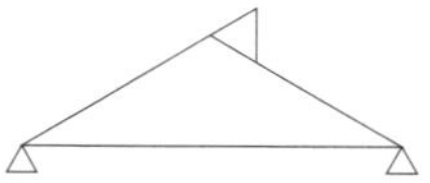	Ridge Truss	The ridge truss provides a stepped roof appearance.
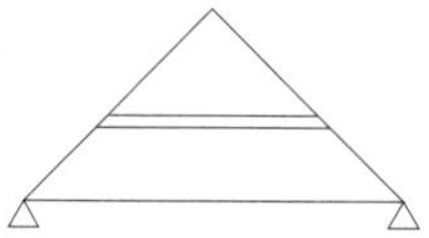	Piggyback	The piggyback truss is a combination of a gable end truss on top of a hip truss, which can be transported in two sections. It is used when a single triangular truss is too large to transport.
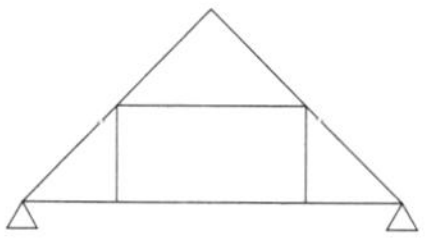	Attic	The attic truss provides useable area within the roof space.
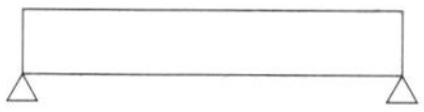	Flat	The flat truss is used in roofs or floors. It may be designed as top or bottom chord bearing, or for simple or multiple spans. It may also be cantilevered at one or both ends.
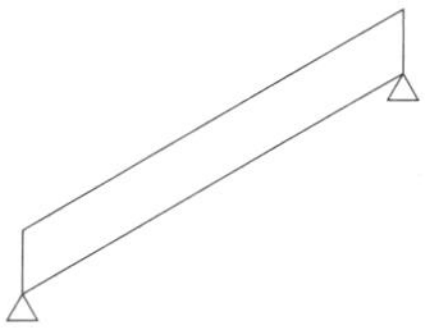	Sloping Flat	This shape is used to create a vaulted ceiling. It may be top or bottom chord bearing.

FIGURE 6.15
(continued)

Truss shapes

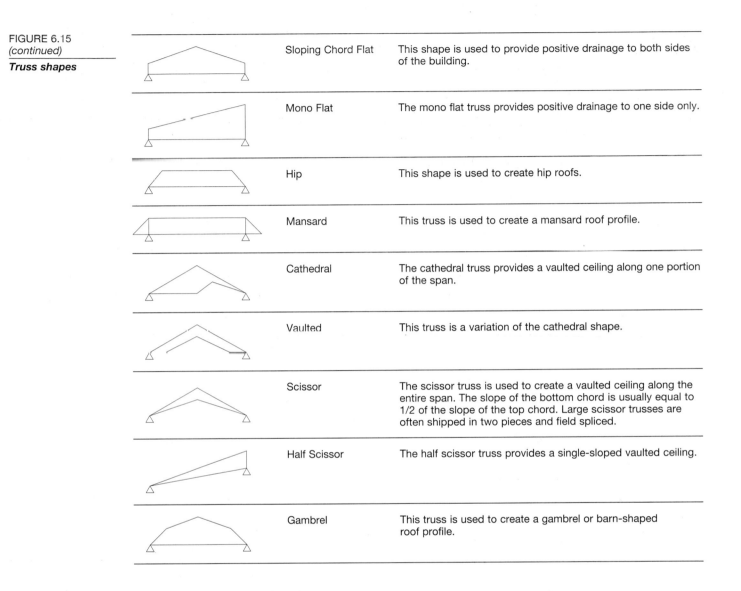

Shape	Name	Description
	Sloping Chord Flat	This shape is used to provide positive drainage to both sides of the building.
	Mono Flat	The mono flat truss provides positive drainage to one side only.
	Hip	This shape is used to create hip roofs.
	Mansard	This truss is used to create a mansard roof profile.
	Cathedral	The cathedral truss provides a vaulted ceiling along one portion of the span.
	Vaulted	This truss is a variation of the cathedral shape.
	Scissor	The scissor truss is used to create a vaulted ceiling along the entire span. The slope of the bottom chord is usually equal to 1/2 of the slope of the top chord. Large scissor trusses are often shipped in two pieces and field spliced.
	Half Scissor	The half scissor truss provides a single-sloped vaulted ceiling.
	Gambrel	This truss is used to create a gambrel or barn-shaped roof profile.

WOOD I-JOISTS

Wood I-joists are made by gluing solid sawn lumber (usually MSR) or LVL flanges to a plywood or oriented strandboard web using a waterproof adhesive to produce a dimensionally stable lightweight member with known engineering properties (Figures 6.16 and 6.17). Because high strength material that can be spliced into long lengths is used, wood I-joists are capable of spanning further than conventional sawn wood joists. They are also dimensionally stable since the materials are dried prior to manufacture.

Wood I-joists are available in a number of standard sizes (Table 6.12) and in lengths up to 20 m. The I shape of these products gives a high strength to weight ratio. For example, wood I-joists 241 mm deep and 8 m long weigh between 23 and 32 kg (depending on the flange size) which means that they can be installed manually. Most suppliers also stock standard joist hangers and other prefabricated connection hardware specially designed for use with wood I-joists.

Wood I-joists are proprietary products. Each manufacturer uses a different combination of web and flange materials and a different connection between the web and the flanges.

As a result, each manufacturer produces a joist with unique strength and stiffness characteristics. Design values for I-joists are derived using the procedures in Clause 13 of CSA O86. I-joist manufacturers register their products with the Canadian Centre for Materials in Construction (CCMC). Sample EI values are shown in Table 6.13.

Manufacturers' literature contains allowable load tables and span tables similar to those found in the NBCC for lumber joists. Their literature also contains recommended installation procedures that may differ from solid sawn joists. Chapter 2 of the Wood Design Manual contains further information on installation of I-joists. Most suppliers will provide layout drawings for a particular job showing the required size and location of joists and installation details.

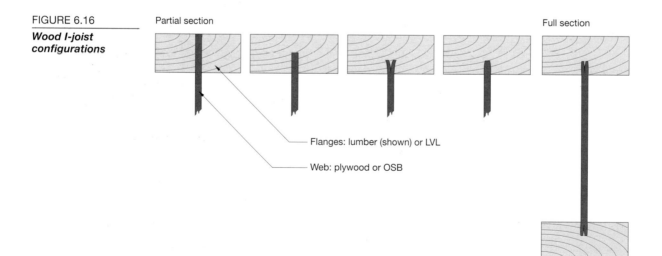

FIGURE 6.16

Wood I-joist configurations

Partial section

Full section

Flanges: lumber (shown) or LVL

Web: plywood or OSB

Applications

The uniform stiffness, strength, and light weight of these prefabricated structural products makes them well suited for longer span joist and rafter applications for both residential and commercial construction.

However, some special installation measures are required for these products. Wood I-joists are designed to carry floor loads. They are not designed to accept loads from bearing walls and column loads above. Therefore, rim framing and squash blocks are used to transfer vertical loads around I-joists rather than through them. Web stiffeners are required when the floor load exceeds the capacity of the wood I-joist at supports.

Wood I-Joists

Principal Applications	Joists
Applicable Manufacturing Standards	Proprietary products — Check with the manufacturer
Applicable Service Conditions	Dry — Check with the manufacturer
Treatability With Wood Preservatives	Not recommended
Applicable Fastenings	Joist Hangers

FIGURE 6.17

Manufacture of wood I-joists

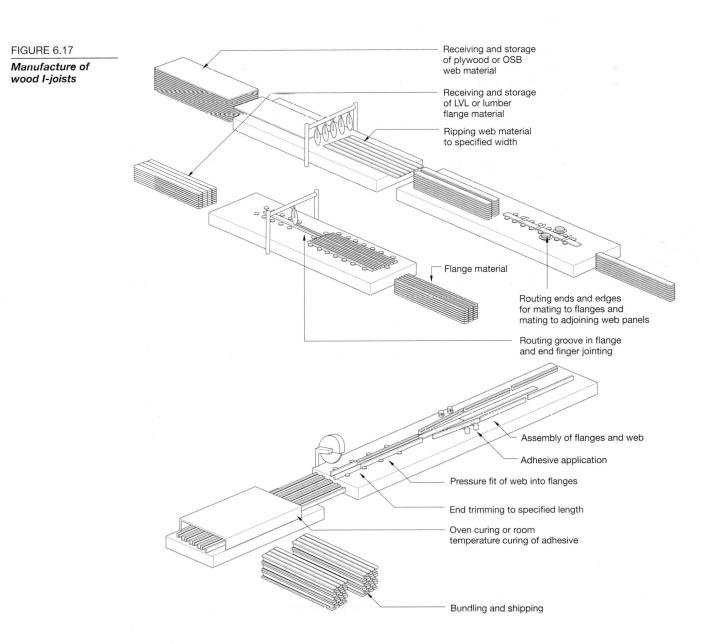

- Receiving and storage of plywood or OSB web material
- Receiving and storage of LVL or lumber flange material
- Ripping web material to specified width
- Flange material
- Routing ends and edges for mating to flanges and mating to adjoining web panels
- Routing groove in flange and end finger jointing
- Assembly of flanges and web
- Adhesive application
- Pressure fit of web into flanges
- End trimming to specified length
- Oven curing or room temperature curing of adhesive
- Bundling and shipping

6.3   Sheathing and Decking

INTRODUCTION

This section describes sheathing and decking wood products that are used as secondary structural members. These products provide rigidity to the supporting main structural members in addition to their important function of constituting a nailing surface for the attachment of building envelopes. In addition, they are often an integral component of the system resisting lateral forces.

SHEATHING

Sheathing is manufactured from a wide variety of wood-based materials. Plywood, oriented strandboard (OSB) and waferboard are the most common panel products for structural roof, wall and floor sheathing. In the past, 19 mm sawn lumber boards were common, but they are rarely used today. Fibreboard and synthetic insulating panels are also used as wall sheathing in houses.

FIGURE 6.18

Plywood manufacture

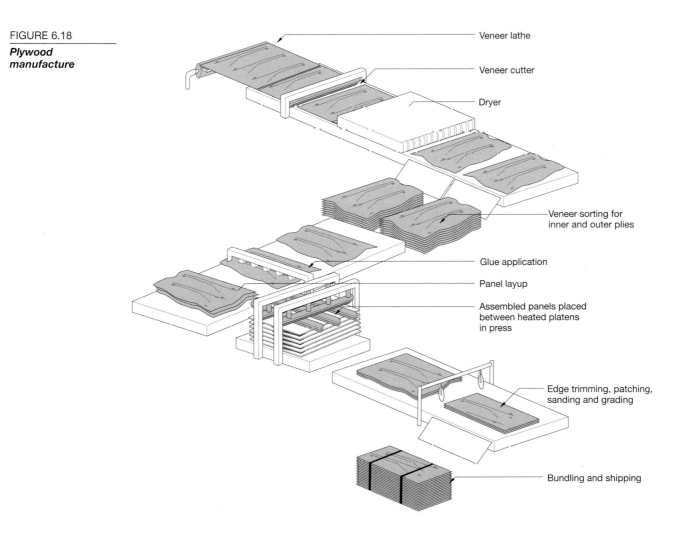

Veneer lathe

Veneer cutter

Dryer

Veneer sorting for inner and outer plies

Glue application

Panel layup

Assembled panels placed between heated platens in press

Edge trimming, patching, sanding and grading

Bundling and shipping

FIGURE 6.19

*Appearance of
plywood grades*

Douglas fir plywood (DFP) and Canadian softwood plywood (CSP) vary in appearance according to grade.

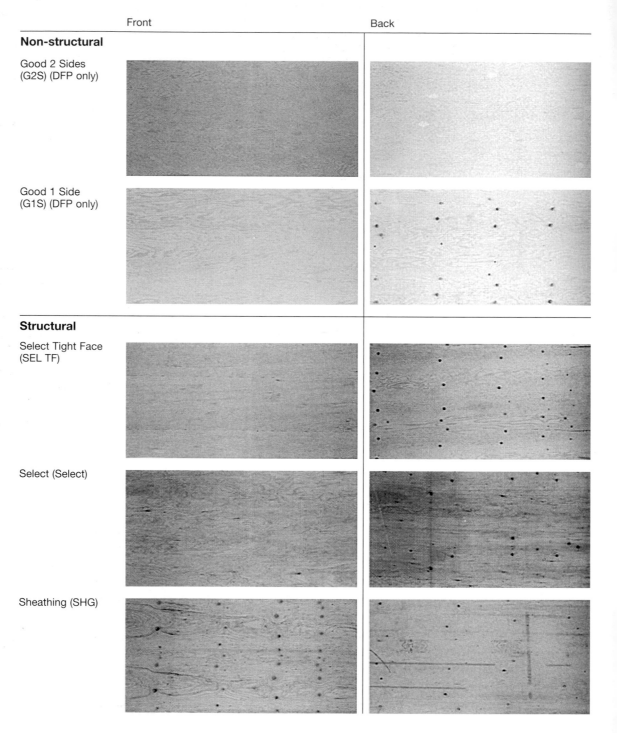

Front   Back

Non-structural

Good 2 Sides
(G2S) (DFP only)

Good 1 Side
(G1S) (DFP only)

Structural

Select Tight Face
(SEL TF)

Select (Select)

Sheathing (SHG)

Plywood

Plywood panels manufactured for structural applications are built up from sheets of softwood veneer glued together with waterproof adhesive (Figure 6.18). The grain direction of each sheet is alternated and the panel is symmetrical about the centreline. Two types of structural softwood plywood are manufactured in Canada (Figure 6.19):

- Douglas Fir Plywood (DFP) conforming to CSA O121
- Canadian Softwood Plywood (CSP) conforming to CSA O151

A number of plywood grades are available (Table 6.14), but unsanded sheathing grade plywood is most commonly used for sheathing applications and is the type of plywood referenced in CSA O86. Unsanded sheathing grade is available in either metric or imperial sizes (Table 6.15). Metric panel thicknesses are similar to the imperial sizes. The length and width of the metric panels, which are slightly less than the imperial sizes, are for use with members spaced at 300, 400 or 600 mm on centre.

FIGURE 6.20

Typical panel marks for Canadian plywood

Face Stamp

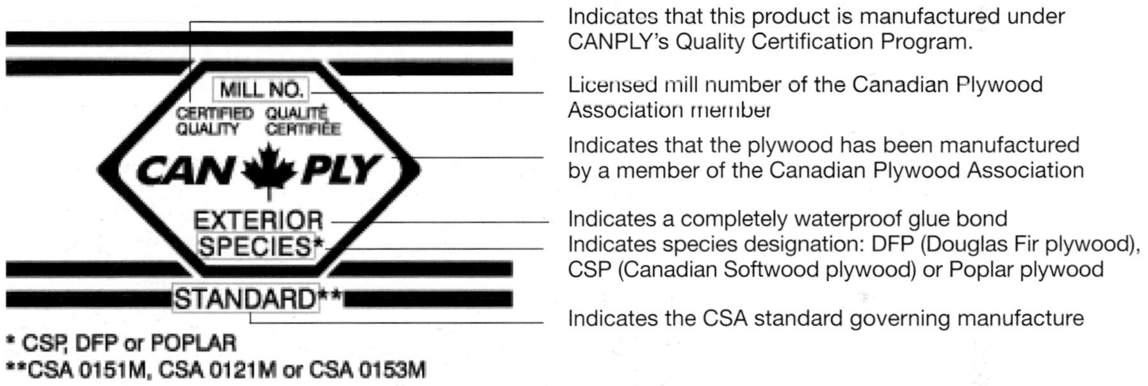
MILL NO.
CERTIFIED QUALITY
QUALITÉ CERTIFIÉE
CAN PLY
EXTERIOR
SPECIES*
STANDARD**
Indicates that this product is manufactured under CANPLY's Quality Certification Program.
Licensed mill number of the Canadian Plywood Association member
Indicates that the plywood has been manufactured by a member of the Canadian Plywood Association
Indicates a completely waterproof glue bond
Indicates species designation: DFP (Douglas Fir plywood), CSP (Canadian Softwood plywood) or Poplar plywood
Indicates the CSA standard governing manufacture
* CSP, DFP or POPLAR
**CSA 0151M, CSA 0121M or CSA 0153M

Edge Stamp

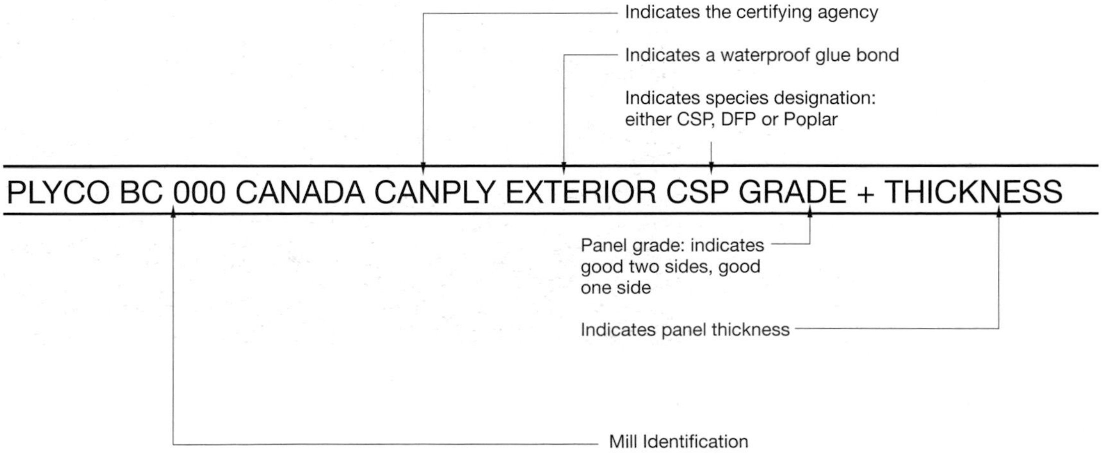
Indicates the certifying agency
Indicates a waterproof glue bond
Indicates species designation: either CSP, DFP or Poplar
PLYCO BC 000 CANADA CANPLY EXTERIOR CSP GRADE + THICKNESS
Panel grade: indicates good two sides, good one side
Indicates panel thickness
Mill Identification

Depending on appearance requirement, either a face stamp or edge stamp is used.
Where a face stamp is used, the grade designation is shown separately on the edge stamp.

Tongue and groove (T&G) plywood is often used for floor sheathing. It has a factory machined tongue along one of the long edges and a groove along the other, which when interlocked, eliminates the need for blocking the edges from below.

All structural plywood products are marked with a grade stamp that indicates the CSA Standard to which it is produced (Figure 6.21).

Plywood

Principal Applications	Roof Sheathing, Floor Sheathing, Wall Sheathing, Sheathing in Preserved Wood Foundations
Applicable Manufacturing Standards	CSA O121 *Douglas Fir Plywood* CSA O151 *Canadian Softwood Plywood*
Applicable Service Conditions	Dry or Wet
Treatability With Wood Preservatives	Treatable
Applicable Fastenings	Nails, screws

Oriented Strandboard (OSB) and Waferboard

OSB and waferboard are structural panels made from poplar wafers that are laminated together with a waterproof phenolic adhesive (Figure 6.21).

The wafers from which waferboard is manufactured are randomly oriented making the strength properties along both the width and length identical.

Oriented strandboard is similar to waferboard, but the wafers are narrower and oriented in the long direction of the panel in the outer layers. This gives the panel added strength and stiffness in the long direction.

Oriented Strandboard (OSB)

Principal Applications	Roof Sheathing, Floor Sheathing, Wall Sheathing
Applicable Manufacturing Standards	CSA O437 *OSB and Waferboard* CAN/CSA O325 *Construction Sheathing*
Applicable Service Conditions	Dry
Treatability With Wood Preservatives	Not Recommended
Applicable Fastenings	Nails, screws

OSB is by far the most common type of structural panel made from wafers. The manufacture of waferboard (panels with randomly distributed wafers) is on the decline.

The general product standard is CSA O437, *OSB and Waferboard*. The product standard contains three designations O-1 and O-2 indicate an oriented panel (OSB) (Figure 6.22), while R-1 indicates a random panel (waferboard).

Another standard that applies to OSB and waferboard, as well as to plywood, is a performance standard: CSA O325, *Construction Sheathing*. This standard sets performance ratings for specific end uses such as floor, roof and wall sheathing in light-frame construction. For example, a panel marked with a 1R24 indicates roof sheathing on supports spaced 24 inches on centre and without support on the long edges of the panel. A typical example of panel marking on construction sheathing is shown in Figure 6.23.

Sheathing conforming to CSA O325 is referenced in Part 9 of the NBCC. In addition, design values for construction sheathing OSB conforming to CSA O325 are listed in CSA O86 allowing engineering design of roof sheathing, wall sheathing and floor sheathing using CSA O325 rated OSB.

OSB and waferboard are available in square edged or tongue and groove edges. Typical sizes for OSB are shown in Table 6.16. Standard performance ratings for specific end uses of OSB and waferboard are provided in Table 6.17.

PLANK DECKING

Plank decking is sawn lumber that is milled into a tongue and groove profile (Figure 6.25). Decking is produced in three thicknesses: 38, 64, and 89 mm. The 38 mm thickness has a single tongue and groove while the thicker sizes have a double tongue and groove. The 64 and 89 mm decking also have 6 mm diameter holes predrilled through the centre of the piece at 760 mm spacing so that each piece may be nailed to the adjacent one with deck spikes.

Decking is generally available in the following species:

- Douglas fir
- Pacific coast hemlock
- Various species from the spruce–pine–fir species combinations
- Western red cedar

Plank decking is available in two grades, Select and Commercial. Select grade has a higher quality appearance than Commercial grade and is also stronger and stiffer. Verification of the grade, since plank decking is not grade marked, should be obtained in writing from the supplier or a qualified grading agency should be retained to check the supplied material.

FIGURE 6.21

Manufacture of OSB and waferboard

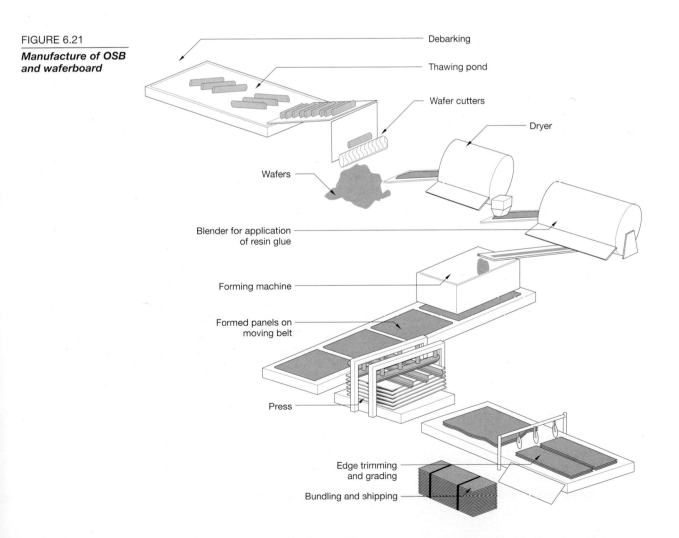

Debarking

Thawing pond

Wafer cutters

Dryer

Wafers

Blender for application of resin glue

Forming machine

Formed panels on moving belt

Press

Edge trimming and grading

Bundling and shipping

FIGURE 6.22

Strand orientation for OSB and waferboard

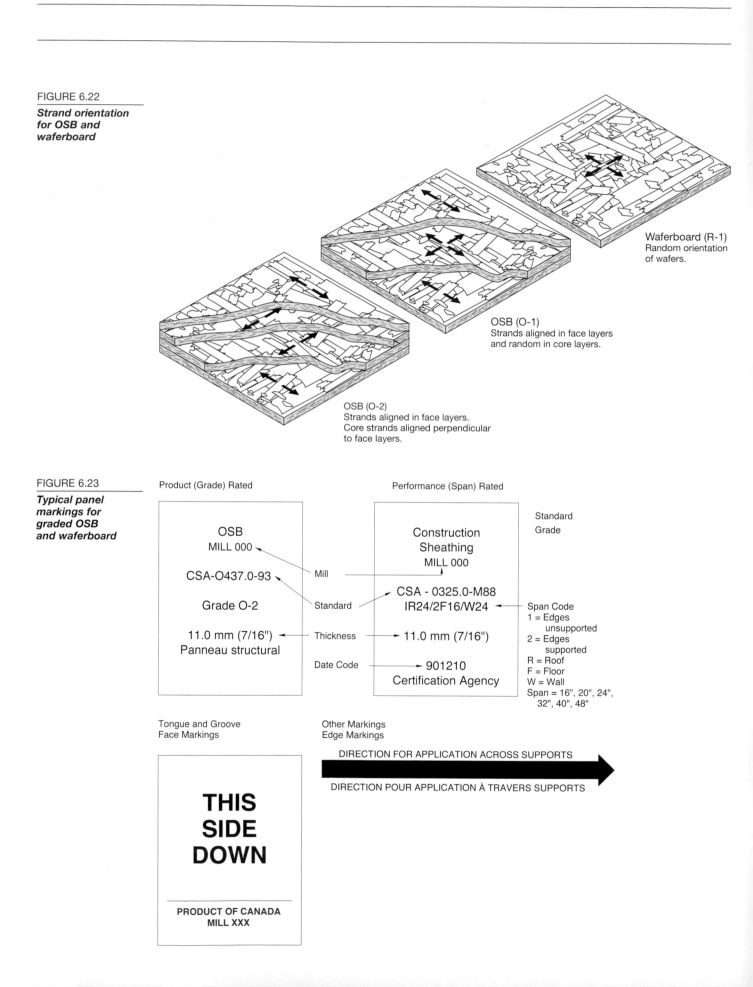

Waferboard (R-1)
Random orientation of wafers.

OSB (O-1)
Strands aligned in face layers and random in core layers.

OSB (O-2)
Strands aligned in face layers. Core strands aligned perpendicular to face layers.

FIGURE 6.23

Typical panel markings for graded OSB and waferboard

Product (Grade) Rated

OSB
MILL 000

CSA-O437.0-93

Grade O-2

11.0 mm (7/16")
Panneau structural

Performance (Span) Rated

Construction
Sheathing
MILL 000

CSA - 0325.0-M88
IR24/2F16/W24

11.0 mm (7/16")

901210
Certification Agency

Mill

Standard

Thickness

Date Code

Standard
Grade

Span Code
1 = Edges
      unsupported
2 = Edges
      supported
R = Roof
F = Floor
W = Wall
Span = 16", 20", 24",
      32", 40", 48"

Tongue and Groove
Face Markings

**THIS
SIDE
DOWN**

PRODUCT OF CANADA
MILL XXX

Other Markings
Edge Markings

DIRECTION FOR APPLICATION ACROSS SUPPORTS

DIRECTION POUR APPLICATION À TRAVERS SUPPORTS

Plank decking is most readily available in random lengths of 1.8 to 6.1 m and longer. Decking may be ordered in specific lengths, but designers should expect limited availability and extra costs. It is usual to specify that at least 90% of the decking be 3.0 m and longer, and between 10 to 50% be 4.9 m and longer.

Decking should always be kiln or air dried to an average moisture content of 15% (maximum 19%) which will reduce shrinkage after installation. Excessive shrinkage due to the use of green decking will result in the loosening of the tongue and groove joint, which is unsightly and structurally unacceptable.

Grade	Principal uses
Select	For roof and floor decking where strength and fine appearance are required.
Commercial	For roof and floor decking where strength is required but appearance is not so important.

FIGURE 6.24

Faces, sizes, and nailing patterns for plank decking

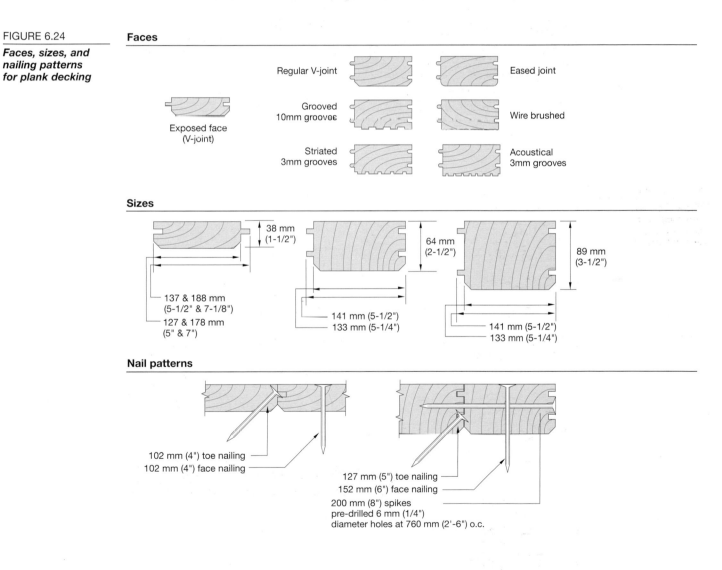

Faces

Exposed face (V-joint)

Regular V-joint

Eased joint

Grooved 10mm grooves

Wire brushed

Striated 3mm grooves

Acoustical 3mm grooves

Sizes

38 mm (1-1/2")

64 mm (2-1/2")

89 mm (3-1/2")

137 & 188 mm (5-1/2" & 7-1/8")
127 & 178 mm (5" & 7")

141 mm (5-1/2")
133 mm (5-1/4")

141 mm (5-1/2")
133 mm (5-1/4")

Nail patterns

102 mm (4") toe nailing
102 mm (4") face nailing

127 mm (5") toe nailing
152 mm (6") face nailing
200 mm (8") spikes pre-drilled 6 mm (1/4") diameter holes at 760 mm (2'-6") o.c.

The quantity of random length plank decking required for a deck is:

$$Q = K\,A\,t\,/\,1000$$

where

Q = quantity of decking, m^3

K = wastage factor, usually 1.05

A = area of deck, m^2

t = thickness of deck, mm

If the decking is sloped, the actual area of the deck should be used, not the horizontal surface area.

The ends of plank decking are usually manufactured square-end-trim, within a squareness tolerance of about 0.4 mm, measured on face sides. Wide pieces (171 mm) might exceed this tolerance.

The underside of plank decking, the face, is sometimes patterned for aesthetic appeal, especially in thick decking. All decking is V-grooved on the underside. Thick decking (64 and 89 mm) has drilled holes to receive nails that are driven through the width of the decking.

Plank Decking

Principal Applications	Roof Decks, Floor Decks
Applicable Manufacturing Standards	CAN/CSA O141-05 *Softwood Lumber* NLGA *Standard Grading Rules for Canadian Lumber*
Applicable Service Conditions	Dry or Wet
Treatability With Wood Preservatives	Treatable but species dependent
Applicable Fastenings	Nails

6.4 Tables

TABLE 6.1

Commercial species groups of lumber

Species combination	Abbreviations	Species included in combination	Characteristics	Colour ranges
Douglas Fir-Larch	D.Fir-L	Douglas fir western larch	• high degree of hardness • good resistance to decay	reddish brown to yellowish
Hem-Fir	Hem-Fir	Pacific coast hemlock Amabilis fir	• works easily • takes paint well • holds nails well • good gluing characteristics	yellow brown to white
Spruce-Pine-Fir	S-P-F	Spruce (all species except Coast sitka spruce) Jack pine Lodgepole pine Balsam fir Alpine fir	• works easily • takes paint well • holds nails well	white to pale yellow
Northern Species	North	Western red cedar	• exceptional resistance to decay • moderate strength • high in appearance qualities • works easily • takes fine finishes • lowest shrinkage	reddish brown heartwood light sapwood
		Red pine	• works easily	reddish to pale brown heartwood
		Ponderosa pine	• takes finish well • holds nails well • holds screws well • seasons with little checking or cupping	pale yellow colour sapwood
		Western white pine Eastern white pine	• softest of Canadian pines • works easily • finishes well • does not tend to split or splinter • hold nails well • low shrinkage • takes stains, paints, varnishes well	creamy white to light straw brown heartwood almost white sapwood
		Trembling aspen Largetooth aspen Balsam poplar	• works easily • finishes well • holds nails well	almost white to greyish-white
		Any other Canadian species graded in accordance with the NLGA rules		

TABLE 6.2

Typical structural lumber sizes, grades, and moisture content

Use	Common sizes		Visual grades	Moisture content
	mm	in. (nom.)		
Wall studs	38 × 89 38 × 140 38 × 184	2 × 4 2 × 6 2 × 8	Stud*	S-Dry or S-Grn
Joists, rafters, and built-up beams	38 × 184 to 38 × 286	2 × 8 to 2 × 12	Select Structural No.1 No.2 No.3	S-Dry or S-Grn
Purlins	64 × 184 to 89 × 286	3 × 8 to 3 × 12	Select Structural No.1 No.2 No.3	S-Grn only

Note: 38 × 184 mm is available as No.3, No.2, No.1, or Select Structural only

TABLE 6.3	Nominal size in.	Surfaced green (S-Grn) size in.	Surfaced dry (S-Dry) size in.	Metric size mm
Dimension lumber sizes	2 × 2	1-9/16 × 1-9/16	1-1/2 × 1-1/2	38 × 38
	3	2-9/16	2-1/2	64
	4	3-9/16	3-1/2	89
	6	5-5/8	5-1/2	140
	8	7-1/2	7-1/4	184
	10	9-1/2	9-1/4	235
	12	11-1/2	11-1/4	286
	3 × 3	2-9/16 × 2-9/16	2-1/2 × 2-1/2	64 × 64
	4	3-9/16	3-1/2	89
	6	5-5/8	5-1/2	140
	8	7-1/2	7-1/4	184
	10	9-1/2	9-1/4	235
	12	11-1/2	11-1/4	286
	4 × 4	3-9/16 × 3-9/16	3-1/2 × 3-1/2	89 × 89
	6	5-5/8	5-1/2	140
	8	7-1/2	7-1/4	184
	10	9-1/2	9-1/4	235
	12	11-1/2	11-1/4	286

Notes:

1. 38 mm (2") lumber is readily available as S-Dry.

2. S-Dry lumber is surfaced at a moisture content of 19% or less.

3. After drying, S-Grn lumber sizes will be approximately the same as S-Dry lumber.

4. Tabulated metric sizes are equivalent to imperial S-Dry sizes, rounded to the nearest millimetre.

TABLE 6.4		Common sizes		
Typical sizes and grades of sawn timber for structural applications	Use	mm	in. nom.	Visual grade
	Posts (square sections)	140 × 140 to 394 × 394	6 × 6 to 16 × 16	Select Structural No.1 No.2
	Beams (rectangular sections)	140 × 241 to 292 × 394	6 × 10 to 12 × 16	Select Structural No.1 No.2

Notes:

1. Availability of large sizes should be checked with suppliers.

2. S-P-F and Northern species groups may not be available in sizes larger than 241 × 241 mm (10" × 10" nom.).

3. All material is available as S-Grn only.

TABLE 6.5	Nominal size in.	Surfaced green (S-Grn) size in.	Metric size mm
Typical sizes sawn timber	6 × 6	5-1/2 × 5-1/2	140 × 140
	8	7-1/2	191
	10	9-1/2	241
	12	11-1/2	292
	14	13-1/2	343
	16	15-1/2	394
	8 × 8	7-1/2 × 7-1/2	191 × 191
	10	9-1/2	241
	12	11-1/2	292
	14	13-1/2	343
	16	15-1/2	394
	10 × 10	9-1/2 × 9-1/2	241 × 241
	12	11-1/2	292
	14	13-1/2	343
	16	15-1/2	394
	12 × 12	11-1/2 × 11-1/2	292 × 292
	14	13-1/2	343
	16	15-1/2	394

Notes:

1. Timbers are always surfaced green.

2. Tabulated metric sizes are equivalent to imperial dimensions.

TABLE 6.6		Stress grades		
Glulam species and stress grades	Species combination	Beams	Columns	Tension members
	Douglas Fir-Larch	20f-E	16c-E	18t-E
		20f-EX		
		24f-E		
		24f-EX		
	Spruce-Pine	20f-E	12c-E	14t-E
		20f-EX		

Note: Glulam may also be manufactured with Hem-Fir species.

TABLE 6.7	Width		Depth range[1]	
Standard glulam sizes	mm	in.	mm	in.
	80	3	114 to 570	4-1/2 to 22-1/2
	130	5	152 to 950	6 to 37-1/2
	175	6-7/8	190 to 1254	7-1/2 to 49-1/2
	215	8-1/2	266 to 1596	10-1/2 to 62-3/4
	265	10-1/4	342 to 1976	13-1/2 to 77-3/4
	315	12-1/4	380 to 2128	15 to 83-3/4
	365	14-1/4	380 to 2128	15 to 83-3/4

Note:

1. Intermediate depths are multiples of the lamination thickness, which is 38 mm (1-1/2" nom.) except for some curved members that require 19 mm (3/4" nom.) laminations.

TABLE 6.8	Grade	Description
Glulam appearance grades	Industrial Grade	Intended for use where appearance is not a primary concern such as in industrial buildings; laminating stock may contain natural characteristics allowed for specified stress grade; sides planed to specified dimensions but occasional misses and rough spots allowed; may have broken knots, knot holes, torn grain, checks, wane and other irregularities on surface.
	Commercial Grade	Intended for painted or flat-gloss varnished surfaces; laminating stock may contain natural characteristics allowed for specified stress grade; sides planed to specified dimensions and all squeezed-out glue removed from surface; knot holes, loose knots, voids, wane or pitch pockets are not replaced by wood inserts or filler on exposed surface.
	Quality Grade	Intended for high-gloss transparent or polished surfaces, displays natural beauty of wood for best aesthetic appeal; laminating stock may contain natural characteristics allowed for specified stress grade; sides planed to specified dimensions and all squeezed-out glue removed from surface; may have tight knots, firm heart stain and medium sap stain on sides; slightly broken or split knots, slivers, torn grain or checks on surface filled; loose knots, knot holes, wane and pitch pockets removed and replaced with non-shrinking filler or with wood inserts matching wood grain and colour; face laminations free of natural characteristics requiring replacement; faces and sides sanded smooth.

TABLE 6.9	Depth	
Typical depths of laminated veneer lumber (LVL)	mm.	in.
	184	7-1/4
	235	9-1/4
	241	9-1/2
	286	11-1/4
	292	11-1/2
	302	11-7/8
	318	12-1/2
	356	14
	406	16
	457	18
	476	18-3/4

Notes:

1. Available in a thickness of 45 mm (1-3/4"). Wider members may be built-up by nailing or bolting two or more plies together.

TABLE 6.10

Typical dimensions of parallel strand lumber (PSL)

Member type	Size (b×d) mm		in.	
Beams	44 ×	235	1-3/4 ×	9-1/4
		241		9-1/2
		286		11-1/4
		302		11-7/8
		356		14
		406		16
		483		19
	68 ×	235	2-11/16 ×	9-1/4
		241		9-1/2
		286		11-1/4
		302		11-7/8
		356		14
		406		16
		483		19
	89 ×	235	3-1/2 ×	9-1/4
		241		9-1/2
		286		11-1/4
		302		11-7/8
		356		14
		406		16
		483		19
	133 ×	235	5-1/4 ×	9 1/4
		241		9-1/2
		286		11-1/4
		302		11-7/8
		356		14
		406		16
		483		19
	178 ×	235	7 ×	9-1/4
		241		9-1/2
		286		11-1/4
		302		11-7/8
		356		14
		406		16
		483		19
Columns	89 ×	89	3-1/2 ×	3-1/2
		133		5-1/4
		178		7
	133 ×	133	5-1/4 ×	5-1/4
		178		7
	178 ×	178	7 ×	7

TABLE 6.11

Sample specified strengths (MPa) for structural composite lumber (PSL and LVL) for LSD

Property	Value
Modulus of elasticity E	13800
Allowable bending stress, f_b (300 mm depth)	37.0
Allowable shear stress, f_v (perpendicular to glueline or wide face of strand)	3.7
Allowable bearing stress, f_{cp} (parallel to glueline or wide face of strand)	9.4

Notes:

1. Both PSL and LVL are proprietary products whose specified strengths vary by manufacturer. For exact values for specific products, contact the manufacturer.

TABLE 6.12

Typical depths of prefabricated wood I-joists

Depth mm.	in.
241	9-1/2
292	11-1/2
302	11-7/8
318	12-1/2
356	14
406	16
457	18
508	20
559	22
610	24

Note:

1. Refer to manufacturer's literature for widths and specific load bearing capacity.

TABLE 6.13

Depths and EI ($\times 10^9$) values for typical wood I-joists

Depth mm	in	EI chord dimensions Nominal 3" $\times$ 2" 2-5/8" $\times$ 1-1/2"	Nominal 4" $\times$ 2" 3-1/2" $\times$ 1-1/2"
241	9-1/2	700	900
292	11-1/2	1100	1400
302	11-7/8	1200	1500
318	12-1/2	1300	1700
356	14	1600	2200
406	16	2200	2900
457	18	2800	3700
508	20	3500	4700
559	22	4300	5700
610	24	5200	6900

Notes:

1. Refer to manufacturer's literature for widths and specific load bearing capacity.

2. Wood I-joists are proprietary products whose specified strengths vary by manufacturer. For exact values for specific products, contact the manufacturer.

TABLE 6.14

Grades of softwood plywood

Type	Grade
DFP (sanded architectural grades)	Good 2 Sides (G2S) Good 1 Side (G1S)
CSP and DFP (unsanded structural grades)	Select Tight Face (SEL TF) Select (SELECT) Sheathing (SHG)

TABLE 6.15

Plywood sizes

	Panel size mm	Square-edged panel thickness mm	Tongue and groove panel thickness mm
Metric sizes	1220 × 2440	7.5	–
	1200 × 2400	9.5	11*
		12.5	12.5
		15.5	15.5
		10.5	18.5
		20.5	20.5

	Panel size ft	Square-edged panel thickness in.	Tongue and groove panel thickness in.
Imperial sizes	4 × 8	5/16	–
		3/8	7/16*
		1/2	1/2
		5/8	5/8
		3/4	3/4
		13/16	13/16

Note: *Available as COFI – Roof panels

TABLE 6.16

OSB sizes

	Panel size mm	Square-edged panel thickness mm	Tongue and groove panel thickness mm
Metric sizes	1200 × 2400	6.0	–
		7.5	–
		9.5	–
		11.0	–
		12.0	–
		12.5	–
		15.0	–
		15.5	15.5
		18.0	18.0
		18.5	18.5
		22.0	22.0
		28.5	28.5

	Panel size ft	Square-edged panel thickness in.	Tongue and groove panel thickness in.
Imperial sizes	4 × 8	1/4	–
		5/16	5/16
		3/8	3/8
		7/16	7/16
		15/32	15/32
		1/2	1/2
		19/32	19/32
		5/8	5/8
		23/32	23/32
		3/4	3/4

TABLE 6.17

CSA O325
performance marks

Assumed end use		Spacing in inches (mm)					
		16 (400)	20 (500)	24 (600)	32 (800)	40 (1000)	48 (1200)
Subflooring	(1F)	1F16	1F20	1F24	1F32	– [3]	1F48
Subflooring used with a panel-type underlay	(2F)	2F16	2F20	2F24	– [3]	– [3]	– [3]
Roof sheathing used without edge support	(1R)	1R16	1R20	1R24	1R32	1R40	1R48
Roof sheathing used with edge support	(2R)	2R16	2R20	2R24	2R32	2R40	2R48
Wall sheathing	(W)	W16	W20	W24	– [3]	– [3]	– [3]

Notes:

1. Panel marks consist of an end use mark followed by the appropriate span mark.

2. Multiple panel marks may be used on panels qualified for more than one end use, e.g., 1R24/2F16 or 2R48/2F24/1F24.

3. Not covered by this Standard.

Bending Members

7.1   General Information

Bending members are structural elements that are subjected to loads applied more or less perpendicular to their long axis. Joists, headers, lintels, purlins, beams, and girders are all bending members named according to the function they perform.

Bending members are usually but not always horizontal, and are usually but not always loaded on their narrow face.

The design of bending members must consider bending moment, longitudinal shear, deflection, and other factors such as lateral stability and bearing.

The following general statements apply to bending members:

- for average loads and spans, bending moment usually governs the design
- for heavy loads and short spans, shear usually governs the design
- for light loads and long spans, deflection usually governs the design

The design of proprietary products such as wood I-joists is similar in principle to those for sawn lumber and glulam, but detailed information should be obtained from the manufacturer.

This chapter covers the following:

7.2   Sawn Lumber Bending Members

7.3   Glulam Bending Members

7.4   Tables

7.2   Sawn Lumber Bending Members

INTRODUCTION

Design of sawn lumber bending members can be governed by:

- bending moment resistance,
- shear resistance,
- deflection, or
- bearing (compression resistance perpendicular to grain).

The factored resistances for the species and grade of lumber used must be greater than the applied load effects. In addition, deflection induced by loading must be less than the appropriate deflection criterion. In general, for average loads and spans, design will usually be governed by bending moment resistance. For heavy loads and short spans, shear resistance may control. Deflection may be the limiting factor for light loads and long spans, such as for most floor joists. Bearing resistance is seldom the limiting factor in the design of sawn lumber, but may be limiting where large beams are used in light-frame construction.

The usual procedure in the design of bending members is to calculate moment and shear in the beam and then select an appropriate member size from beam or joist selection tables. The designer then checks that the stiffness, EI, of the member is adequate for the required deflection criteria.

After a member is selected to meet all three criteria, its bearing resistance is checked.

BENDING MOMENT RESISTANCE

In bending, it is assumed that stress is proportional to strain. Stress and strain are linearly related by the modulus of elasticity E, up to the proportional limit, and strain increases in direct proportion to the distance from the neutral axis (assuming that plane sections before bending remain plane after bending) (Figure 7.1).

These assumptions lead to the following well-known formula for bending stress:

$$f_b = M\,y\,/\,I$$

where

f_b = unit bending stress at a given fibre

M = bending moment at the section

y = distance of the given fibre from the neutral axis

I = moment of inertia of the section about the neutral axis

FIGURE 7.1

Bending stress distribution

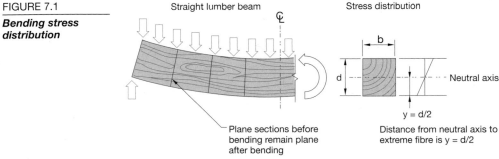

Straight lumber beam

Stress distribution

Plane sections before bending remain plane after bending

$y = d/2$

Distance from neutral axis to extreme fibre is $y = d/2$

Neutral axis

Therefore the bending moment resistance of lumber, M_r, can be calculated by

$$M_r = \phi\, F_b\, S\, K_{Zb}\, K_L$$

where

ϕ = 0.9

F_b = $f_b\,(K_D\, K_H\, K_{Sb}\, K_T)$

f_b = specified strength in bending, MPa (CSA O86 Tables 5.3.1A, 5.3.1B, 5.3.1C, 5.3.1D, 5.3.2 and 5.3.3)

K_D = load duration factor (CSA O86 Table 4.3.2.2)

K_H = system factor (CSA O86 Table 5.4.4)

K_{Sb} = service condition factor in bending (CSA O86 Table 5.4.2)

K_T = treatment factor (CSA O86 Table 5.4.3)

S = section modulus = $\left[\dfrac{b\,d^2}{6}\right]$ mm^3

K_{Zb} = size factor in bending (CSA O86 Table 5.4.5)

K_L = lateral stability factor

The resistance to bending moment may be governed by the strength or by lateral stability.

Beam Stability

When a beam is loaded, the upper fibres, which are in compression, act like a column and have a tendency to buckle as the compression stress reaches a certain critical value (Figure 7.2). Since a beam is relatively stiff in the vertical direction (which is one of the main design criteria), it is not likely that buckling would occur in that direction. This leaves the weaker lateral direction as the only possible path of instability.

A beam will resist lateral buckling through a combination of lateral bending stiffness and torsional stiffness. The critical moment which causes lateral buckling is:

$$M_{crit} = \frac{\pi}{L_e}\sqrt{EI_y\,G\,J}$$

Notice that bending strength does not appear in the formula. This is because, for slender beams, lateral buckling and not bending strength is the governing factor. EI_y is the bending stiffness in the lateral direction and $G\,J$ is the St. Venant torsional stiffness.

L_e is the effective length and depends on the unsupported length of a beam. By definition the unsupported length is the length between those supports that prevent the beam from buckling. That is, those supports that keep the compression fibres restrained from lateral movement. Where purlins provide lateral support to a beam, the unsupported length of the beam is the distance between the purlins. Where a member is continually supported by decking, the unsupported length of the beam can be taken as zero.

The lateral-torsional resistance is inversely proportional to the unsupported length of the beam. Other factors also play a role and add complexity. Most are taken into account in the design rules and it might be appropriate to realize their influence on the moment resistance.

The beam slenderness determines the lateral stability of the beam. The slenderness is defined as either stocky, intermediate or slender. Stocky beams are governed by bending strength, and slender beams are governed by stability. Intermediate beams are governed by a combination of bonding strength and stability. CSA O86 provides a transition formula for this intermediate region that is based on experimental results (Figure 7.3).

FIGURE 7.2

Lateral torsional buckling of beams

FIGURE 7.3

Determination of K_L

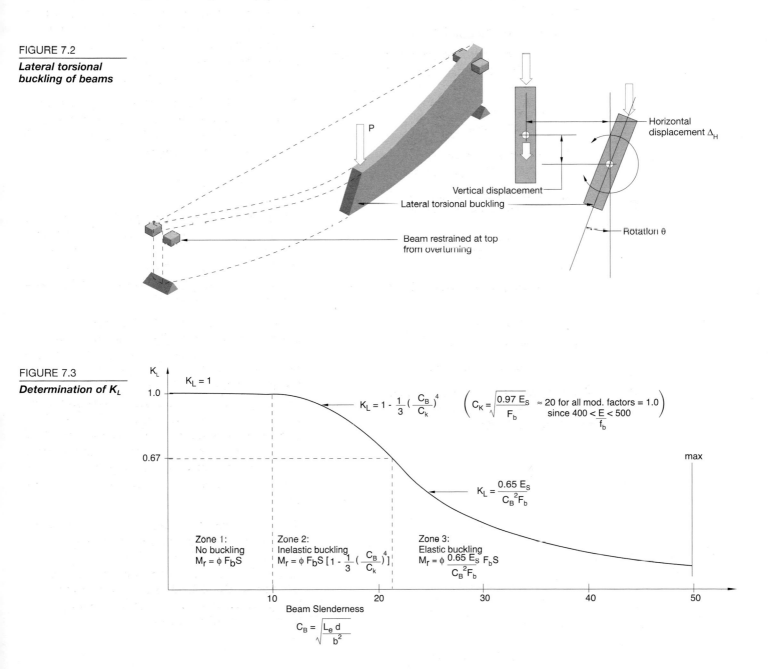

$K_L = 1$

$K_L = 1$

$K_L = 1 - \frac{1}{3}\left(\frac{C_B}{C_k}\right)^4$

$\left(C_K = \sqrt{\frac{0.97\,E_S}{F_b}} \approx 20 \text{ for all mod. factors} = 1.0 \text{ since } 400 < \frac{E}{f_b} < 500\right)$

1.0

0.67

max

$K_L = \frac{0.65\,E_S}{C_B^{\,2}F_b}$

Zone 1:
No buckling
$M_r = \phi\,F_b S$

Zone 2:
Inelastic buckling
$M_r = \phi\,F_b S\left[1 - \frac{1}{3}\left(\frac{C_B}{C_k}\right)^4\right]$

Zone 3:
Elastic buckling
$M_r = \phi\,\dfrac{0.65\,E_S}{C_B^{\,2}F_b}\,F_b S$

10   20   30   40   50

Beam Slenderness

$C_B = \sqrt{\dfrac{L_e\,d}{b^2}}$

Beams with a slenderness ratio, C_B, of less than 10 are generally considered to be stocky. Intermediate beams have a C_B of 10 to about 20, and slender beams have a C_B between about 20 and 50.

The stability rules for sawn lumber and glulam are essentially the same. Since sawn lumber beams are usually stocky, simple check rules to guard against lateral-torsional buckling are adequate (Table 7.1). Glulam beams are typically much larger and more slender, and design measures must be taken to ensure stability.

The lateral stability factor, K_L, is used to determine the effective critical moment. For stocky lumber beams meeting the slenderness and support conditions shown in Table 7.1 (CSA O86 clause 5.5.4.2.1), $K_L = 1$. For intermediate and slender beams, the K_L must be calculated (Figure 7.3) and be used to modify the critical moment.

Imperfections such as out-of-straightness of the beam, knots and grain irregularities can affect the lateral stability, especially for very slender beams. These factors are implicitly considered in the design values.

Beam stability is an important consideration, but is not overly complicated. The design procedure involves determining the degree of lateral support and selecting a trial section based on the assumption that no buckling occurs. If the beam is stocky, the design can be finalized. If the trial section is not stocky, the K_L factor must be calculated and used to determine the effective critical moment. If this is less than the allowable moment, iterative design must be performed to select a section which meets the stability and strength criteria for the given slenderness and support conditions.

SHEAR RESISTANCE

In the calculation of maximum shear force, the loads within a distance from the support equal to the depth of the member may be neglected. This is because these loads are considered to be distributed down through the member in compression perpendicular to the grain without affecting shear resistance.

For rectangular cross sections (the most commonly used with sawn wood), longitudinal shear stress is parabolically distributed over the depth of members. The maximum value, at mid-depth (the neutral axis) is 1.5 times the average shear stress (Figure 7.4).

FIGURE 7.4

***Shear stress
distribution***

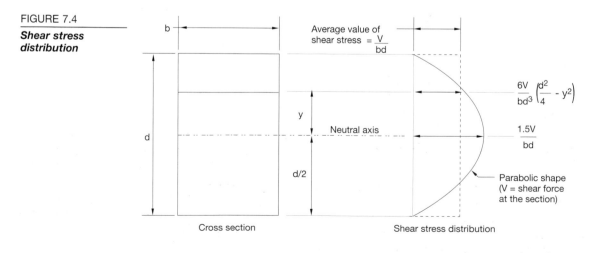

FIGURE 7.5

***Notched and drilled
sawn timber beams***

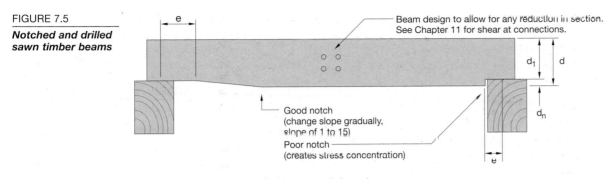

Note: The definition of e is applicable to sawn timber only

As seasoning progresses, checks and splits may develop, especially in large-size lumber beams. The grading rules for sawn lumber prescribe allowable limits for checks and splits that are taken into account in the specified sawn lumber shear values.

Sometimes the ends of beams are notched at the bottom to increase clearance or to bring the top surface level with other beams or girders (Figure 7.5). Notches may also occur between supports to make room for pipes or for framing of other beams, but should not be permitted in areas of high bending moment, such as near mid-span.

Notches can create stress concentrations that affect both shear and other stresses. Sharp or abrupt changes in beam sections should be avoided because they can produce tension perpendicular to grain. Since wood is weak in tension perpendicular to grain, splitting can occur at notches.

Stress concentrations causing compression perpendicular to grain are less critical because wood is stronger in compression perpendicular to grain than in tension perpendicular to grain. Thus, a notch at the top of a beam is less critical than a notch at the bottom.

Holes are drilled in beams for beam-to-beam connections and for other reasons such as accomodating building services. The effective depth of the member must be considered in the shear calculation at connection locations (see Chapter 11). Beam design must allow for any reduction in section.

The factored shear resistance, V_r, on the neutral plane of members at the section of maximum shear force must equal or exceed the maximum shear force, V_f.

Factored shear resistance, V_r, may be calculated as

$$V_r = \phi F_v \left[\frac{2A_n}{3} \right] K_{Zv}$$

where

ϕ = 0.9

F_v = $f_v (K_D K_H K_{Sv} K_T)$

f_v = specified strength in shear, MPa (CSA O86 Tables 5.3.1A, 5.3.1B, 5.3.1C, and 5.3.1D Note: For MSR lumber, specified strengths in shear are not grade-dependent and shall be taken from Table 5.3.1 A for the appropriate species.)

A_n = net area of cross section, mm^2

K_{Zv} = size factor in shear (CSA O86 Table 5.4.5)

If a member is notched on the tension face at a support, an additional capacity check must be made to insure that stress concentrations in the member will not cause splitting at the notch. For a simply supported beam, the tension face at a support is the lower face of the beam.

For sawn members notched on the tension side at the support, the factored reaction resistance must also be greater than or equal to the reaction at the support. The factored reaction resistance may be calculated as:

$$F_r = \phi F_f \, A \, K_N$$

where

ϕ = 0.9

F_f = $f_f(K_D K_H K_{Sf} K_T)$

f_f = specified notch shear force resistance, MPa

= 0.50 for all sawn members

K_{Sf} = service factor

= 1.00 for dry service

= 0.70 for wet service

K_N = notch factor (see below)

A = gross cross-section area, mm²

The notch factor for rectangular sawn members with notches on the tension face at the support is determined as follows:

$$K_N = \left[0.006d\left[1.6\left[\frac{1}{\alpha} - 1\right] + \eta^2\left[\frac{1}{\alpha^3} - 1\right]\right]\right]^{-\frac{1}{2}}$$

where

d = depth of the member

d_n = depth of the notch, mm, which must not exceed 0.25d

α = 1– (d_n/d)

η = e/d

e = length of notch, mm, measured parallel to the member axis from the centre of the nearest support to re-entrant corner of notch. For a member notched over an end support the minimum required bearing length may be used as the length of the support (Figure 7.5). For a continuous member, the length of support equals the actual bearing length.

Refer to section 7.3 for the design of notches in glulam bending members.

DEFLECTION

Under service load, wood beam deflection is calculated according to elastic theory. Consequently, conventional methods for evaluation of deflection in elastic structures due to bending moment are applied to wood beams; standard formulae can be found in the *Wood Design Manual* or in engineering handbooks, textbooks, or software.

Limits are placed on deflections in structures to ensure buildings are serviceable and finishing materials are not damaged. Deflection limits should be restricted to no more than L/360 for structures with rigid ceiling finishes such as gypsum and plaster, which may crack if deflection is not limited. Deflection should also be limited to avoid poor fit over doors, windows and partitions.

Control of deflection is largely left to the judgement of designers. Certain guidelines, however, are given in CSA O86 which stipulate that structural members be designed so that elastic deflection under total specified loads does not exceed 1/180 of the span and is limited to avoid damage to structural elements or attached nonstructural elements. CSA O86 also requires that excessive permanent deformation be avoided and that ponding and vibration be carefully assessed.

CSA O86 requires that structural members supporting more than 50% of total design loads on a continual basis be designed to avoid excessive permanent deformation. An upper limit on deflection equal to span divided by 360 under continuously applied loads must be used in lieu of more accurate evaluation of these cases.

Because ponding of rainwater or ice can cause safety problems due to excessive deflections which could lead to different and potentially cascading load distributions than assumed in design, CSA O86 requires that roof framing systems be investigated by rational analysis to ensure adequate performance under ponding conditions unless:

a. the roof slopes sufficiently towards points of free drainage to prevent accumulation of rain water on the roof surface, or

b. for a simply supported system subjected to a uniformly distributed load, the following condition is satisfied:

$$\frac{\Sigma\Delta}{w} < 65$$

where

Δ = deflection due to w, mm

w = total uniformly distributed load, kN/m^2

$\Sigma\Delta$ = sum of deflections due to this load of all components of the system, (decking, secondary beams, primary beams, etc.), mm

The *National Building Code of Canada* (NBCC) has deflection guidelines for buildings that fall under Part 9 (*Housing and Small Buildings*). CSA O86 defines minimum deflection criteria, and there are other deflection guidelines that are commonly followed. Table 7.2 provides a summary of suggested deflection limits for wood bending members.

Deflection of wood members can increase under continuous loads of long duration. Some of this deflection may be plastic or non-recoverable deflection when the load is removed.

For wood, the most serious condition occurs when full design load is applied continuously to green wood (or wood that has not been dried) in wet locations where the wood will not dry. In this extreme case, the non-recoverable deflection may equal the initial elastic deflection when the load is first applied.

For normal loading of dry wood and a limiting deflection/span ratio of L/360, there may be no plastic deformation. In general, plastic or non-recoverable deformation will depend upon the ratio of dead to live load, the cumulative effect of live load during the life of the structure, and whether or not wood is used in fluctuating wet and dry service conditions. Dry wood is not particularly susceptible to plastic deformation.

The modulus of elasticity for deflection calculations, E_S, is:

$$E_S = E (K_{SE} K_T)$$

where

E = specified modulus of elasticity, MPa

K_{SE} = service condition factor for modulus of elasticity

K_T = treatment factor

Springy floors are not comfortable to walk on. A deflection limit of L/360, based on specified live load, has generally proven satisfactory for light-frame wood construction (based on surveys), provided that the floor system has good lateral load distributing properties. Floors can be made stiffer by using thicker subfloor sheathing, using more nails, using bridging or blocking between the joists or by applying an appropriate type of glue between the subfloor and joists. Common practice is to use bridging, full blocking, strapping, or some combination of these to distribute loads over more than one member.

The *National Building Code of Canada* includes span tables for lumber joist floors that are used in housing. To avoid the human perception that floors are too springy or bouncy, a means of estimating vibration-acceptable spans is used to limit floor vibrations.

The span is determined for which the calculated deflection of a single floor member under a 1 kN concentrated load at mid-span is 2 mm. Then a factor K is used to multiply that span to obtain a vibration-controlled span for the floor system, which is compared with the strength-controlled span and deflection-controlled span due to uniformly distributed load. The least of these three spans governs. The factor K is found from an expression given in the NBCC Appendix.

Appendix A.4.5.2 of CSA O86 provides additional guidance on deflection of wood frame systems.

BEARING

Once a beam section has been selected to meet the criteria for bending moment resistance, deflection, and shear resistance, bearing must be checked to ensure that compression resistance perpendicular to grain for the beam selected is adequate at the supports and at locations of concentrated loads. Refer to Chapter 8 for a discussion of the bearing design process.

TORSION OF BEAMS

The design of beams should take into account the torsion that may develop due to eccentricity of applied loads, as for example where one beam frames into the side of another beam. Shear strength under torsion may be taken as similar to longitudinal shear strength. Torsion causes shear, and the shear stress developed for compact cross sections is much less than for the more efficient cross sections (considering bending moment only) usually used for rectangular wood beams. When torsion-causing-details must be used for wood beams, designers should try to avoid high torsional shear by selecting compact (or nearly square) cross sections. Such cross sections are inherently better able to resist shear stress.

EXAMPLE 7.1: JOIST DESIGN

Structural framing details of the first floor of a store are shown in Figure 7.6. Joists J1 frame into the sides of glulam beams B1 and are supported on hangers with bearing length of 50 mm. The specified dead and live loads for the joists are 1.2 kN/m^2 and 4.8 kN/m^2 respectively. Beams are to be 130 mm in width. Design the joists J1 using No.2 grade Spruce-Pine-Fir.

Load Effects and Combinations

From CSA O86 and NBCC:

Total factored load

$$= 1.25 \, D + 1.5 \, L$$

$$= 1.25 \times 1.2 + 1.5 \times 4.8$$

$$= 1.5 + 7.2$$

$$= 8.7 \text{ kN/m}^2$$

Specified Strengths

For No.2 Grade Structural Joist and Plank, S-P-F CSA O86 Table 5.3.1A

f_b = 11.8 MPa

f_v = 1.5 MPa

f_{cp} = 5.3 MPa

E   = 9500 MPa

Modification Factors

K_D = 1.0
(Standard duration of load, CSA O86 Table 4.3.1.2)

K_H = 1.40
(System factor, Case 2. CSA O86 Table 5.4.4)

K_{Sb} = 1.0

K_{Sv} = 1.0

$K_{Scp} = 1.0$

$K_{SE} = 1.0$

$K_T = 1.0$

K_{Zb}, K_{Zv} to be decided when member size chosen (CSA O86 Table 5.4.5)

$K_L = 1.0$, Provide support as required (Table 7.1)

$M_r = 0.9 \times 11.8 \times 1.40 \times S \times K_{Zb}$

$\quad = 14.87\ S \times K_{Zb}$

$V_r = 0.9 \times 1.5 \times 1.40 \times \left[\dfrac{2A}{3}\right] K_{Zv}$

$\quad = 1.26\ A \times K_{Zv}$

FIGURE 7.6

Retail floor layout

Plan

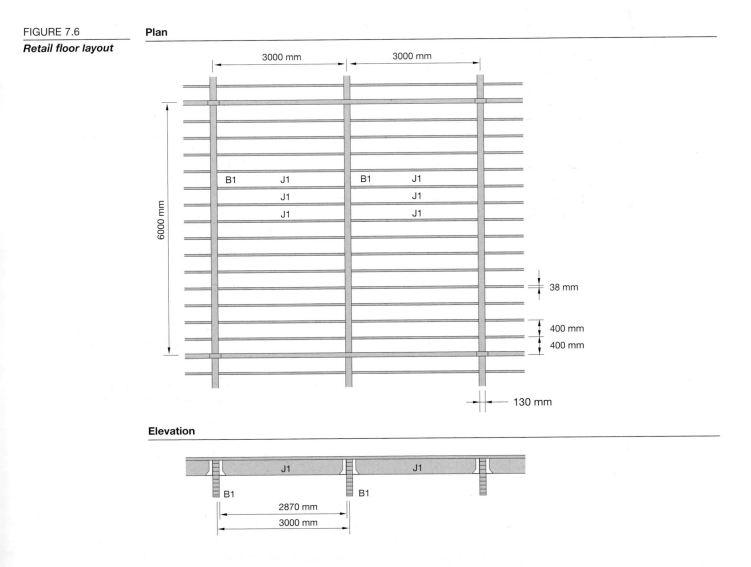

Elevation

Procedure

Because joists may be governed by bending strength, find section to provide:

$$M_r \geq M_f$$

Joists spaced at 400 mm, thus tributary width is 0.4 m.

Total factored uniformly distributed load on a joist

$$w_f = 8.7 \text{ kN/m}^2 \times 0.4 \text{ m}$$

$$= 3.48 \text{ kN/m}$$

Span, L = 3000 mm minus support beam width, estimated at 130 mm

$$= 3000 - 130 = 2870 \text{ mm}$$

Maximum factored bending moment M_f

$$M_f = (w_f L^2) / 8 = (3.48 (2870)^2) / 8$$

$$= 3.58 \times 10^6 \text{ N•mm} = 3.58 \text{ kN•m}$$

Try 38 × 184 mm

$$K_{Zb} = 1.2$$

$$M_r = 14.87 \times \frac{38 \times 184^2}{6} \times 1.2$$

$$= 3.83 \text{ kN•m}$$

$$(> M_f = 3.58) \qquad \textit{(Acceptable)}$$

Note:
The *Wood Design Manual* gives factored moment resistances which are applicable when the checklist conditions for joists are met.

Check whether the bending stiffness of 38 × 184 mm joists is sufficient to limit deflection to L / 360 under specified live load.

$$w_L = 4.8 \times 0.4$$

$$= 1.92 \text{ kN/m (or N/mm)}$$

$$\Delta \text{ limit} = L / 360$$

$$= 2870 / 360$$

$$= 8.0 \text{ mm}$$

$$\Delta = \left[\frac{5 \, w_L \, L^4}{384 \, E_s I} \right]$$

$$E_s I = E \, (K_{SE} \, K_T) \, I$$

$$= 9500 \, (1.0 \times 1.0) \, \frac{38 \times 184^3}{12}$$

$$= 187 \times 10^9 \text{ N•mm}^2$$

Note:
The *Wood Design Manual* lists $E_s I$ for joists in the Joist Selection Tables

$$\Delta = \left[\frac{5 \times 1.92 \times 2870^4}{384 \times 187 \times 10^9} \right]$$

$$= 9.0 \text{ mm}$$
(exceeds Δ limit of 8.0 mm)

$$\textit{(Not Acceptable)}$$

$$E_s I_{REQ'D} = \frac{9}{8} \times 187 \times 10^9$$

$$= 210 \times 10^9 \text{ N•mm}^2$$

For next larger joist size, 38 × 235 mm,

$$E_s I = 390 \times 10^9 \text{ N•mm}^2$$

Thus, for 38 × 235 mm,

$$\Delta = 187 / 390 \times 9.0$$

$$= 4.3 \text{ mm} \qquad \textit{(Acceptable)}$$

Check shear resistance for 38 × 235 mm

$$V_f = \frac{w_f L}{2}\left[1 - \frac{2\,d}{L}\right]$$

$$= \frac{3.48 \times 2870}{2}\left[1 - \frac{2 \times 235}{2870}\right]$$

$$= 4176 \text{ N (4.2 kN)}$$

$$V_r = 1.26\,A\,K_{Zv}$$

$$= 1.26 \times 38 \times 235 \times 1.1$$

$$= 12\,380 \text{ N}$$
$$(12.38 \text{ kN} > V_f) \qquad \textit{(Acceptable)}$$

Note:
The *Wood Design Manual* lists V_r values in the Joist Selection Tables. For shear, 38 × 235 mm is adequate

Check bearing capacity. For bearing length of 50 mm as provided by the joist hangers stipulated:

$$Q_f = w_f\,L\,/\,2$$

$$= 3.48 \times 2870\,/\,2$$

$$= 4990 \text{ N}$$

Factored bearing resistance (compression perpendicular to grain)

$$Q_r = \phi\,F_{cp}\,A_b\,K_B\,K_{Zcp}$$

$$= 0.8\,f_{cp}\,(K_{Scp}\,K_T)\,A_b\,K_B\,K_{Zcp}$$

$$= 0.8 \times 5.3 \times (1.0 \times 1.0) \times 38 \times 50 \times 1.0 \times 1.0$$

$$= 8060 \text{ N } (> Q_f) \qquad \textit{(Acceptable)}$$

Therefore 38 × 235 mm joists are adequate for bending moment, shear and bearing capacity as well as stiffness.

Verify that lateral stability provisions are satisfied.

$$d/b = 235\,/\,38$$

$$= 6.2$$

CSA O86 Clause 5.5.4.2 provides that: the lateral stability factor, K_L, may be taken as unity (i.e. = 1.0) provided the d/b ratio does not exceed 6.5 and the compressive edges of the joists are held in line by direct connection of sheathing. Lateral support must also be provided at points of bearing to prevent lateral displacement and rotation. These conditions are met.

Use 38 × 235 mm joists of No.2 grade S-P-F.

From Section 2.3 of the *Wood Design Manual*, other sections which would work: 38 × 235 mm joists of No. 2 grade Northern 38 × 184 mm joists of Select Structural grade D.Fir-L.

EXAMPLE 7.2: BUILT-UP BEAM, NOTCHED AT SUPPORT

A built-up beam supporting bedroom floor joists in a single storey nursing home spans 2.7 m between a support post and the foundation wall. The floor joists are 184 mm deep and span 3.0 m and 3.5 m respectively. The built-up beam is to be 3 or 4 plies wide. At the foundation wall, the depth of the built-up beam is limited to 220 mm. (Figure 7.7). Design the built-up beam using No.2 grade Douglas Fir-Larch.

Load Effects and Combinations

From in the NBCC, as well as CSA O86

Specified residential floor live loads: 1.9 kPa
Specified dead load: 1.2 kPa

Total factored load

$$= 1.25\,D + 1.5\,L$$
$$= 1.25 \times 1.2 + 1.5 \times 1.9$$
$$= 1.5 + 2.85$$
$$= 4.35\ kN/m^2$$

Specified Strengths

For No.2 Grade Structural Joist and Plank, D.Fir-L

$$f_b = 10.0\ MPa$$
$$f_v = 1.9\ MPa$$
$$f_{cp} = 7.0\ MPa$$
$$E = 11000\ MPa$$

Modification Factors

$$K_D = 1.0$$
$$K_H = 1.1$$

(System factor, Case 1 for 3-ply beam. CSA O86 Table 5.4.4)

$$K_{Sb} = 1.0$$
$$K_{Sv} = 1.0$$
$$K_{St} = 1.0$$
$$K_{Scp} = 1.0$$
$$K_{SE} = 1.0$$
$$K_T = 1.0$$

K_{Zb}, K_{Zv} vary. CSA O86 Table 5.4.5

$$K_L = 1.0,\ Provide\ adequate\ restraint$$
$$K_{Zcp} = 1.0$$
$$M_r = 0.9 \times 10.0 \times 1.1 \times S \times K_{Zb}$$
$$= 9.9\ S \times K_{Zb}$$
$$V_r = 0.9 \times 1.9 \times 1.1 \times \left[\frac{2A_n}{3}\right] K_{Zv}$$
$$= 1.25\ A_n \times K_{Zv}$$
$$F_r = 0.9 \times 0.5 \times 1.1\ A \times K_N$$
$$= 0.495\ A \times K_N$$

Procedure

Check Bending Moment

Find a section to provide

$$M_r \geq M_f$$

$$\text{Tributary width} = \frac{(3.0\ m + 3.5\ m)}{2} = 3.25\ m$$

Total factored uniformily distributed load on beam

$$w_f = 4.35\ kN/m^2 \times 3.25\ m$$
$$= 14.14\ kN/m\ (N/mm)$$

Maximum factored bending moment, M_f

$$M_f = \frac{14.14\ N/mm \times (2700\ mm)^2}{8}$$
$$= 12.89 \times 10^6\ N\bullet mm$$
$$= 12.89\ kN\bullet m$$

Try $3 - 38 \times 235$ mm

$$K_{zb} = 1.1$$
$$M_r = 9.9 \times \left[\frac{3 \times 38 \times 235^2}{6}\right] \times 1.1$$
$$= 11.4\ kN\bullet m \qquad (Not\ Acceptable)$$

Try $3 - 38 \times 286$ mm

$K_{Zb} = 1.0$

$M_r = 9.9 \times \left[\dfrac{3 \times 38 \times 286^2}{6} \right] \times 1.0$

$\qquad = 15.4$ kN•m *(Acceptable)*

Check Shear

d at foundation = 220 mm

$A_n = 3 \times 38 \times 220$

$\qquad = 25080$ mm^2

$K_{Zv} = 1.0$

$V_f = \dfrac{14.14 \times 2700}{2} \left[1 - \dfrac{2 \times 220}{2700} \right]$

$\qquad = 15978$ N (16.0 kN)

$V_r = 1.25 \times 25080 \times 1.0$

$\qquad = 31\,350$ N (31.3 kN) *(Acceptable)*

Check Deflection

Deflection limit = L/360 under specified
live load

$\qquad\qquad\quad = 7.5$ mm

$w_L = 6.18$ N/mm

$E_S I = E(K_{SE} K_T) I$

$\qquad = 11000\,(1.0 \times 1.0) \left[\dfrac{3 \times 38 \times 286^3}{12} \right]$

$\qquad = 2445 \times 10^9$ N•mm^2

$\Delta = \dfrac{5 \times 6.18\,(2700\ \text{mm})^4}{384 \times 2445 \times 10^9}$

$\qquad = 1.7$ mm *(Acceptable)*

Define Bearing Length Required

$Q_f = 14.14 \times \dfrac{2700}{2}$

$\qquad = 19089$ N (19.1 kN)

Bearing width = 3×38 mm

$\qquad\qquad\quad = 114$ mm

$Q_r = 0.8 \times 7.0$ MPa $\times A_b$

$\qquad = 5.6\ A_b$

A_b req'd $= \dfrac{19089}{5.6}$

$\qquad\qquad = 3409$ mm^2

Bearing length req'd $= \dfrac{3409\ \text{mm}^2}{114\ \text{mm}}$

$\qquad\qquad\qquad = 29.9$ mm
$\qquad\qquad\qquad$ (Use 30 mm)

Normally, beams have a minimum 38mm
bearing length. However, 30 mm is acceptable.

Check Notch Effect at Support

d $\ = 286$ mm

$d_n = 286 - 220$

$\quad\ = 66$ mm

Check that notch depth is not greater than
25% of member

0.25d = 71.5 mm > 66 mm *(Acceptable)*

e $\ = \dfrac{30\ \text{mm}}{2} + 2\text{mm}$

$\quad = 17$ mm

$\alpha\ = 1 - \dfrac{d_n}{d}$

$\quad = 1 - \dfrac{66}{286}$

$\quad = 0.769$

$\eta\ = \dfrac{e}{d}$

$\quad = \dfrac{17}{286}$

$\quad = 0.060$

$$K_N = \left[0.006d\left(1.6\left(\frac{1}{\alpha}-1\right)+\eta^2\left(\frac{1}{\alpha^3}-1\right)\right)\right]^{-1/2}$$

$$= \left[0.006\times286\left(1.6\left(\frac{1}{0.769}-1\right)\right.\right.$$

$$\left.\left.+0.060^2\left(\frac{1}{0.769^3}-1\right)\right)\right]^{-\frac{1}{2}}$$

$$= 1.1$$

Check that $F_r \geq Q_f$

$$F_r = \phi F_t A K_N$$

$$= 0.9\times0.5\times1.1\times3\times38\times286\times1.1$$

$$= 17753 \text{ N} \qquad \textit{(Not Acceptable)}$$

Add an additional ply.
K_N can be estimated as 1.1

$$F_r = 0.9\times0.5\times1.1\times4\times38\times286\times1.1$$

$$= 23670 \text{ N} \qquad \textit{(Acceptable)}$$

Check Lateral Stability

$$d/b = 286 \text{ mm}/(4\times38)$$

$$= 1.9$$

No lateral restraint is required, provided 4 plies are acting as a unit. Normal practice is to nail plies together with 2 rows of nails. Nails should be spaced at 450 mm.

Use 4 – 38 × 286 mm D.Fir-L No.2 grade. Provide 38 mm bearing length. Notch at foundation to be no larger than 40 mm long by 66 mm deep.

FIGURE 7.7

Floor and main beam details

Plan

Section at Foundation

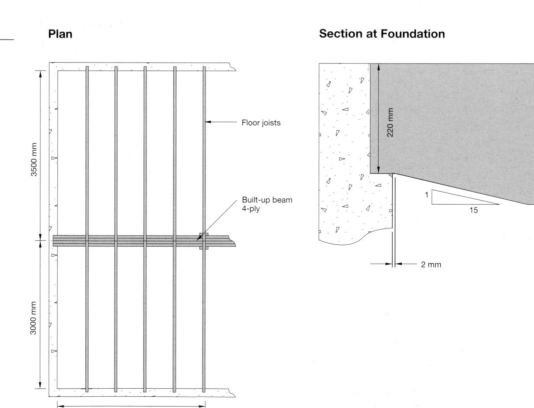

EXAMPLE 7.3: MEMBERS SUBJECT TO BENDING ABOUT BOTH PRINCIPAL AXES

Design oblique sawn timber roof purlins for the following circumstances:

Purlin spacing	1.8 m
Purlin span	6 m
Roof pitch	3/12 (14.04°)
Specified dead load	0.50 kPa
Specified snow load strength	2.16 kPa (I_S=1.0)
Specified snow load serviceability	1.94 kPa (I_S=0.9)
Duration of load	Standard
Service conditions	Dry
Treatment	None

Use D.Fir-L Select Structural grade

Load Effects and Combinations

Total factored load

$$= 1.25 \times 0.5 + 1.5 \times 2.16$$
$$= 3.87 \text{ kPa}$$

Purlin load

$$w_f = 3.87 \times 1.8$$
$$= 6.97 \text{ kN/m}$$

$$w_s = 1.94 \times 1.8$$
$$= 3.50 \text{ kN/m}$$

Procedure

Resolve load as normal and tangential components (Figure 7.8)

$$w_{fN} = 6.97 \cos 14.04°$$
$$= 6.75 \text{ kN/m}$$

$$w_{fT} = 6.97 \sin 14.04°$$
$$= 1.69 \text{ kN/m}$$

$$w_{SN} = 3.50 \cos 14.04°$$
$$= 3.40 \text{ kN/m}$$

$$w_{ST} = 3.50 \sin 14.04°$$
$$= 0.85 \text{ kN/m}$$

Compute factored moments

About the strong (X–X) axis

$$M_{fX} = (6.75/8) \times 6^2$$
$$= 30.4 \text{ kN•m}$$

About the weak (Y-Y) axis

$$M_{fY} = (1.69/8) \times 6^2$$
$$= 7.61 \text{ kN•m}$$

FIGURE 7.8

Oblique sawn timber purlin

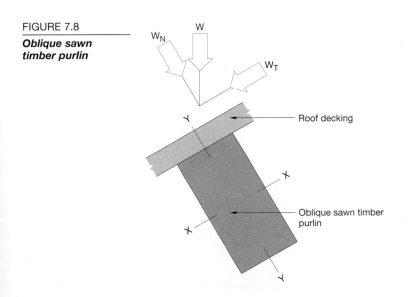

Roof decking

Oblique sawn timber purlin

Trial section (using rule of thumb suggested in the *Wood Design Manual*, Section 2.7)

$$M_{rX} = 1.2 (30.4 + 7.61)$$

$$= 45.6 \text{ kN•m}$$

Choose D.Fir-L Select Structural
191×292 mm

$$M_{rX} = \phi f_b (K_D K_H K_{Sb} K_T) S_X K_{Zb} K_L$$

$$= 0.9 \times 19.5 (1.0 \times 1.0 \times 1.0 \times 1.0) \times 2.71 \times 10^6 \times 1.1 \times 1.0$$

$$= 52.4 \text{ kN•m}$$

$$M_{rY} = \phi f_b (K_D K_H K_{Sb} K_T) S_Y K_{Zb} K_L \times$$
(factor for wide face loading)

From Table 5.3.1C of CSA O86, the factor for wide face loading is 0.88 for Select Structural Grade.

$$M_{rY} = 0.9 \times 19.5 (1.0 \times 1.0 \times 1.0 \times 1.0) \times 1.78 \times 10^6 \times 1.1 \times 1.0 \times 0.88$$

$$= 30.2 \text{ kN•m}$$

$$E_s I_X = E(K_{SE} K_T) I_X$$

$$= 12000 (1.0 \times 1.0) \times 396 \times 10^6$$

$$= 4760 \times 10^9 \text{ N•mm}^2$$

$$E_s I_Y = E(K_{SE} K_T) I_Y \times \text{(factor for wide side loading)}$$

$$= 12000 \times (1.0 \times 1.0) \times 170 \times 10^6 \times 1.0$$

$$= 2030 \times 10^9 \text{ N•mm}^2$$

Check interaction

$$\frac{M_{fX}}{M_{rX}} + \frac{M_{fY}}{M_{rY}} \leq 1.0$$

$$= \frac{30.4}{52.4} + \frac{7.61}{30.2}$$

$$= 0.58 + 0.25$$

$$= 0.83 < 1.0 \qquad \textit{(Acceptable)}$$

Check deflection. Δ under specified live load $< L/240$ (as suggested in Table 7.2)

$$\Delta \text{ limit} = 6000/240$$

$$= 25 \text{ mm}$$

$$\Delta_X = \left[\frac{5 w_{SN} L^4}{384 E_s I_X} \right]$$

$$= 12.1 \text{ mm}$$

$$\Delta_Y = \left[\frac{5 w_{ST} L^4}{384 E_s I_Y} \right]$$

$$= 7.05 \text{ mm}$$

$$\Delta = \sqrt{\Delta_X^2 + \Delta_Y^2}$$

$$= 14.0 \text{ mm} < 25 \text{ mm} \qquad \textit{(Acceptable)}$$

Use 191 x 292 mm Select Structural grade D. Fir-L. purlins

7.3   Glulam Bending Members

INTRODUCTION TO GLULAM DESIGN

Glulam is frequently used for intermediate and long-span bending applications. This is due to the wide range of sizes, lengths and shapes available (Chapter 6).

Because bending stresses vary from zero at the neutral axis to a maximum at the top and bottom of a bending member (Figure 7.9), the stiffest and strongest laminations are located in the outer portions. The lowest grade, weakest lumber laminations are used in the inner portions of glulam bending grades. Laminations on the tension face are generally stronger than those on the compression face. This applies to both visual requirements and minimum E (modulus of elasticity) values established by non-destructive testing. There are no restrictions on minimum E values for middle laminations of bending grades.

In some cases, stresses may be reversed in a bending member, so that the side normally subject to compression becomes the tension side, and *vice versa*. The 20f-E and 24f-E grades have a limited capacity for stress reversal and may be used where a small tensile component might occur due to reverse bending moments.

For arches, continuous beams or cantilevered beams, the design may develop equal flexural tension stresses on both sides of a member. A designer wishing to use the same specified bending strength for both sides should specify the stress grades 20f-EX or 24f-EX. These grades require high grade laminations on both the compression and tension faces.

Specified strengths in bending are not species-dependent; however, other properties such as shear and E are species-dependent.

Because glulam is usually custom-made for specific applications, it is most efficient to use bending grade members for flexural uses, and compression and tension grade members for such things as columns or heavy duty trusses. (In the grade designation, the bending grades use **f** and the compression and tension grades use **c** and **t** respectively.)

Glued-laminated timber members are made in many sizes, but standard sizes are more economical than non-standard sizes. Furthermore, since most glulam is made to order, it is possible to use many different sizes for a specific project.

GLULAM BENDING MEMBER DESIGN

Similar to sawn lumber, the design of glulam bending members can be governed by:

- bending moment resistance,
- shear resistance,
- deflection, or
- bearing (compression resistance perpendicular to grain).

The procedure for determining the bending moment capacity of glued-laminated members depends on their shape. The capacity of straight glulam members of constant depth is a function of the bending moment resistance. An additional aspect of glulam bending member design is the influence of curvature on the capacity of curved or doubled-tapered glulam members. Both the bending moment resistance and the tensile capacity perpendicular to grain (in the radial direction) must be checked.

Similar to sawn lumber, glulam bending stress is assumed to be proportional to strain (linearly related by E up to the proportional limit), and strain is directly proportional to the distance from the neutral axis (it is assumed that plane sections remain plane after bending) (Figure 7.9).

FIGURE 7.9

Bending stress distribution

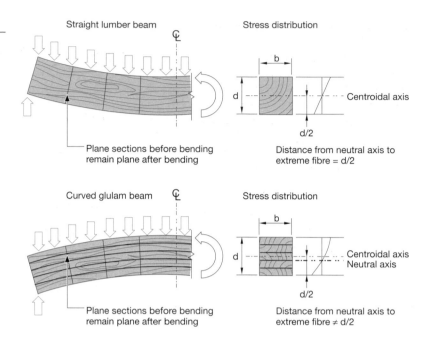

Straight lumber beam

Stress distribution

Plane sections before bending remain plane after bending

Distance from neutral axis to extreme fibre = d/2

Curved glulam beam

Stress distribution

Centroidal axis
Neutral axis

Plane sections before bending remain plane after bending

Distance from neutral axis to extreme fibre ≠ d/2

Bending Resistance

The factored bending moment resistance, M_r, of glued-laminated timber members is the lesser of M_{r1} and M_{r2} calculated as:

$$M_{r1} = \phi \, F_b \, S \, K_{Zbg} \, K_X$$

$$M_{r2} = \phi \, F_b \, S \, K_L \, K_X$$

where

ϕ = 0.9

F_b = $f_b (K_D \, K_H \, K_{Sb} \, K_T)$

f_b = specified strength in bending, MPa (CSA O86 Table 6.3)

K_{Zbg} = size factor for glulam beams

= $1.03 \, (BL)^{-0.18} \leq 1.0$

B = beam width (for single piece laminations), or width of the widest piece of lamination (for multiple piece laminations)

L = length of the glulam beam from point of zero moment to zero moment

K_L = lateral stability factor

K_X = curvature factor (K_X = 1.0 for straight members; and $K_X \leq 1$ for curved member)

S = section modulus

Tests have shown that the tensile strength of the end joints in laminations may control the bending strength of glulam beams. The size factor, K_{Zbg}, accounts for the variability in strength, and the number and location of end joints used in outer tension laminations. The factor "L" used in the K_{Zbg} equation equals the length of the beam when the beam is simply supported. For multi-span or cantilever beams, L is the length between the points of inflection. The moment resistance, as modified by K_{Zbg}, must be calculated for each beam segment and compared to the maximum factored moment within that segment.

K_{Zbg} is used to calculate the moment resistance on the tension side of the beam. K_L is used to determine the lateral buckling on the compression side of the beam. Therefore, K_{Zbg} and K_L are not used simultaneously to determine beam capacity.

The lateral stability factor, K_L, is used to control lateral buckling (Section 7.2). This factor is based on tests and analyses carried out on clear lumber, and is applicable to glulam because of the restriction placed on location and dispersion of knots and other characteristics.

For glulam subjected to combined bending moment and axial loads, designers may omit calculations for K_L and apply the rules of thumb for lateral stability used in lumber design. These rules have been proven satisfactory by experience. For an appropriate degree of lateral support, the depth to width ratio of the member should not exceed the values given in Table 7.1. If these limits are met, the value of K_L is unity. Otherwise, the lateral stability factor should be calculated.

The following method is used for calculating K_L:

a. If the maximum depth to width ratio of a bending member does not exceed 2.5:1, K_L may be taken as 1.00.

    Where the ratio of depth to width is greater than 2.5, lateral support must be provided at points of bearing to prevent lateral displacement and rotation, and K_L is determined by steps b or c.

b. If the compression edge of a bending member is supported throughout its length so as to prevent lateral displacement, $K_L = 1.00$ (for decking to provide such support, it must be fastened securely to bending members and adjacent framing to provide a rigid diaphragm).

c. If the compression edge of a bending member is not supported throughout its length, K_L is determined by considering the bending member slenderness ratio, C_B, as calculated by:

$$C_B = \sqrt{\frac{L_e d}{b^2}}$$

where

L_e = effective length, mm, (CSA O86 Table 6.5.6.4.3)

b = width, mm

d = depth, mm

where C_B is 10 or less

$K_L = 1.00$

where $C_B > 10$ but $\leq C_K$

$$K_L = 1 - \frac{1}{3}\left[\frac{C_B}{C_K}\right]^4$$

$$C_K = \sqrt{\frac{0.97\, E\, K_{SE}\, K_T}{F_b}}$$

where

K_{SE} = service condition factor for modulus of elasticity

F_b = specified strength in bending

where C_B is greater than C_K but ≤ 50

$$K_L = \frac{0.65\, E\, K_{SE}\, K_T}{C_B^2\, F_b\, K_X}$$

where

F_b = $f_b\,(K_D\, K_H\, K_{Sb}\, K_T)$

f_b = specified strength in bending, MPa (CSA O86 Table 6.3)

K_X = curvature factor

Shear Resistance

There are two methods of calculating shear for glulam. One is the simple method used for lumber that also applies to glued-laminated beams less than 2.0 m³ in volume. This method is also used for glued-laminated members other than beams.

The other method is more advanced and requires a trial-and-error procedure to determine the required area. The more advanced method takes into account the effects of beam volume and load configuration on beam shear capacity. Designers may find it easier to first use the simple method in the case where the beam volume is less than 2 m³. If the shear capacity is not adequate using the simple method, designers may then check the capacity using the advanced method.

The simple equation for factored shear resistance, V_r, is:

$$V_r = \phi F_v \frac{2A_g}{3} K_N$$

where

$\phi = 0.9$

$F_v = f_v (K_D K_H K_{Sv} K_T)$

$f_v = $ specified strength in shear (CSA O86 Table 6.3), MPa

$A_g = $ gross cross-sectional area, mm²

$K_N = $ notch factor for glulam

CSA O86 provides the following K_N factors for notched rectangular glulam beams.

Notched at lower (tension) face at the support

$$K_N = \left[1 - \frac{d_n}{d} \right]^2$$

Notched at upper (compression) face where e > d

$$K_N = 1 - \frac{d_n}{d}$$

FIGURE 7.10

Notched and drilled glulam beams

Beam notched on lower face at the ends

Beam notched on upper face at the ends

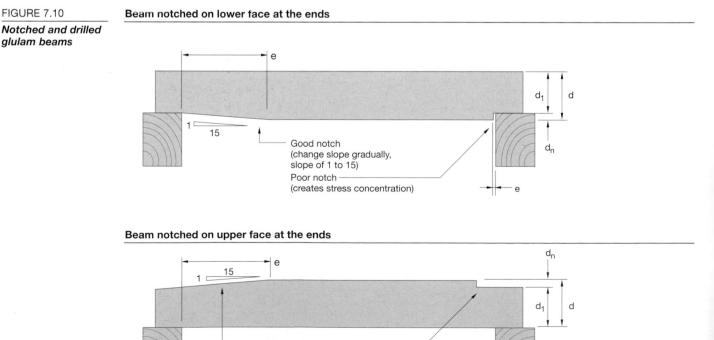

Notched at upper (compression) face where e < d

$$K_N = 1 - \frac{d_n e}{d(d - d_n)}$$

where

   d = total beam depth, mm

   d_n = depth of notch ($d_n \leq 0.25\,d$), mm

(For notches located on the tension side of the beam it is recommended that designers apply a more restrictive limit, for example 10% of the beam depth.)

   e = length of the notch measured along the beam span from the inner edge of the support to the farthest edge of the notch, mm (Figure 7.10)

The simple method may be conservative where the beam volume is less than 2.0 m³. However, where the beam volume is 2.0 m³ or greater, CSA O86 requires the designer to use the following method.

For a glulam beam with volume exceeding 2.0 m³, the factored shear resistance is required to be no less than the sum of all factored loads acting on the beam, W_f, and is taken as:

$$V_r = \phi\, F_v\, 0.48 A_g\, K_N\, C_v\, Z^{-0.18} \geq W_f$$

where

   ϕ = 0.9

   F_v = $f_v\, (K_D\, K_H\, K_{Sv}\, K_T)$

   f_v = specified strength in shear, MPa (CSA O86 Table 6.3)

   A_g = gross cross-sectional area, mm²

   K_N = notch factor for glulam

   C_v = shear load coefficient (CSA O86 Clause 6.5.7.3)

   Z = beam volume, m³

   W_f = sum of all factored loads acting on the beam, kN

The shear load coefficient, C_v, depends on beam shape, configuration, load distribution and loading type and is tabulated for typical cases in CSA O86. For load patterns not given in the tables, the shear load coefficient C_v must be calculated.

It is important designers recognize that the principle of superposition cannot be applied in determining C_v due to the interactive effects of volume and loading pattern on shear resistance.

Deflection

CSA O86 requires that elastic deflection under the specified loads be no greater than the span divided by 180. There are some additional requirements for certain cases to prevent plastic (non-recoverable) deformation. Under continuous loads of long duration, or severe ponding conditions, some non-recoverable deflection can occur. This is more likely where wood is wet and cannot dry out since wet wood is more susceptible to deformation.

Limits on deflection may be imposed to prevent either elastic or plastic deformation. They may also be intended to control unacceptable performance. A deflection limit of span divided by 360 under live loading is commonly used to prevent cracking in ceiling finishes such as gypsum board and plaster. A deflection limit may also be appropriate in some cases to prevent vibration in floors.

For glulam, it is possible to build in some camber to offset the deflections due to applied dead and live loads. Camber is curvature opposite to the anticipated deflection in service. This is not usually done for stock beams which are pre-manufactured for stocking in a distribution depot and which may be cut to length on order. However, most glulam beams and arches are made to order and may be cambered to suit the particular design conditions by gluing the laminations to the slightly curved shape required for camber.

For glulam beams of approximately 6 m in length or more, it is usual practice in the Canadian laminating industry to incorporate camber (Table 7.3). The camber used may range from approximately 24 mm for a simple beam spanning 6 m to 80 mm for a simple beam on a span of 20 m. Generally, designers should specify camber to counteract at least the deflection due to dead load. CSA O86 relaxes the elastic deflection limit to span/180 due to specified live loading where the camber provided is equal to calculated dead load deflection. Glulam fabricators may recommend camber based on their experiences.

The modulus of elasticity for deflection calculations, E_S, may be calculated by:

$$E_S = E (K_{SE} K_T)$$

where

E = modulus of elasticity, MPa

K_{SE} = service condition factor for modulus of elasticity

K_T = treatment factor

Bearing

Compressive resistance perpendicular to grain, Q_r, determines the required bearing area at support points and at points of concentrated loads. The bearing area is determined partly by the width of beams that are used. Beam supports are generally the same width as the beams themselves. (Refer to the discussion of the design process for bearing presented in Chapter 8.)

EXAMPLE 7.4: GLULAM BEAM DESIGN

Design the glulam beams B1 as shown in Figure 7.6 using 20f-E bending grade Spruce-Pine. Because joists are closely spaced, the loading on beam B1 may be considered as uniformly distributed.

Tributary width for B1

$$- 3.0 \text{ m}$$

Dead load (not including self weight)

$$= 1.2 \times 3.0$$

$$= 3.6 \text{ kN/m}$$

Estimated self weight of beam

$$= 0.4 \text{ kN/m}$$

Total dead load

$$D = 4.0 \text{ kN/m}$$

Live load due to use and occupancy

$$L = 4.8 \times 3.0$$

$$= 14.4 \text{ kN/m}$$

Load Effects and Combinations

As in CSA O86 and the NBCC:

Total factored load on beam

$$= 1.25 \, D + 1.5 \, L$$

$$= 1.25 \times 4.0 + 1.5 \times 14.4$$

$$= 5.0 + 21.6$$

$$= 26.6 \text{ kN/m (or N/mm)}$$

Specified strengths

For 20f-E bending grade Spruce-Pine from CSA O86 Table 6.3

$$f_b = 25.6 \text{ MPa}$$

$$f_v = 1.75 \text{ MPa}$$

$$f_{cp} = 5.8 \text{ MPa}$$

$$E = 10300 \text{ MPa}$$

Modification factors

Note that for glulam the lateral stability factor K_L is not based on the rules of thumb used for lumber. Thus:

$$K_D = 1.0$$

$$K_H = 1.0$$

$$K_{Sb} = 1.0$$

$$K_{Sv} = 1.0$$

$$K_{Scp} = 1.0$$

$$K_{SE} = 1.0$$

$$K_T = 1.0$$

Procedure

The design approach is to determine the maximum factored bending moment and shear force and the deflection limit to be met. Maximum factored bending moment:

$$M_f = (w_f \, L^2) / 8$$

$$= 26.6 \, (6000)^2 / 8$$

$$= 120 \times 10^6 \text{ N•mm}$$

$$= 120 \text{ kN•m}$$

Select a beam to provide $M_r \geq M_f$. Note the *Wood Design Manual* contains a list of factored resisting moments, shears and stiffnesses. Keeping in mind that the joist span was based on use of 130 mm wide beams, select a beam of 20f-E Spruce-Pine 130 × 494 mm.

Calculate K_{Zbg}:

$$B = 0.13 \text{ m}$$

$$L = 6.0 \text{ m}$$

$$K_{Zbg} = 1.03 \, (0.13 \times 6.0)^{-0.18} \text{ but not greater than 1.0}$$

$$= 1.08 \text{ therefore use 1.0}$$

Calculate K_L:

From CSA O86 Table 6.5.6.4.3:

$$L_e = 1.92 \times 400$$
$$= 768 \text{ mm}$$

$$C_B = \sqrt{\frac{L_e d}{b^2}}$$
$$= \sqrt{\frac{768 \times 494}{130^2}}$$
$$= 4.7 < 10$$

$$K_L = 1.0$$

Calculate S:

$$S = \left[\frac{b d^2}{6}\right]$$
$$= \frac{130 \times 494^2}{6}$$
$$= 5.29 \times 10^6 \text{ mm}^3$$

$$M_{r1} = 0.9 (25.6 \times 1 \times 1 \times 1 \times 1) \, 5.29 \times 10^6 \times 1 \times 1$$
$$= 122 \text{ kN•m} \qquad \textit{(Acceptable)}$$

$$M_{r2} = 0.9 (25.6 \times 1 \times 1 \times 1 \times 1) \, 5.29 \times 10^6 \times 1 \times 1$$
$$= 122 \text{ kN•m} \qquad \textit{(Acceptable)}$$

For this beam

$$V_r = 0.9(1.75 \times 1 \times 1 \times 1 \times 1)\left[\frac{2 \times 130 \times 494}{3}\right]$$
$$= 67400 \text{ N}$$

$$E_s I = 10300 \times 1.0 \times 1.0 \left[\frac{130 \times 494^3}{12}\right]$$
$$= 13500 \times 10^9 \text{ N•mm}$$

For the beam selected to satisfy the bending moment requirement, check the stiffness to ensure that deflection is limited to the appropriate criterion and check the shear resistance.

The deflection limit is to be L / 360 due to specified live load:

$$\Delta \text{ allowable} = 6000 / 360 = 16.7 \text{ mm}$$

Specified live load = 14.4 kN/m (or N/mm)

$$\Delta = \frac{5 \, w_L \, L^4}{384 \, E_s I}$$
$$= \frac{5 \times 14.4 \times 6000^4}{384 \times 13500 \times 10^9}$$
$$= 18.0 \text{ mm (exceeds 16.7 mm)}$$

(Not Acceptable)

$$E_s I_{\text{REQ'D}} = \frac{18.0}{16.7} \times 13500 \times 10^9$$
$$= 14600 \times 10^9 \text{ N•mm}$$

Check $E_s I$ for next larger glulam beam.
Try 130×532 mm

$$E_s I = 16800$$
$$\Delta = 18.0 \, (13500/16800)$$
$$= 14.5 \text{ mm } (< 16.7 \text{ mm}) \quad \textit{(Acceptable)}$$

For stiffness, a beam 130×532 mm is required.

Check lateral stability for 130×532 mm beam.

$$C_B = \sqrt{\frac{L_e d}{b^2}}$$
$$= \sqrt{\frac{768 \times 532}{130^2}}$$
$$= 4.9 < 10$$

$$\therefore K_L = 1.0$$

Check shear resistance for the 130×532 mm beam. Maximum factored shear force:

$$V_f = \frac{w_f L}{2}\left[1 - \frac{2 \, d}{L}\right]$$
$$= \frac{26.6 \times 6000}{2}\left[1 - \frac{2 \times 532}{6000}\right]$$
$$= 65600 \text{ N}$$
$$= 65.6 \text{ kN}$$

The beam selected on the basis of bending moment, 130×494 mm, has $V_r = 67.4$ kN so the 130×532 mm beam meets the design requirement.

Use a 130 x 532 mm 20f-E Spruce-Pine glulam beam.

EXAMPLE 7.5: CANTILEVERED GLULAM BEAM DESIGN

Design the cantilevered roof beam illustrated in Figure 7.11. The uniform dead load is 6 kN/m. The uniform snow load is 30 kN/m for strength calculations (I_s=1.0) and 27 kN/m for serviceability calculations (I_s=0.9). A concentrated equipment live load of 200 kN is applied at the free end of the beam. The beam is laterally supported along its top surface by a roof deck.

Load Effects and Combinations

For equipment live loads the NBCC specifies a minimum companion load factor of 1.0. Therefore the load combinations for strength are:

Case 1:

$$1.25D + 1.5L + 0.5S \qquad \textit{(Governs)}$$

Uniform factored load on beam

$$\begin{aligned} &= 1.25\,D + 0.5S \\ &= 1.25 \times 6 + 0.5 \times 30 \\ &= 22.5 \text{ kN/m} \end{aligned}$$

Factored point load on beam

$$\begin{aligned} &= 1.5 \times 200 \\ &= 300 \text{ kN} \end{aligned}$$

Case 2:

$$1.25\,D + 1.5\,S + 1.0\,L$$

Uniform factored load on beam

$$\begin{aligned} &= 1.25\,D + 1.5\,S \\ &= 1.25 \times 6 + 1.5 \times 30 \\ &= 52.5 \text{ kN/m} \end{aligned}$$

Factored point load on beam

$$\begin{aligned} &= 1.0 \times 200 \\ &= 200 \text{ kN} \end{aligned}$$

Specified Strengths

Since the beam is subject to positive and negative bending moments, select -EX grade. For this example use Douglas Fir-Larch 20f-EX Grade.

From CSA O86.1 Table 6.3

$$f_b(\text{pos}) = 25.6 \text{ MPa}$$

$$f_b(\text{neg}) = 25.6 \text{ MPa}$$

$$f_v = 2.0 \text{ MPa}$$

$$E = 12400 \text{ MPa}$$

FIGURE 7.11

Shear and moment diagrams

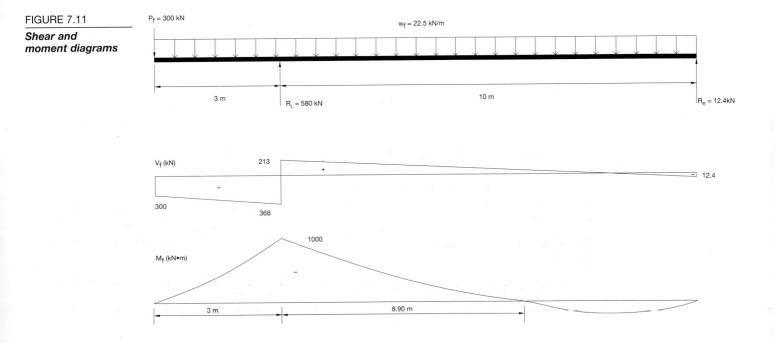

Modification Factors

$$K_D = 1.0$$

$$K_H = 1.0$$

$$K_{Sb} = 1.0$$

$$K_{Sv} = 1.0$$

$$K_{Scp} = 1.0$$

$$K_{SE} = 1.0$$

$$K_T = 1.0$$

Procedure

Select a beam size based on bending moment assuming $K_{Zbg} = 1.0$ and $K_L = 1.0$. Check M_{r1} and M_{r2}, and then check for shear and deflection.

See Figure 7.11,

$$M_{f(max)} = -1000 \text{ kN·m}$$

Try a 215 × 1140 mm member

$$M'_r = 0.9 \times (25.6 \times 1.0 \times 1.0 \times 1.0 \times 1.0)$$

$$\times \frac{215 \times 1140^2}{6}$$

$$= 1070 \text{ kN·m}$$

Check K_{Zbg}: By observation, the bending moment at the cantilever support will govern the design. The distance between points of zero moments is 3 + 8.90 = 11.90 m (Figure 7.11).

$$B = 0.215 \text{ m}$$

$$L = 11.9 \text{ m}$$

$$K_{Zbg} = 1.03 (0.215 \times 11.9)^{-0.18} \text{ but not greater than 1.0}$$

$$= 0.870$$

$$M_{r1} = 1070 \times 0.870$$

$$= 933 \text{ kN·m} \qquad \textit{(Not Acceptable)}$$

Check K_L – Decking is only provided on the upper surface of the beam. Therefore, where the beam is subjected to negative bending moments, lateral restraint is not provided to the compression face. Lateral restraint

is provided at the supports. The unsupported length is the greater of:

• The length of the cantilever = 3.0 m
• The distance between supports = 10.0 m (Governs)

From CSA O86 Table 6.5.6.4.3

$$L_e = 1.92 l_u$$

$$= 1.92 \times 10.0$$

$$= 19.2 \text{ m}$$

$$C_B = \sqrt{\frac{L_e d}{b^2}}$$

$$= \sqrt{\frac{19200 \times 1140}{(215)^2}}$$

$$= 21.7$$

$$C_K = \sqrt{\frac{0.97 E K_{SE} K_T}{F_b}}$$

$$= \sqrt{\frac{0.97 \times 12400 \times 1.0 \times 1.0}{25.6 \times 1.0 \times 1.0 \times 1.0 \times 1.0}}$$

$$= 21.7$$

$$K_L = 1 - \frac{1}{3} \left(\frac{C_B}{C_K} \right)^4$$

$$= 1 - \frac{1}{3} \left(\frac{21.7}{21.7} \right)^4$$

$$= 0.667$$

$$M_{r2} = 1070 \times 0.667$$

$$= 713 \text{ kN·m} \qquad \textit{(Not Acceptable)}$$

Check a variety of sizes:

Width (mm)	215	215	215	265
Depth (mm)	1178	1368	1444	1444
K_{Zbg}	0.870	0.870	0.870	0.838
M_{r1} (kN·m)	996	1340	1500	1780
C_B	22.1	23.8	24.5	19.9
K_L	0.643	0.554	0.525	0.765
M_{r2} (kN·m)	737	856	904	1620
A (mm²)	253000	294000	310000	383000

265 × 1444 is the lightest section that meets moment criteria

Check Shear

$$V_f \quad = \quad 368 \text{ kN} \qquad \text{(from Figure 7.11)}$$

Beam Volume

$$= \quad 13.0 \text{ m} \times 0.265 \text{ m} \times 1.444 \text{ m}$$

$$= \quad 4.97 \text{ m}^3 > 2.0 \text{ m}^3$$

Use detailed calculation for beam volume > 2.0 m³

$$V_r \quad = \quad \phi F_v 0.48 A K_N C_v Z^{-0.18} \geq W_f$$

$$W_f \quad = \quad (22.5 \times 13.0) + 300$$

$$= \quad 593 \text{ kN}$$

C_V from CSA O86 Table 6.5.7.3C

$$r \quad = \quad \frac{300 \text{ kN}}{22.5 \text{kN/m} \times 13 \text{ m}} = 1.03$$

$$L_1/L_2 \quad = \quad \frac{3 \text{ m}}{10 \text{ m}}$$

$$= \quad 0.3$$

$$C_V \quad = \quad 3.30 \text{ (Extrapolating from CSA O86 Table 6.5.7.3C)}$$

$$V_r \quad = \quad 0.9 \times 2.0 \ (1 \times 1 \times 1 \times 1) \ 0.48 \times (265 \times 1444) \times 1 \times 3.30 \times 4.97^{-0.18}$$

$$= \quad 818 \text{ kN} > 593 \text{ kN}$$

(Acceptable)

Check shear for Case 2

$$W_f \quad = \quad (52.5 \times 13.0) + 200$$

$$= \quad 883 \text{ kN}$$

C_V from CSA O86 Table 6.5.7.3C

$$r \quad = \quad \frac{200 \text{ kN}}{52.5 \text{kN/m} \times 13 \text{ m}} = 0.293$$

$$L_1/L_2 \quad = \quad \frac{3 \text{ m}}{10 \text{ m}}$$

$$= \quad 0.3$$

$$C_V \quad = \quad 4.26 \text{ (Extrapolating from CSA O86 Table 6.5.7.3C)}$$

$$V_r \quad = \quad 0.9 \times 2.0 \times (1 \times 1 \times 1 \times 1) \ 0.48 \times (265 \times 1444) \times 1 \times 4.26 \times 4.97^{-0.18}$$

$$= \quad 1055 \text{ kN} > 883 \text{ kN} \quad \textit{(Acceptable)}$$

Check Deflection

By observation, the deflection at the end of the cantilever will govern cantilever live load deflection.

$$\text{Limit} \quad = \quad \text{span/180}$$

$$E_s I \quad = \quad 12400 \times 1 \times 1 \times \left(\frac{265 \times 1444^3}{12} \right)$$

$$= \quad 8.24 \times 10^{14} \text{ N} \bullet \text{mm}^2$$

$$\Delta_{overhang} \quad = \quad \frac{w_L a}{24 E I} \ (4a^2 l - l^3 + 3a^3)$$

$$+ \frac{Pa}{6EI} \ (2al + 2a^2)$$

$$= \quad \frac{27 \times 3000}{24 \times 8.24 \times 10^{14}} \times (4 \times 3000^2 \times$$

$$10000 - 10000^3 + 3 \times 3000^3)$$

$$+ \frac{200000 \times 3000}{6 \times 8.24 \times 10^{14}} \times$$

$$(2 \times 3000 \times 10000 + 2 \times 3000^2)$$

$$= \quad 7.18 \text{ mm}$$

$$= \quad \text{span/418} \qquad \textit{(Acceptable)}$$

Use a 265 × 1444 mm 20f-EX Douglas Fir-Larch glulam beam.

Note: In some cases engineers may choose an alternate approach to determine unsupported length based on the greater of:

• The length of the cantilever, or

• Where the member is subject to negative bending,

  • The distance between the support and zero moment, or

  • The distance between zero moments within a span.

See example 13.3.

7.4 Tables

TABLE 7.1

Maximum depth to width ratio for lumber beams or joists from the **Wood Design Manual**

Degree of lateral support	max d / b
If lateral restraint is provided at points of bearing to prevent lateral displacement and rotation (e.g., at ends of beam).	4
If, in addition, the member is held in line as by purlins or tie rods.	5
If lateral restraint is provided at points of bearing and the compression edge is held in line as by direct connection of decking or joists, or joists spaced not more than 610mm o.c.	6.5
If, in addition, adequate blocking or bridging is provided between members at intervals not exceeding eight times their depth.	7.5
If lateral restraint is provided at points of bearing and both edges of the member are held firmly in line.	9

Note:

b and d refer to width and depth respectively (mm); for vertically laminated beams, b may be based on the total width of the beam if laminations are securely fastened together at intervals not exceeding 4d.

TABLE 7.2

Deflection guidelines from the **Wood Design Manual**

		Loading	Δ_{max}	Limitation
Roofs and Floors		Total Load	L/180	CAN/CSA O86
Plastered or Gypsum Ceilings:	Glulam	Live Load	L/360	Suggested
	Lumber	Total Load	L/360[1]	Suggested
Roofs		Live Load	L/240[2]	Suggested
Floors		Live Load	L/360	Suggested
Wind Columns		Wind Load	L/180	Suggested

Notes:

1. Part 9 of the NBCC permits L/360 deflection limitation based on live load for all roofs and floors with plaster or gypsum board.

2. In Part 9, this is required for use with ceilings other than plaster or gypsum. Where no ceilings exist, L/180 based on live load is permitted.

TABLE 7.3

Recommended camber for glulam beams from the **Wood Design Manual**

Application	Simple, continuous or cantilevered	Simple span only (empirical)
Roof beam	deflection due to DL + 50% of LL	4 mm per m of span
Floor beam	deflection due to DL + 25% of LL	2 mm per m of span
Bridge girder	deflection due to DL + 200% of LL	not used

Compression Members

8.1   Compression Members

INTRODUCTION

The load carrying capacity of an axially loaded wood compression member depends on both the compression strength of the wood and on stability. Column stability in turn depends on stiffness which is affected by the slenderness of the member.

For wood columns, which are usually rectangular in shape, the slenderness ratio shall be calculated for both axes. The measure of slenderness, C_c, is the ratio of the effective length to the associated dimension. The effective length is used to account for conditions of end restraint considering the possible buckled shape for a given column.

As slenderness increases, load carrying capacity decreases (as a cubic function of slenderness) so that a short column can support more load than a long column of the same cross section, grade and species. The size effect on material strength also affects columns and is taken into account separately from slenderness by using the factor K_{Zc}.

SAWN LUMBER COLUMNS

For sawn lumber, the slenderness ratio, C_c, is restricted to a maximum value of 50 (at which sawn lumber columns may have only about 10 to 25% of the capacity they have at a slenderness ratio of about 5).

The slenderness factor, K_C, is used to relate slenderness to load capacity for lumber columns. The formulation used for K_C in CSA O86 is one based on a cubic Rankine-Gordon expression. The reliability assessments leading to selecting the performance factor, ϕ, for lumber columns incorporated a nominal load eccentricity of 5% of the member width, on average.

To design a sawn lumber column to support a given factored load, determine the effective length, select a member size, grade and species group and calculate the factored compressive resistance parallel to grain for both areas. If the resistance is less than the load, select another size and recalculate.

Factored compressive resistance parallel to grain, P_r, may be calculated as the lesser of

$$P_{rd} = \phi \, F_c \, A \, K_{Zcd} \, K_{Cd}$$

$$P_{rb} = \phi \, F_c \, A \, K_{Zcb} \, K_{Cb}$$

where

ϕ = 0.8

F_c = $f_c \, (K_D \, K_H \, K_{SC} \, K_T)$

f_c = specified strength in compression parallel to grain, MPa (CSA O86 Tables 5.3.1A, 5.3.2B, 5.3.1C, 5.3.1D, 5.3.2 and 5.3.3)

A = area of the cross-section, mm^2

K_{Zc} = size factor

K_{Zcd} = $6.3(dL_d)^{-0.13} \leq 1.3$ for buckling in direction of d

K_{Zcb} = $6.3(bL_b)^{-0.13} \leq 1.3$ for buckling in direction of b

K_C = slenderness factor

$$K_{Cd} = \left[1.0 + \frac{F_c \, K_{Zcd} \, C_{Cd}^3}{35 \, E_{05} \, K_{SE} \, K_T} \right]^{-1}$$

for buckling in direction of d

$$K_{Cb} = \left[1.0 + \frac{F_c \, K_{Zcb} \, C_{Cb}^3}{35 \, E_{05} \, K_{SE} \, K_T} \right]^{-1}$$

for buckling in direction of d

Where

$$C_{cd} = \frac{K_e L_d}{d}$$

$$C_{cb} = \frac{K_e L_b}{b}$$

K_e = effective length factor given in CSA O86 Table A5.5.6.1

E_{05} = modulus of elasticity for design of compression members, MPa

    = as specified in Tables 5.3.1A to 5.3.1D for visually graded lumber

    = 0.82 E for MSR lumber

    = 0.75 E for MEL lumber

The value used for modulus of elasticity for design of columns is taken as a 5th percentile value because column strength is a function of E.

Another category of sawn lumber columns is described as "built-up" columns where two to five pieces are joined with prescribed fasteners at specified spacings. Nails, bolts or split rings may be used to join the pieces. For built-up columns, CSA O86 permits using a portion of the load for a solid column with equivalent cross section, (60% for nails, 75% for bolts and 80% for split rings), provided the fastenings used to join the pieces meet the stipulated requirements for size and spacing (see CSA O86 Clause 5.5.6.4).

Perhaps the largest quantity of lumber used as compression members is in stud walls in housing. This is a very efficient use of wood because the wall sheathing provides support against buckling about the weak axis of the studs. Thus, the depth of the stud (which is perpendicular to the sheathing) is used in determining the slenderness ratio.

GLULAM COLUMNS

The column design approach for glulam is essentially the same as the approach for sawn lumber. Tests have confirmed that the formulation used for K_C for sawn lumber can also be used for glulam.

The slenderness ratio, C_c, is restricted to a maximum value of 50 for glulam columns as it is for lumber columns. At $C_c = 50$, glulam columns have only 10 to 20% of the capacity they have at a slenderness ratio of 10. The slenderness ratio is given by:

$$C_c = \text{the greater of:}$$

$$\frac{\text{effective length associated with width}}{\text{member width}}$$

or

$$\frac{\text{effective length associated with depth}}{\text{member depth}}$$

The design of a glulam column to support a given factored load consists of determining the effective length, selecting a member size, grade and species group and calculating the factored compressive resistance parallel to grain (trial and checking approach). The stress grade to be used for glulam columns depends on whether there is only compression force applied or whether there is compression combined with bending, as in the case of an exterior column subject to wind force.

For compression only, it is most economical to use the compression grades, 16c-E and 12c-E in Douglas Fir-Larch or Spruce-Pine, respectively. Where there is compression combined with bending, it is generally most economical to use bending grades in either of the foregoing species group combinations.

Factored compressive resistance parallel to grain, P_r, may be calculated as

$$P_r = \phi F_c A K_{Zcg} K_C$$

where

ϕ = 0.8

F_c = $f_c (K_D K_H K_{Sc} K_T)$

f_c = specified strength in compression parallel to grain, MPa (CSA O86 Table 6.3)

A = cross-sectional area, mm²

K_{Zcg} = $0.68(Z)^{-0.13} \le 1.0$

Z = member volume, m³

K_C = slenderness factor

$$K_C = \left[1.0 + \frac{F_c K_{Zcg} C_C^3}{35 E_{05} K_{SE} K_T} \right]^{-1}$$

where

E_{05} = modulus of elasticity for design of glulam columns, defined as $E_{05} = 0.87 E$ (the value used for modulus of elasticity for design of long columns is taken as a 5th percentile value because strength is at issue.)

CSA O86 Table A5.5.6.1 gives effective length factors, K_e, for compression members. Effective length is defined as $L_e = K_e L$ where L is the distance between centres of lateral support of a compression member in the plane where buckling is being considered (Table 8.1).

The *Wood Design Manual* includes Column Selection Tables which assist in determining appropriate column sections.

COMPRESSIVE RESISTANCE PERPENDICULAR TO GRAIN: BEARING

The behaviour of wood in compression perpendicular to grain depends on the size of the loaded area. When a load is transmitted to a beam in compression perpendicular to the grain, the wood fibres at the edges of the bearing area create a localized tension component along the grain (Figure 8.1). This tension force helps to support the load on the beam.

For short bearing lengths, the tension component is important in supporting the load. For bearing lengths of 150 mm or longer, the tension component is not significant.

For bearings of any lengths at the ends of a member and for bearings 150 mm or more in length at any other position, the resistance in compression perpendicular to grain for the grade and species apply.

When lengths of bearings or diameters of washers (such as for bolted fastenings) are less than 150 mm and no part of the bearing area is closer to the end of the member than 75 mm, the specified strength may be multiplied by the appropriate modification factor, K_B (CSA O86 Table 5.5.7.6). This modification is permitted only if the bearing does not occur in a position of high bending stress; otherwise, local crushing of wood fibres could distort the cross section, resulting in stress concentrations, as discussed earlier for notches.

Tests have shown that wood used in a flat orientation has improved crushing resistance compared with edge orientation. The specified strength may be multiplied by the K_{Zcp} factor (CSA O86 Table 5.5.7.5) to account for flat orientation.

In the general case, the compression resistance perpendicular to grain under the effect of all factored applied loads is calculated as:

$$Q_r = \phi \, F_{cp} \, A_b \, K_B \, K_{Zcp}$$

where

$\phi = 0.8$

$F_{cp} = f_{cp} \, (K_D \, K_{Scp} \, K_T)$

$f_{cp} =$ specified strength in compression perpendicular to grain, MPa (CSA O86 Tables 5.3.1A, 5.3.1B, 5.3.1C, 5.3.1D, 5.3.2, 5.3.3 and 6.3)

$A_b =$ bearing area, mm²

$K_B =$ bearing factor (CSA O86 Table 5.5.7.6)

$K_{Zcp} =$ size factor for bearing used when the width of a member loaded perpendicular to grain is greater than the depth of the member. For glulam members, the thickness of the lamination is used for the depth of the member. CSA O86 Table 5.5.7.5

At a beam support, bearing must be checked for two cases. The first case is the general case described previously. An additional check for "critical" bearing is required for loads applied to both sides of a member within a distance "d" from the centre of the support (Figure 8.2). In the critical case, the stress can extend through the full depth of the member, in contrast to the general bearing case where the bearing stress is typically limited to the outer fibres of the bending member. Due to the increased volume under stress and the resulting increase in probability of deformation over time, the resistance for the critical case is reduced.

The factored compressive resistance perpendicular to the grain under the effect of only those loads applied within a distance from the centre of the support equal to the depth of the member is determined by:

$$Q_r' = (2/3) \, \phi \, F_{cp} \, A_b' \, K_B \, K_{Zcp}$$

$\phi = 0.8$

$A_b' =$ average bearing area

$A_b' = b\left(\dfrac{L_{b1} + L_{b2}}{2}\right)$, but $\leq 1.5 \, b(L_{b1})$

$L_{b1} =$ lesser bearing length, mm

$L_{b2} =$ larger bearing length, mm

$b =$ average bearing width (perpendicular to grain), mm

FIGURE 8.1

Bearing example

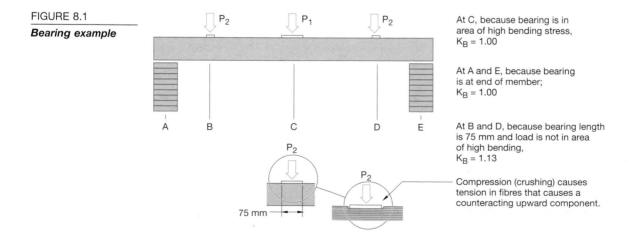

At C, because bearing is in area of high bending stress, $K_B = 1.00$

At A and E, because bearing is at end of member; $K_B = 1.00$

At B and D, because bearing length is 75 mm and load is not in area of high bending, $K_B = 1.13$

Compression (crushing) causes tension in fibres that causes a counteracting upward component.

COMPRESSION AT AN ANGLE TO GRAIN

The factored compressive resistance, N_r, at an angle to grain is determined by

$$N_r = \frac{P_r Q_r}{P_r \sin^2 \theta + Q_r \cos^2 \theta}$$

where

P_r = factored compressive resistance parallel to grain for short columns

Q_r = factored compressive resistance perpendicular to grain

θ = angle between direction of grain and direction of load, degrees

EXAMPLE 8.1: SAWN LUMBER COLUMNS

For a one storey industrial building with 3.0 m long wood columns spaced at 3.0 m in both directions, check the design of the columns. The designer has specified 140×191 mm No.1 grade D.Fir-L. Specified loads on the columns are dead load = 20 kN and snow load on the roof = 80 kN. (Note: specified snow load is calculated using $I_S = 1.0$). Consider that the columns are not subject to sway forces because the wood frame exterior walls transfer wind forces to the foundation.

Load Effects and Combinations

Total factored load

= 1.25 D + 1.5 S

= $1.25 \times 20 + 1.5 \times 80$

= 25 + 120

= 145 kN

Calculations

Specified strength, for No.1 grade Post and Timber in D.Fir-L from CSA O86 Table 5.3.1D

f_c = 12.2 MPa

E = 10500 MPa

E_{05} = 6500 MPa

Because full fixity of wood columns is difficult to attain and to maintain, the degree of end restraint will hold the ends in position but will not prevent rotation. Thus:

K_e = 1.0

Effective length

= actual length (no lateral bracing specified)

= 3000 mm

FIGURE 8.2

Compression perpendicular to grain procedure

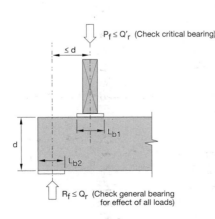

$P_f \leq Q'_r$ (Check critical bearing)

$\leq d$

L_{b1}

d

L_{b2}

$R_f \leq Q_r$ (Check general bearing for effect of all loads)

Column capacity P_r is the lesser of:

$$P_{rd} = \phi\, F_c\, A\, K_{Zcd}\, K_{Cd}$$

$$P_{rb} = \phi\, F_c\, A\, K_{Zcb}\, K_{Cb}$$

where

$\phi = 0.8$

$K_D = 1.0$ (standard duration of load)

$K_H = 1.0$ (no system as defined in CSA O86 5.4.4)

$K_{Sc} = 1.0$ (dry service conditions)

$K_T = 1.0$ (no treatment)

$F_C = f_c(K_D K_H K_{Sc} K_T) =$
$12.2 \times (1 \times 1 \times 1 \times 1) = 12.2$

$K_{Zcd} = 6.3\,(dL_d)^{-0.13} = 6.3\,(191 \times 3000)^{-0.13}$
$= 1.12\ (\leq 1.3\ ok)$

$K_{Zcb} = 6.3\,(bL_b)^{-0.13} = 6.3\,(140 \times 3000)^{-0.13}$
$= 1.17\ (\leq 1.3\ ok)$

$C_{cd} = \dfrac{3000}{191} = 15.7$

$C_{cb} = \dfrac{3000}{140} = 21.4$

$K_{Cd} = \left[1.0 + \dfrac{F_c\, K_{Zcd}\, C_{Cd}^3}{35 E_{05}\, K_{SE}\, K_T}\right]^{-1}$

$\quad = \left[1.0 + \dfrac{12.2 \times 1.12 \times 15.7^3}{35 \times 6500 \times 1 \times 1}\right]^{-1}$

$\quad = 0.811$

$K_{Cb} = \left[1.0 + \dfrac{F_c\, K_{Zcb}\, C_{Cb}^3}{35 E_{05}\, K_{SE}\, K_T}\right]^{-1}$

$\quad = \left[1.0 + \dfrac{12.2 \times 1.17 \times 21.4^3}{35 \times 6500 \times 1 \times 1}\right]^{-1}$

$\quad = 0.619$

$P_{rd} = \phi\, F_c\, A\, K_{Zcd}\, K_{Cd}$
$\quad = 0.8 \times 12.2 \times (140 \times 191) \times 1.12$
$\quad\ \times 0.811$
$\quad = 238\ kN$

$P_{rb} = \phi\, F_c\, A\, K_{Zcd}\, K_{Cd}$
$\quad = 0.8 \times 12.2 \times (140 \times 191) \times 1.17 \times$
$\quad\ 0.619$
$\quad = 189\ kN$

Therefore,

$$P_r = 189\ kN > P_f = 145\ kN$$

(Acceptable)

Note:
The *Wood Design Manual* has tabulated capacities for columns.

Use 140 × 191 mm No.1 grade D Fir-L columns.

EXAMPLE 8.2: INTERNAL STUD WALL

An internal stud wall in an industrial building supports floor and roof loads. The studs are spaced at 400 mm centres and are sheathed on both sides. The table below specifies the loading conditions on the stud wall. The studs are 3.0 m long.

	Dead load (kPa)	Snow/live load (kPa)	Tributary width (m)
Roof	1.0	1.5 snow	8
Floor	1.5	4.8 live	4

Dead Load $= 1.0 \times 8 + 1.5 \times 4 = 14.0$ kN/m

Live Load $= 4.8 \times 4 = 19.2$ kN/m

Snow Load $= 1.5 \times 8 = 12$ kN/m

Load Effects and Combinations

Factored load on stud

Case 1:
$1.25\, D + 1.5\, L + 0.5\, S$

$\quad = 1.25\,(14.0 \times 0.4) + 1.5\,(19.2 \times 0.4) +$
$\quad\ \ 0.5\,(12 \times 0.4)$

$\quad = 20.92$ kN *(Governs)*

Case 2:
$1.25\, D + 1.5\, S + 0.5\, L$

$\quad = 1.25\,(14.0 \times 0.4) + 1.5\,(12 \times 0.4) +$
$\quad\ \ 0.5\,(19.2 \times 0.4)$

$\quad = 18.04$ kN

Specified Strengths

Use S-P-F Stud Grade. Try 38×140 mm stud.

From CSA O86 Table 5.3.1A

$f_c = 9.0$ MPa

$E = 9000$ MPa

$E_{05} = 5500$ MPa

Stud is fully restrained in the narrow direction by sheathing

K_e = 1.0

L_e = actual length
(no lateral bracing specified)

= 3000 mm

Slenderness ratio

C_c = L_e/d

= 3000/140

= 21.4

Column capacity

P_r = $\phi F_c A K_{Zc} K_c$

ϕ = 0.8

F_c = $f_c(K_D K_H K_{Sc} K_T)$

K_{Zc} = $6.3(dL)^{-0.13} \leq 1.3$

K_c = $\left[1.0 + \dfrac{F_c K_{Zc} C_C^3}{35 E_{05} K_{SE} K_T}\right]^{-1}$

For this design

K_D = 1.0

K_H = 1.10
(CSA O86 Table 5.4.4 Case 1)

K_{Sc} = 1.0

K_T = 1.0

Calculations

F_c = 9.0 (1.0 × 1.1 × 1.0 × 1.0)

= 9.9 MPa

K_{Zc} = $6.3(140 \times 3000)^{-0.13}$

= 1.17

K_c = $\left[1.0 + \dfrac{9.9 \times 1.17 \times 21.4^3}{35 \times 5500 \times 1 \times 1}\right]^{-1}$

= 0.629

P_r = 0.8 × 9.9 (38 × 140) × 1.17 × 0.629

= 31.0 kN *(Acceptable)*

Use 38 × 140 mm Stud Grade S-P-F studs at 400 mm centres.

Note: the designer may also wish to check stud bearing on the bottom plate. See Stud Tables in the Wood Design Manual.

EXAMPLE 8.3: GLULAM COLUMN DESIGN

Design a glulam column for the conditions given in Example 8.1 using 12c-E grade Spruce-Pine.

Load Effects and Combinations
Total factored load

P_f = 131 kN

Calculations
Specified strength for 12c-E grade Spruce-Pine glulam from CSA O86 Table 6.3

f_c = 25.2 MPa

E = 9700 MPa

E_{05} = 0.87 × 9700

= 8440 MPa

Because fixity is difficult to attain and to maintain, the degree of end restraint will hold the ends in position but will not prevent rotation. Thus:

K_e = 1.0

Effective length

L_e = actual length
(no lateral bracing specified)

= 3000 mm

Using the Tables in the *Wood Design Manual*, select a column 130 × 152 mm with effective length of 3 m and a factored capacity of 193 kN with no bracing. Now check the capacity using CSA O86.

$$C_c = 3000/130$$

$$= 23.1$$

Column capacity

$$P_r = \phi \, F_c A K_{Zcg} K_C$$

$$\phi = 0.8$$

$$F_c = f_c(K_D K_H K_{Sc} K_T)$$

$$= 25.2 \, (1 \times 1 \times 1 \times 1)$$

$$= 25.2 \text{ MPa}$$

$$A = 130 \times 152$$

$$= 19760 \text{ mm}^2$$

$$K_{Zcg} = 0.68(Z)^{-0.13} \le 1.0$$

$$= 0.68 \, (0.13 \times 0.152 \times 3)^{-0.13}$$

$$= 0.982$$

$$K_C = \left[1.0 + \frac{F_c K_{Zcg} C_C^3}{35 E_{05} K_{SE} K_T}\right]^{-1}$$

$$\left[1.0 + \frac{29.0 \times 0.982 \times 23.1^3}{35 \times 8440 \times 1 \times 1}\right]^{-1}$$

$$= 0.492$$

$$P_r = 0.8 \times 25.2 \times 19760 \times 0.982 \times 0.492$$

$$= 192 \text{ kN} \qquad \textit{(Acceptable)}$$

Note: Manual calculations may differ slightly from the *Wood Design Manual* due to rounding differences.

Use 130 × 152 mm 12c-E Spruce-Pine columns.

Another acceptable section is 130 × 114 mm 16c-E Douglas Fir-Larch columns.

8.2   Tables

TABLE 8.1

*K_e factor for columns
(from CSA O86
Table A5.5.6.1)*

Degree of end restraint of compression member	Effective length factor K_e	Symbol
Effectively held in position and restrained against rotation at both ends	0.65	
Effectively held in position at both ends, restrained against rotation at one end	0.80	
Effectively held in position at both ends, but not restrained against rotation	1.00	
Effectively held in position and restrained against rotation at one end, and at the other restrained against rotation but not held in position	1.20	
Effectively held in position and restrained against rotation at one end, and at the other partially restrained against rotation but not held in position	1.50	
Effectively held in position at one end but not restrained against rotation, and at the other end restrained against rotation but not held in position	2.00	
Effectively held in position and restrained against rotation at one end but not held in position nor restrained against rotation at the other end	2.00	

Note:

Effective length $L_e = K_e L$ where L is the distance between centres of lateral supports of the compression member in the plane in which buckling is being considered. At a base or cap detail, the distance should be measured from the outer surface of the base or cap plate. The effective length factor K_e shall be not less than what would be indicated by rational analysis. Where conditions of end restraint cannot be evaluated closely, a conservative value for K_e should be used.

Tension Members

9.1 Tension Members

INTRODUCTION

For wood members designed to carry tension, such as bottom chords of trusses, capacity may be governed by the strength of connections to other members or by the strength of the wood at reduced cross sections.

Steel tension rods are sometimes used in conjunction with wood diagonals in trusses and are also used to carry tensile loads in tied arches.

The net area of cross section, A_n, is the gross area of cross section minus the projected area of all material removed by boring, grooving, dapping and notching. Bolts, lag screws and timber connectors require removal of wood to install and thus result in a reduced section. When these fasteners are installed in staggered rows, adjacent fasteners are considered to be in the same critical section unless the parallel to grain spacing is greater than S_N.

For bolted and lag screw joints, $S_N = 8 \times$ nominal diameter of the bolt; for timber connector joints, $S_N = 2 \times$ the diameter of the connector.

A table is provided in Chapter 11 listing the projected area of material removed by drilling and grooving for timber connectors. It is important to recognize that CSA O86 limits the area removed by boring, grooving, dapping and notching at the net section to no more than 25% of the area of the gross section.

SAWN LUMBER TENSION MEMBERS

Factored resistance in tension parallel to grain, T_r, may be calculated as

$$T_r = \phi F_t A_n K_{Zt}$$

where

$\phi = 0.9$

$F_t = f_t (K_D K_H K_{St} K_T)$

f_t = specified strength in tension parallel to grain, MPa (CSA O86 Tables 5.3.1 A, 5.3.1 B, 5.3.1 C, 5.3.1 D, 5.3.2 and 5.3.3)

A_n = net area of cross section, mm^2

K_{Zt} = size factor in tension (CSA O86 Table 5.4.5)

GLULAM TENSION MEMBERS

Tension parallel to grain can control the design of glulam used for the bottom chords of trusses and for bracing members.

There are two grades of glulam intended primarily for use as tension members: 18t-E Douglas Fir-Larch and 14t-E Spruce-Pine. All other stress grades of glulam have lower specified strengths in tension due to lower grade requirements for inner laminations; however, these may be adequate for a given application.

Where tension parallel to grain is combined with bending stress, designers may consider using 20f-EX or 24f-EX grades of any available species group. The tensile values of these grades are lower, but bending values are higher than for the tension grades.

The specified strengths for the tension grades permit the greatest efficiency in material utilization for tension applications. There are two values to be considered in tension member design, namely the tension at the net section and the tension at the gross cross section.

According to brittle fracture theory the probability of failure is less with a smaller volume of material, so tensile resistance at the net section is greater than at the gross section. To determine load capacity, it is necessary to check capacity at both the net section and at the gross section.

Where tension and bending occur at the same section, for economy, the bending grades are often specified by experienced designers in preference to the tension grades.

The factored tensile resistance parallel to grain, T_r, is calculated as the lesser of

$$T_r = \phi \, F_{tn} \, A_n$$

or

$$T_r = \phi \, F_{tg} \, A_g$$

where

$\phi = 0.9$

$F_{tn} = f_{tn} \, (K_D \, K_H \, K_{St} \, K_T)$

$F_{tg} = f_{tg} \, (K_D \, K_H \, K_{St} \, K_T)$

$f_{tn} =$ specified strength in tension parallel to grain at the net section, MPa (CSA O86 Table 6.3)

$f_{tg} =$ specified strength in tension parallel to grain at the gross section, MPa (CSA O86 Table 6.3)

$A_n =$ net area of cross section, mm^2

$A_g =$ gross area of cross section, mm^2

TENSION AT AN ANGLE TO GRAIN

Wherever possible, designers should avoid details which may cause tensile stresses not parallel to the grain in wood.

The only specified strengths in tension perpendicular to grain for wood are provided for glulam because of the radial stresses developed under load in curved and double-tapered glulam members.

EXAMPLE 9.1: DESIGN OF A TENSION MEMBER

MSR Lumber is to be used for the bottom chord of metal plate-connected wood roof trusses used in a warehouse roof system where trusses are to be spaced at 600 mm on centre. Preliminary truss analysis has found the factored tensile force to be 36.7 kN due to snow plus dead loads. Select a size and grade of S–P–F lumber to provide the required tensile capacity (without considering the metal plate connections).

Factored tensile resistance

$$T_r = \phi\, F_t\, A_n\, K_{Zt}$$

where

$\phi = 0.9$

$F_t = f_t\, (K_D\, K_H\, K_{St}\, K_T)$, MPa

$f_t =$ specified tensile strength, MPa

$A_n =$ net area of cross section, mm^2

$K_{Zt} =$ size effect factor in tension parallel to grain

Try 38 × 89 mm MSR 1650F$_b$-1.5E S-P-F

$f_t = 11.4$ MPa

For snow plus dead load

$K_D = 1.0$

For a roof truss system (for Case 1)

$K_H = 1.1$ may be used

For the warehouse consider service conditions to be dry

$K_{St} = 1.0$

With no treatment specified, use

$K_T = 1.0$

Calculations

There is no material removed when metal plate connectors are pressed into the lumber, thus:

$$A_n = A_g = 38 \times 89 = 3380 \text{ mm}^2$$

For 38 × 89, $K_{Zt} = 1.5$ would be used for visually graded lumber but CSA O86 assigns a value for K_{Zt} of 1.0 for MSR lumber for tension because the MSR process already accounts for the size effect by grading full size lumber. Therefore use $K_{Zt} = 1.0$.

$$T_r = 0.9 \times 11.4\ (1 \times 1.1 \times 1 \times 1)\ 3380 \times 1.0$$

$$= 38\ 100 \text{ N}\ \ (> 36.7 \text{ kN})$$

(Acceptable)

Use 38 × 89 mm 1650F$_b$-1.5E S-P-F MSR lumber.

Combined Axial Loads and Bending Members

10.1 Combined Compression and Bending Members

BEAM COLUMNS

The upper chords of trusses and wall framing members subject to wind or earth pressure loads must be designed for bending plus axial loads (usually compression) (Figure 10.1). Accounting for combined bending and compression is essentially the same for sawn lumber and for glulam.

The resistance of most members subjected to bending and compressive axial loads must be considered using the equation:

$$\left(\frac{P_f}{P_r}\right)^2 + \frac{M_f}{M_r}\left[\frac{1}{1-\dfrac{P_f}{P_E}}\right] \leq 1$$

where

P_f = factored compressive axial load

P_r = factored compressive load resistance parallel to grain calculated in accordance with the requirements of CSA O86

M_f = factored bending moment

M_r = factored bending moment resistance calculated in accordance with the requirements of CSA O86

P_E = Euler buckling load in the direction of the applied moment

$$= \frac{\pi^2 E_{05} K_{SE} K_T I}{\left(K_e L\right)^2}$$

where:

E_{05} = modulus of elasticity for design of compression members, MPa

= 0.82E for MSR lumber

= 0.75E for MEL lumber

= as specified in Tables 5.3.1A to 5.3.1D for visually graded lumber

= 0.87E for glulam

K_{SE} = service condition factor

K_T = treatment factor

$K_e L$ = effective length in the direction of the applied bending moment

CSA O86 provides alternate interaction equations for metal plate connected truss members and preserved wood foundation studs subject to combined compression and bending loads.

For sawn lumber members used in truss applications that meet the requirements of CSA O86 Clause 5.5.13:

$$\left(\frac{P_f}{P_r}\right)^2 + \frac{M_f}{K_M M_r} \leq 1.0$$

where:

K_M = bending capacity modification factor (CSA O86 Table 5.5.13.5)

FIGURE 10.1

Combined bending and axial loads

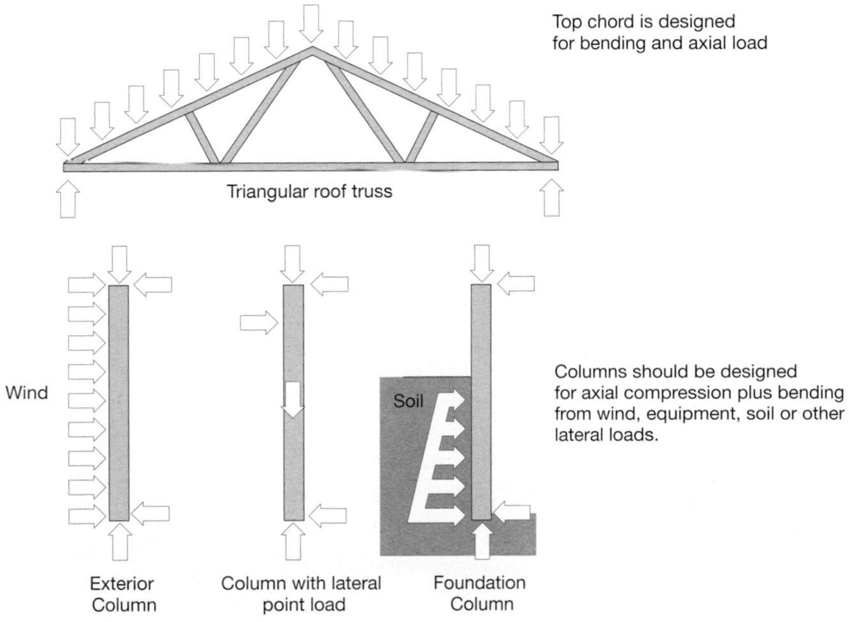

Top chord is designed for bending and axial load

Triangular roof truss

Wind

Soil

Columns should be designed for axial compression plus bending from wind, equipment, soil or other lateral loads.

Exterior Column

Column with lateral point load

Foundation Column

For studs used in preserved wood foundations:

$$\left(\frac{P_f}{P_r}\right)^2 + \frac{M_f}{M_r}\left[\frac{1}{1-\dfrac{P_f}{P_E}}\right] \leq 1 \text{ (CSA O86}$$
$$\text{Clause A5.5.12.6)}$$

where:

M_f = maximum factored bending moment on stud

To ensure lateral stability of members due to increased buckling potential, the maximum depth to width ratios should not exceed the values given in Table 7.1. For members subject to possible stress reversal, the maximum depth to width ratio should be limited to four, unless both edges of the members are held in line.

The factored bending moment, M_f, is augmented by the P-Δ effects caused by a deflection, Δ, (or an eccentricity) that combines with the compressive axial load, P_f, to generate a secondary bending moment effect. The total bending moment may be estimated with reasonable accuracy by amplifying the factored moment. The moment amplification factor in CSA O86 (Clause 5.5.10, Clause 6.5.12 and Clause A.5.5.12.6) is given as $1/(1-P_f/P_E)$ where P_E is the Euler buckling load, calculated using the 5th %ile value (E_{05}) for the species and grade. This simplified approach is slightly more conservative than the detailed amplification approach, provided in Clause A.5.5.10 as an alternative. The more exact approach uses the product of axial load and lateral deflection (Δ), calculated using serviceability load combinations, times the amplification factor to augment the applied moment.

It is possible that in some cases the secondary bending moment may not act in the same direction as the primary moment (for example, where end eccentricity is involved). Analysis of secondary moments may require sophisticated methods.

The bending stresses and compressive stresses may not be caused by the same load. In the combined formula, however, the same duration of load factor, K_D, is generally used to calculate both P_r and M_r (even though different values are used to check the individual stresses separately).

One exception is the design of studs in preserved wood foundations where lateral loads are due to soil pressures and vertical loads are primarily due to snow and live loads. A K_D factor of 0.65 applies to the calculation of M_r and a K_D factor of 1.0 applies to the calculation of P_r.

EXAMPLE 10.1: COLUMN SUBJECT TO SNOW, WIND AND DEAD LOADS

Design a glulam column using 20f-EX grade Spruce-Pine for the conditions given in Example 8.3, specified dead load 18 kN and specified snow load 72 kN, and taking wind load into account. Specified wind load on the exterior columns is 1.0 kN/m, uniformly distributed along the length of the column. Try a 130 × 152 mm column.

Load Effects and Combinations

Case 1:

Factored axial load (I_s = 1.0)

$$\begin{aligned} P_f &= 1.25\,D + 1.5\,S \\ &= 1.25 \times 18 + 1.5 \times 72 \\ &= 131 \text{ kN} \end{aligned}$$

Factored wind load (I_w = 1.0)

$$\begin{aligned} w_f &= 0.4\,w \\ &= 0.4 \times 1.0 \\ &= 0.4 \text{ kN/m (N/mm)} \end{aligned}$$

Factored moment due to wind load

$$\begin{aligned} M_f &= (0.4 \times 3000^2) / 8 \\ &= 0.45 \times 10^6 \text{ N·mm} \end{aligned}$$

Case 2:

$$\begin{aligned} P_f &= 1.25\,D + 0.5\,S \\ &= 1.25 \times 18 + 0.5 \times 72 \\ &= 58.5 \text{ kN} \end{aligned}$$

$$\begin{aligned} w_f &= 1.4\,w \\ &= 1.4 \times 1.0 \\ &= 1.4 \text{ kN/m} \end{aligned}$$

$$\begin{aligned} M_f &= (1.4 \times 3000^2) / 8 \\ &= 1.58 \times 10^6 \text{ N·mm} \end{aligned}$$

Calculations

The secondary moment due to the axial load from the roof acting on the deflected shape of the column from lateral wind load bending need to be accounted for.

Using the interaction equation from CSA O86:

$$\left(\frac{P_f}{P_r}\right)^2 + \frac{M_f}{M_r}\left[\frac{1}{1-\frac{P_f}{P_E}}\right] \leq 1$$

P_E = Euler buckling load in the direction of the applied moment

$$= \frac{\pi^2 E_{05} K_{SE} K_T I}{(K_e L)^2}$$

where

E = 10300 MPa

E_{05} = 0.87E MPa

     = 8960 MPa

K_{SE} = 1.0

K_T = 1.0

$K_e L$ = 1.0 × 3000 = 3000 mm

I = $\left(\frac{130 \times 152^3}{12}\right)$

   = 380 × 10⁵ mm⁴

P_E = $\frac{\pi^2 \times 0.87 \times 10300 \times 380 \times 10^5}{3000^2}$

     = 374 kN

Moment Capacity

The resisting moment capacity of the 130 × 152 mm column of 20f-EX Spruce-Pine about its strong axis, M_r, is the lesser of M_{r1} and M_{r2}

M_{r1} = $\phi F_b \, S \, K_{Zbg} \, K_X$

M_{r2} = $\phi F_b \, S \, K_L \, K_X$

K_{Zbg} = 1.03 $(BL)^{-0.18} \leq 1.0$

       = 1.03 $(0.13 \times 3)^{-0.18}$ but not greater than 1.0

       = 1.22 use 1.0

For glulam members subject to combined bending and axial loads, $K_L = 1.0$ if the rules in Table 7.1 are applied. In this example, d/b = 1.17 and no lateral restraint is required for $K_L = 1.0$.

$M_{r1} = M_{r2} = 0.9 \times 25.6 \, (1.15 \times 1 \times 1 \times 1) \times$

$$\frac{130 \times 152^2}{6}$$

= 13.3 kN•m

Compressive Capacity

P_r = $\phi F_c A K_{Zcg} K_C$

ϕ = 0.8

F_c = $f_c(K_D K_H K_{Sc} K_T)$

    = 25.2 $(1.15 \times 1 \times 1 \times 1)$

    = 29.0 MPa

K_{Zcg} = $0.68(Z)^{-0.13} \leq 1.0$

       = 0.68 $(0.13 \times 0.152 \times 3)^{-0.13}$

       = 0.982

C_C = $\frac{3000}{130}$

    = 23.1

K_C = $\left[1.0 + \frac{F_c K_{Zcg} C_C^3}{35 E_{05} K_{SE} K_T}\right]^{-1}$

    = $\left[1.0 + \frac{29.0 \times 0.982 \times 23.1^3}{35 \times 8961 \times 1 \times 1}\right]^{-1}$

    = 0.472

P_r = $0.8 \times 29.0 \, (130 \times 152) \times 0.982 \times 0.472$

    = 212 kN

Combined Capacity

Using the interaction equation, check capacity

$$\left(\frac{P_f}{P_r}\right)^2 + \frac{M_f}{M_r}\left[\frac{1}{1-\frac{P_f}{P_E}}\right] \leq 1$$

Case 1:

$$\left(\frac{131}{212}\right)^2 + \frac{0.45}{13.3}\left[\frac{1}{1-\frac{131}{374}}\right] = 0.43 \leq 1$$

(Acceptable)

Case 2:

$$\left(\frac{58.5}{212}\right)^2 + \frac{1.58}{13.3}\left[\frac{1}{1 - \frac{58.5}{374}}\right] = 0.22 \leq 1$$

(Acceptable)

Thus the same section selected for axial load only is also adequate when subject to the specified wind load. Note that the 130 × 152 mm column section must be used so that bending is about the strong axis. Grade 12c-E is typically specified for columns subjected to axial load only. Grade 20f-EX is typically specified for columns subjected to bending plus axial loads.

Use 130 × 152 mm 20f-EX Spruce-Pine columns.

EXAMPLE 10.2: STUD WALL DESIGN – PERMANENT WOOD FOUNDATION

A new one-storey home is to be built utilizing a permanent wood foundation (PWF). The studs in the PWF must support the roof snow load, the floor live load, the dead load and the soil pressure from the backfill. The studs are 2.4 m long and the backfill height is 1.5 m (Figure 10.2). The factored snow, live and dead vertical load on the wall is 29 kN/m. The specified lateral load from soil pressure has an equivalent-to-fluid-pressure load of 4.7 kN/m^2 per metre of depth. The studs are to be placed at 400 mm centres and are sheathed with plywood. The plywood restrains the studs against buckling about their weak axis.

Some species in the S-P-F and Northern species group (e.g. jack pine and red pine respectively) can be preservative treated to meet the requirements of the Standard CSA O80.15, *Preservative Treatment of Wood for Building Foundation Systems, Basements and Crawl Spaces by Pressure Process.* Lumber used in PWF's must be No.2 grade or better.

Try No.2 grade 38 × 184 mm Northern species.

Load Effects and Combinations
Factored axial load

$$= 29 \text{ kN/m} \times 0.4 \text{ m}$$
$$= 11.6 \text{ kN per stud}$$

FIGURE10.2
**Permanent wood
foundation**

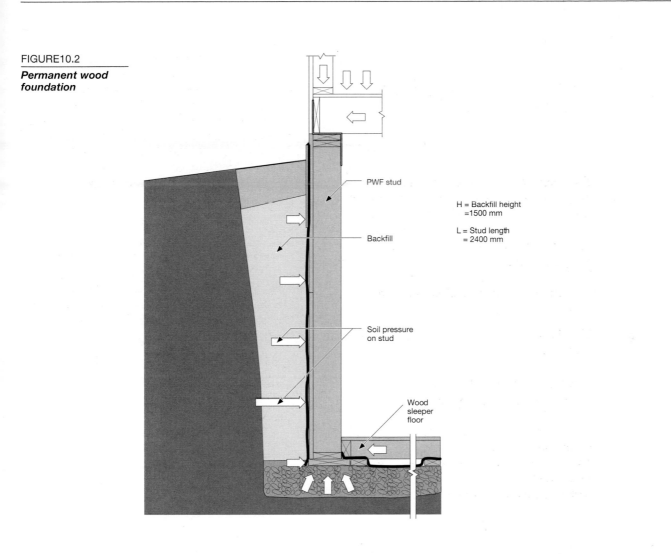

PWF stud

Backfill

Soil pressure
on stud

Wood
sleeper
floor

H = Backfill height
 =1500 mm

L = Stud length
 = 2400 mm

Maximum factored lateral soil pressure

$$= 1.5 \times 4.7 \times 1.5$$

$$= 10.6 \text{ kN/m}^2$$

w_f = maximum factored lateral load per stud

$$= (10.6 \text{ kN/m}^2) \times (0.4 \text{ m})$$

$$= 4.23 \text{ N/mm per stud}$$

From Clause A.5.5.12.6 of CSA O86, combined bending and axial load effects for permanent wood foundations may be evaluated using:

$$\left(\frac{P_f}{P_r}\right)^2 + \frac{M_f}{M_r}\left[\frac{1}{1-\frac{P_f}{P_E}}\right] \le 1$$

where

M_f = maximum factored moment due to lateral load on stud, N•mm

P_f = factored axial load on stud, N

P_r = factored compressive resistance, N

M_r = factored bending moment resistance, N•mm

P_E = Euler buckling load in the plane of the applied moment

Specified Strengths

For No.2 Grade Northern Species CSA O86 Table 5.3.1A

f_b = 7.6 MPa

f_c = 10.4 MPa

E = 7000 MPa

E_{05} = 5000 MPa

Modification Factors

K_D = 0.65 for bending

= 1.0 for compression

K_H = 1.4 for bending

= 1.1 for compression

K_S = 1.0, Dry service is assumed since the studs are behind the moisture barrier on the foundation wall.

K_T = 0.9 for E

= 0.75 for all other properties

K_{Zb} = 1.2

K_L = 1.0, Provide adequate restraint

M_r = $\phi F_b S K_{Zb} K_L$

$$= 0.9 \times 7.6 \, (0.65 \times 1.4 \times 1 \times 0.75) \times$$
$$\frac{38 \times 184^2}{6} \times 1.2 \times 1$$

$$= 1.20 \times 10^6 \text{ N•mm}$$

$$= 1.20 \text{ kN•m}$$

P_r = $\phi F_c A K_{Zc} K_C$

K_{Zc} = $6.3(dL)^{-0.13} \le 1.3$

$$= 6.3 \, (184 \times 2400)^{-0.13}$$

$$= 1.16$$

C_C = $\dfrac{1.0 \times 2400}{184}$

$$= 13.04$$

$$K_C = \left[1.0 + \frac{F_c K_{Zc} C_c^3}{35 E_{05} K_{SE} K_T} \right]^{-1}$$

$$= \left[1.0 + \frac{10.4(1 \times 1.1 \times 1 \times 0.75) \times 1.16 \times 13.04^3}{35 \times 5000 \times 1 \times 0.9} \right]^{-1}$$

$$= 0.877$$

$$P_r = 0.8 \times 10.4 \ (1 \times 1.1 \times 1 \times 0.75) \times 38 \times$$
$$184 \times 1.16 \times 0.877$$

$$= 49.0 \text{ kN} \qquad \textit{(Acceptable)}$$

From CSA O86 Clause A.5.5.12.8

$$M_f = \frac{w_f H^2}{6L} \left[L - H + \frac{2}{3} \sqrt{\frac{H^3}{3L}} \right]$$

$$= \frac{4.23 \times 1500^2}{6 \times 2400} \left[2400 - 1500 + \frac{2}{3} \sqrt{\frac{1500^3}{3 \times 2400}} \right]$$

$$= 897 \ 000 \text{ N} \bullet \text{mm}$$

$$= 0.897 \text{ kN} \bullet \text{m}$$

Check combined bending and compressive capacity:

$$P_E = \frac{\pi^2 E_{05} K_{SE} K_T I}{[K_e L]^2}$$

$$= \frac{\pi^2 \times 5000 \times 1.0 \times 0.9 \times \left(\frac{38 \times 184^3}{12} \right)}{(2400)^2}$$

$$= 152 \text{ kN}$$

$$\left(\frac{P_f}{P_r} \right)^2 + \frac{M_f}{M_r} \left[\frac{1}{1 - \dfrac{P_f}{P_E}} \right] \leq 1$$

$$\left(\frac{11.6}{49.0} \right)^2 + \frac{0.897}{1.20} \left[\frac{1}{1 - \dfrac{11.6}{152}} \right] = 0.86 \leq 1$$

(Acceptable)

For a full design check, the following conditions must also be considered:

1) Lateral deflection
2) Lateral shear

10.2   Combined Tension and Bending Members

COMBINED TENSION AND BENDING

Members subject to bending loads in addition to tensile axial loads are designed to provide resistance to the combined load considering the interaction equation:

$$\frac{T_f}{T_r} + \frac{M_f}{M_r} \leq 1.0$$

where

T_f = factored tensile axial load

T_r = factored tensile resistance parallel to grain

M_f = factored bending moment

M_r = factored bending moment resistance

The values for duration of load factors (K_D) used in the interaction formulas may be different from the values used in the independent formulas for T_r or M_r as, for example, when the load causing tensile stress is different from the load causing bending stress. In the interaction equation the same K_D value should be applied to both resistances, again based on the load acting for the shortest duration.

Connections

11.1   General Information

CSA O86 provides design information for the following fasteners:

- split ring and shear plate connectors
- bolts and dowels
- drift pins
- lag screws
- timber rivets
- truss plates
- nails and spikes
- joist hangers
- wood screws

This chapter will be limited to a discussion of the fasteners outlined in CSA O86.

Two limit states may apply to fastening design in CSA O86. The strength limit state occurs when a connection reaches its maximum load capacity as a result of factored loads on the structure. Serviceability limit states limit connection deformation under specified loads.

For lateral loading of truss plates, the strength and serviceability limit states are identified seperately. For all other fastenings, only the strength limit state is identified. For truss plates, CSA O86 requires the designer to check both strength and serviceability limit states and to base the design on the more limiting condition.

Failure modes for wood connections are complex and vary from connection to connection. Thus, the designer must ensure that there are adequate fastenings in the connection and the individual fastenings are properly placed.

This chapter outlines the design of fasteners in metric units. Since some fasteners are commonly described in imperial units, this nomenclature is used, where appropriate in specific sections.

11.2 General Requirements

SHEAR DEPTH

Where a wood member is loaded at any angle to grain greater than 0°, the load results in a shear force component inducing tension stress perpendicular to the grain of the member. Where the load is imposed by a fastening group, this stress is greatest at a boundary of the fastening group. Therefore, CSA O86 defines an effective shear depth, d_e, that must be used instead of the total member depth, d, when checking for member shear resistance (Figure 11.1).

The factored shear resistance at the connection must be greater than the factored shear stress in the member at the connection. For bending members, the shear force at the connection can be obtained from the shear force diagram.

SERVICE CONDITION FACTOR

CSA O86 Table 10.2.1.5 gives the moisture service condition factor, K_{SF}, for fastenings. K_{SF} reflects two aspects of connection resistance that may be affected by moisture service conditions. First, wood is generally weaker when wet and therefore wood connections used in wet service conditions will have less resistance.

Second, when fasteners are installed in wood that will dry in service or when wood moisture content fluctuates in service, shrinkage will occur. Unless the effects of this shrinkage are accounted for in the design, splitting may occur at the fasteners thus weakening the connection.

Splitting occurs when wood is restrained from moving across the grain (Figure 11.2). Shrinkage in wood is greater perpendicular to grain and splitting results from wood's low resistance to tension forces perpendicular to the grain.

FIGURE 11.1

Shear depth

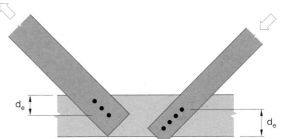
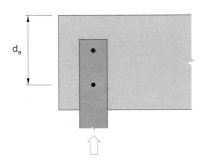

FIGURE 11.2

Splitting occurs when wood is restrained from moving across the grain

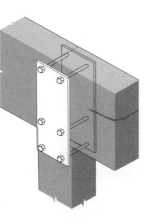

To prevent splitting at the connection one or more of the following precautions may be taken:

- Assemble wood structures at the moisture content that will be used in service.
- Use fasteners such as nails or slender bolts to make more ductile connections.
- Use only one line of fasteners, such as bolts, shear plates, or split rings parallel to the grain, if possible.
- Minimize the spacing of fasteners perpendicular to grain.
- Use separate splice plates for each row of fasteners.
- Slot steel splice plates perpendicular to the grain of the wood, where practical, to allow for movement of the wood.

LOAD DURATION

There is limited data on the effect of load duration on wood connections. Traditionally it has been assumed that the load duration effect on the ultimate strength of wood joints is similar to that of wood itself, and that any effects on the fastener parts (usually steel) can be neglected. To be consistent with sawn lumber, the same load duration definitions and corresponding K_D factors have been applied to fastening design. K_D is not applied to designs for lateral slip resistance. The following K_D factors apply to ultimate resistance calculations for all connections:

- Short term loads, K_D = 1.15
- Standard term loads, K_D = 1.00
- Long term, K_D = 0.65

WOOD TREATMENT AND FASTENERS

Preservative treated wood is typically used in applications where it may be exposed to moisture for considerable periods, thus the fasteners and connectors must also be resistant to these conditions. In addition, common wood preservatives designed for exterior use contain copper that may react with the metals used to fabricate fasteners and connectors, so it is important to use the right type of fastener and/or connector. Hot dip galvanized or stainless steel fasteners are recommended when using a preservative treatment that contains copper. More information on fasteners for use with preservative wood can be found on the wood durability web site at www.durable-wood.com. Where treated wood is used in dry environments to prevent damage by wood-destroying insects, including termites, corrosion is of less concern.

Furthermore, some chemical fire retardants have been shown to cause wood strength loss, thus affecting the ductility and strength of fastenings in wood-based materials. CSA O86 requires that tests be carried out on the effects of fire retardants, or any potentially strength-reducing chemicals used with wood-based materials to determine the appropriate treatment factor.

GROUPS OF FASTENINGS

Tests have shown that the total strength of a joint with small, ductile, widely spaced fastenings is essentially the product of the strength of a single fastener times the number of fasteners. This assumption of equal loads on each fastener was the basis of early design standards.

However, tests on large, heavily loaded connections have shown that each connection can have a total load capacity significantly lower than the strength of one fastener times the number of fasteners. A theoretical analysis by Lantos (1969), based on assumed elasticity of timbers end-connected by wood or steel side members under tension, showed that the end fasteners in each row carried above-average loads whereas the middle fasteners carried loads below the group average. This was confirmed by Cramer (1968) and others, and by comparison of calculated values with the results of tests.

FIGURE 11.3

*Staggered lines
of fasteners*

Single line of staggered fasteners

One row of six

Two rows of three

Even number of multiple lines

Two rows of six

Four rows of three

Odd number of multiple lines

One row of six and one row of three
or three rows of three
(whichever has the least factored
resistance)

Three rows of three

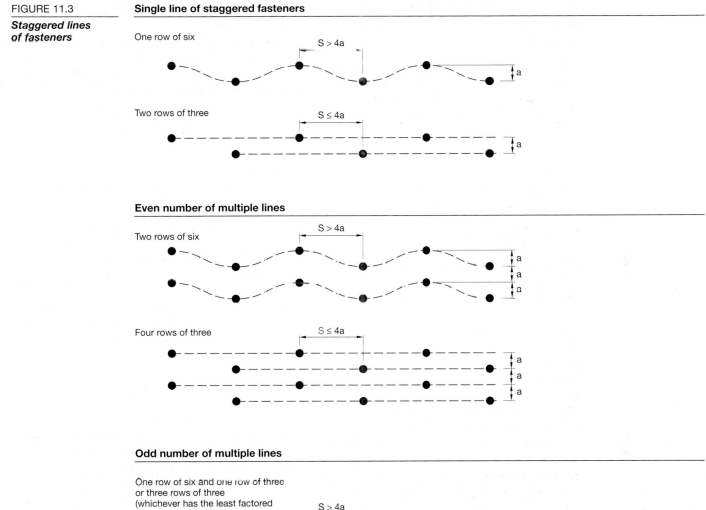

For split rings, shear plates, and lag screws the load carrying capacity per fastener decreases with the number of fasteners in a row parallel to the load but there is no reduction for the number of rows. Tables 10.2.2.3.4A and 10.2.2.3.4B in CSA O86 give the group modification factor, J_G, for shear plates, split rings and lag screw joints used with wood and steel side plates respectively. These factors are based on Lantos's calculations and are dependent on the areas of the main member and side plates and the number of fasteners in a row.

The capacity of a bolted connection is dependent on the number of bolts in a row, the number of rows, and the joint geometry.

A row is defined as one or more bolts, lag screws, shear plates or split rings aligned in the direction of the load. When fasteners are used in staggered lines, the number of rows should be determined as shown in Figure 11.3.

The conventional approach for group effect is not applicable to truss plate or joist hanger design. Since truss plate and joist hanger design values are developed empirically from a series of tests, the group effect is directly incorporated into the resistance values. Likewise, the group effect is intrinsic in the design procedure for timber rivet connections.

Relatively smaller, more ductile joints made with nails and spikes are considered less vulnerable to the group effect. For these fasteners the group effect can be ignored.

WASHERS

Washers are required between wood and the head (or nut) of a bolt, or lag screw, unless a steel strap or plate is used. Standard cut washers may be sufficient with bolts and lag screws used alone for lateral loads, but when used with split rings or shear plate connectors they require bigger, thicker washers in order to draw the connectors into full wood contact. Otherwise, the standard washer may deform, leading to non-uniform bearing stresses and crushing of the wood. Table 11.1 describes washers commonly used in wood connections.

NET SECTION

In connections made using bolts, drift pins, lag screws, split rings, and shear plates, the net section of the members being joined must be checked to ensure there is adequate resistance. The area reduction due to bolt, lag screw or drift pin holes is equal to the diameter of the hole multiplied by the thickness of the member. Table 11.2 contains area reduction information for shear plates and split rings.

Where staggered rows of fasteners are used, adjacent fasteners must be considered to occur at the same cross-sectional plane when the centre-to-centre spacing along the grain is less than the following values:

- 2 × fastener diameter for split rings and shear plates
- 8 × fastener diameter for bolts, lag screws or drift pins

Stress concentrations may occur where the member is grooved, dapped or drilled for the fastenings. In order to limit this effect, the net area must not be less than 75% of the gross area of the member.

LOADING AT AN ANGLE TO GRAIN

The lateral resistance of most fasteners depends upon the angle of load to grain. The angle is 0° where the load is parallel to grain, and 90° where the load is perpendicular to grain. Loading at an intermediate angle to grain may be calculated from the Hankinson formula which is expressed as follows:

$$N_r = \frac{P_r Q_r}{P_r \sin^2\theta + Q_r \cos^2\theta}$$

where

N_r = factored resistance at an angle to grain

P_r = factored resistance parallel to grain

Q_r = factored resistance perpendicular to grain

θ = angle between grain direction and direction of load

STEEL SIDE PLATES

Many wood connections utilize steel side plates. In all cases, steel plates must conform to the requirements of CSA Standard CAN3-S16 *Steel Structures for Buildings-Limit States Design*. The designer must ensure that the steel is adequate to resist all factored loads, and connection details are in accordance with CSA O86.

INSPECTION

Following the erection of wood structures, the connections must be inspected to ensure they were installed in accordance with the design. Items which an inspector must check include:

- All fastenings specified were installed.
- The correct size of fastenings were installed.
- Holes, daps and grooves were properly made and within dimension tolerances.
- The spacings, end and edge distances meet the criteria of CSA O86 and design.
- The fastenings were installed in the correct orientation.
- Washers of the correct size have been installed where required.
- Specified installation procedures were followed.

EXAMPLE 11.1: TENSION SPLICE

An arena roof is to be framed with heavy timber trusses. The bottom chords are 130×342 Douglas-fir glulam. The bottom chord splice is constructed with four 10×100 mm steel side plates and sixteen 2-5/8" shear plates per side. There are two shear plates per 3/4" bolt arranged as two rows of four pairs per side (Figure 11.4).

a) What is the net section of the bottom chord?

b) What is the group modification factor?

c) The arena will be subject to changes in moisture content. What can be done to minimize splitting at the connection?

a) Net section

A_{net} = A_{gross} – Area removed for connection

= $130 \text{ mm} \times 342 \text{ mm} - 2(3.73 \times 10^3 \text{ mm}^2)$

= $37.0 \times 10^3 \text{ mm}^2$

$A_{net} \geq 0.75 A_{gross}$ *(Acceptable)*

b) Determine J_G

A_m = $130 \text{ mm} \times 342 \text{ mm}$

= $44\ 500 \text{ mm}^2$

A_s = $4(10 \text{ mm} \times 100 \text{ mm})$

= 4000 mm^2

A_m/A_s = 11.1

Four fasteners in a row

From CSA O86 Table 10.2.2.3.4B

J_G = 0.95

FIGURE 11.4

Bottom chord tension splice

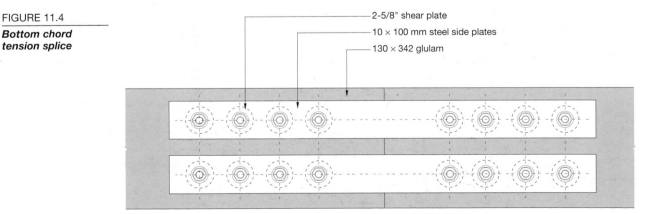

2-5/8" shear plate

10 × 100 mm steel side plates

130 × 342 glulam

c) Details to prevent splitting:

  • Use separate splice plates for each
    row of fastenings.

  • Minimize spacing between rows
    of fastenings.

  • Maximize end distance in the
    connection.

  • Use a different detail which will
    only use one row of fastenings.
    For example: design joint with
    4" diameter shear plates.

11.3 Split Ring and Shear Plate Connectors

Shear plates and split rings are round steel connectors installed in specially cut wood grooves to provide a large diameter connection on the wood surface.

Split rings are used in wood-to-wood connections. Identical grooves are made in the matching faces of the two members to be connected. The split ring is installed so that half of it will sit in one wood member and the other half in the facing member (Figure 11.5). A bolt or lag screw is then used to draw the two members together.

Shear plates can be used in wood-to-wood connections but are best adapted to wood-to-metal connections. In a wood-to-wood connection, two shear plates are used back to back with a separate connector in each of the grooves of the two facing members. Shear is transferred through the bolt or lag screw passing through the centre of the connector unit. In a wood-to-metal connection, only one shear plate is installed on the wood face.

Shear plates and split rings each come in two different sizes. The 2-1/2" split ring is for use with a 1/2" diameter bolt or lag screw and the 4" split ring requires a 3/4" diameter bolt or lag screw. The 2-5/8" shear plate is used with a 3/4" diameter bolt or lag screw and the 4" size may be used with either a 3/4" or 7/8" diameter bolt or lag screw.

Split ring connectors (2-1/2" or 4" diameter) are manufactured from hot-rolled carbon steel SAE 1010, meeting the requirements of the *Society of Automotive Engineers Handbook*. Shear plate connectors may be either pressed steel or malleable iron. The steel shear plates (2-5/8" diameter) are manufactured from hot-rolled carbon steel SAE 1010 and malleable iron shear plates (4" diameter) meet the requirements of ASTM Standard A47, *Malleable Iron Castings Grade 32510* (or ASTM Standard A47M, *Grade 22010*) (Figure 11.6).

The heavy 4" diameter shear plates, which are made of malleable iron, are cast and can sometimes be out of round. They should be checked for dimensions and roundness before assembly. An oval shear plate should not be forced into a round hole.

The grooves for split rings and shear plates must be precision machined to specified tolerances to perform well. Special cutting tools are used to make the grooves (Figure 11.7). A slight taper in the split ring allows it to wedge tightly into each groove at the interface when the members are butted face-to-face.

Shear plates, when assembled, lie flush with the wood surface. Since shear plates and split rings require accurate boring and grooving, plant fabrication is favoured. Assembly of most structures is done on site, with only small transportable units assembled in the plant.

APPLICATIONS

Split ring and shear plate joints are generally used in heavy timber or glulam structures where there are larger loads to be resisted. Typical applications include:

- large trusses
- purlin to beam connections
- column to foundation connections
- arch peaks
- timber bridge construction

Shear plates can be useful in wood-to-wood connections if the parts or members are expected to move (rotate) in use, such as demountable structures that fold up like formwork for repetitive use.

FIGURE 11.5

Split rings and shear plates

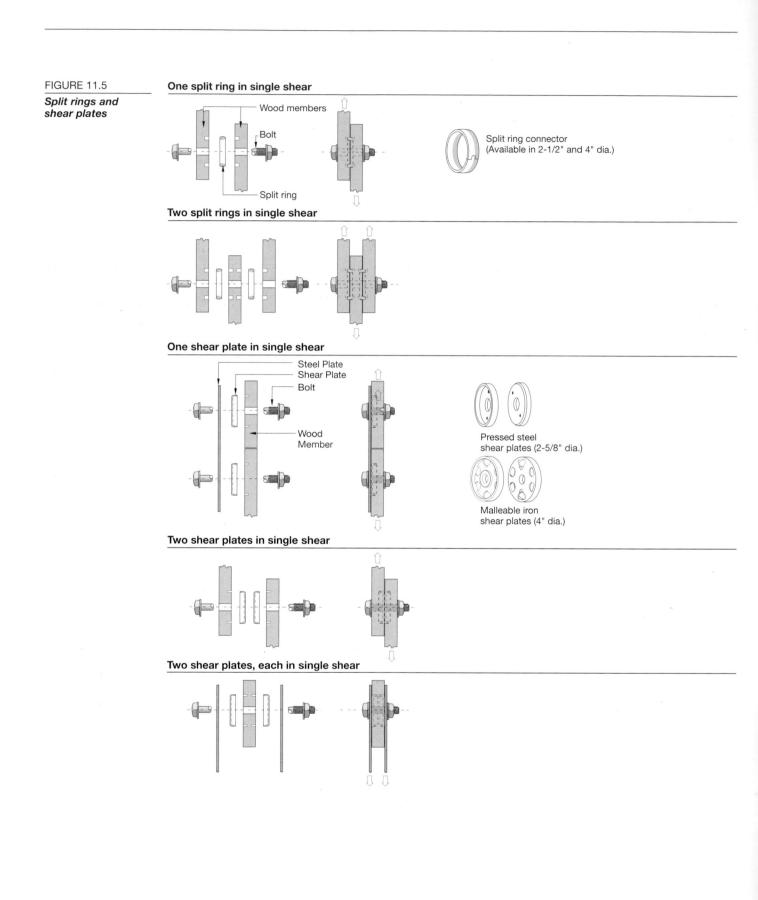

One split ring in single shear

Wood members

Bolt

Split ring

Split ring connector
(Available in 2-1/2" and 4" dia.)

Two split rings in single shear

One shear plate in single shear

Steel Plate
Shear Plate
Bolt

Wood
Member

Pressed steel
shear plates (2-5/8" dia.)

Malleable iron
shear plates (4" dia.)

Two shear plates in single shear

Two shear plates, each in single shear

FIGURE 11.6

Timber connector types and sizes

Split ring connector

Steel ring with tongue and groove division; section of ring is wedge shaped for easy insertion in specially cut grooves.

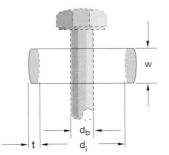

	Split ring dimensions	
	2-1/2"	4"
	mm	mm
Inside diameter at centre when closed, d_i	63.5	101.6
Thickness of steel at centre, t	4.1	4.9
Depth of steel, w	19.0	25.4

Shear plates

For wood to wood joints, two shear plates are placed back to back in connection.

For wood to metal joints, a single shear plate is placed in wood member.

Pressed steel, front

Malleable iron, front

Pressed steel, back

Malleable iron, back

	Shear plate dimensions		
	2-5/8"	4"	
		3/4" bolt	7/8" bolt
	mm	mm	mm
Diameter of plate, d_p	66.5	102.1	102.1
Diameter of bolt hole, d_b	20.6	20.6	23.9
Thickness of plate, t	4.3	5.1	5.1
Depth of flange, w	10.7	15.7	15.7

FIGURE 11.7
Groove cutting tools

Split ring tool   **Shear plate tool**

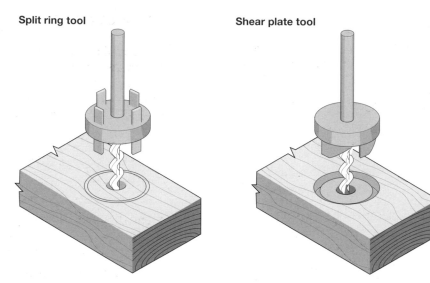

LATERAL RESISTANCE

The resistance of split rings and shear plate connectors is developed through bearing of the connector unit on the wood and/or steel. Stress in the wood is highest in the vicinity of the connector (Figure 11.8).

The relative importance of the bolt and the connector varies according to the type of connector and the method of action of the combination. In all cases, however, the connector unit transfers shear either between the faces of two timber members or between a timber member and a metal side plate. In the shear plate connector, although only a portion of the load is transferred to the wood by shear on the bolt, the unit will not work unless the bolt is in position and securely fastened.

CSA O86 Table 10.3.6C gives maximum factored resistances for shear plates in the case where the connector unit is limited by the shear strength of the bolt. The capacity of a split ring unit is dependent upon the combined action of bolt and ring. Although most of the unit's load capacity comes from the ring, the bolt does carry some load, which is already accounted for in the connector formula. In all cases, it is essential that the proper size of bolt and washers be used with the particular connector.

Lateral strength resistances given in CSA O86 are derived from tests by Scholten (1944). These tests showed that the strength parallel or perpendicular to grain, of a split ring or shear plate connection, is directly proportional to the applicable crushing strength of the wood. The values in CSA O86 are near minimum test values adjusted for the crushing strength of the species group and load duration.

Factored Lateral Strength Resistance

Factored lateral strength resistance parallel to the grain is calculated as

$$P_r = \phi \, P_u \, n_F \, J_F$$

Factored lateral strength resistance perpendicular to the grain is calculated as

$$Q_r = \phi \, Q_u \, n_F \, J_F$$

where

$\phi = 0.6$

$P_u = p_u \, (K_D \, K_{SF} \, K_T)$

p_u = lateral strength resistance parallel to grain, kN
(CSA O86 Table 10.3.6A)

$Q_u = q_u (K_D \, K_{SF} \, K_T)$

q_u = lateral strength resistance perpendicular to grain, kN (CSA O86 Table 10.3.6B)

K_D = load duration factor

K_{SF} = service condition factor (CSA O86 Table 10.2.1.5)

K_T = fire-retardant treatment factor (CSA O86 Clause 10.2.1.7)

n_F = number of fastening units

$J_F = J_G \, J_C \, J_T \, J_O \, J_P$

J_G = factor for groups of fastenings (CSA O86 Tables 10.2.2.3.4A and B)

J_C = minimum configuration factor (CSA O86 Tables 10.3.3A, B, and C)

J_T = thickness factor (CSA O86 Table 10.3.4)

J_O = factor for connector orientation in grain

= 1.00 for side grain installation

= 0.67 for end grain and all other installations

J_P = factor for lag screw penetration (CSA O86 Table 10.3.5)

CONNECTION CONFIGURATION

The location and relative position of connectors in members affects connector resistances. Factors which must be considered in the geometry of a connection made with split ring or shear plate connectors are:

- the angle of load to grain
- the thickness of the members to be joined
- whether one or two faces of the member is to receive connectors
- the distance between the connector and the edge of the wood member measured perpendicular to the grain
- the distance between the connector and the end of the wood member measured parallel to the grain
- the centre to centre spacing of connectors
- whether the connector is in side grain or end grain
- the group effect as discussed in Section 11.2

FIGURE 11.8

Stress distribution in joints

Split ring connector joint

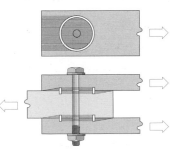

Shear plate connector joint

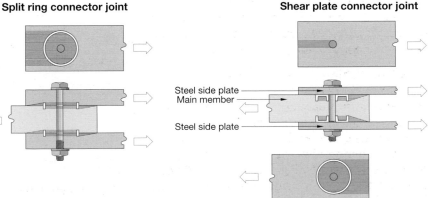

Steel side plate
Main member
Steel side plate

There are three distance factors, J_C, for shear plate or split ring connector joints. These factors are defined for edge distance, end distance and connector spacing. The most efficient end, edge, and spacing distances are those that permit maximum loads. Often, practical considerations, such as economy and smallest size of plates, will govern spacings and edge and end distances.

Depending on the geometry of the connection, each of these factors may be less than one. In determining the resistance of the connection, the lowest of the three J_C factors is used.

The factor for member thickness, J_T, depends on the size of the member and the number of faces containing a connector. Figure 11.9 illustrates configurations for typical shear plate and split ring joints, where $J_C = 1.0$.

Shear plates or split rings may be used in end grain (Figure 11.10), but in this orientation, a factor for connector orientation in grain, J_O, equal to 0.67 is used to calculate resistance.

LAG SCREW CONNECTOR CONNECTIONS

Where lag screws, instead of bolts, are used with connectors, resistance of the connection is dependent on the length of penetration of the lag screw into the member receiving the point. In denser wood species, less penetration is required. CSA O86 Table 10.3.5 gives the lag screw penetration requirements and the corresponding factors for lag screw penetration J_P.

For example, a connection made with 2-5/8" diameter shear plates in Douglas fir timbers would require 19 mm diameter lag screws. In order to utilize the full capacity of the connection, the lag screw would have to penetrate at least 95 mm into the member receiving the point if two wood members were being connected. The minimum penetration allowed would be 67 mm. A wood to wood connection with the minimum penetration would have 75% of the resistance. A wood to steel connection would be assigned full capacity with the minimum penetration.

If lag screws are used with connectors, the holes must be drilled and the lag screws installed in accordance with the general requirements for lag screw connections.

FIGURE 11.9

Shear plate and split ring spacing and edge distances for $J_C = 1.0$, mm

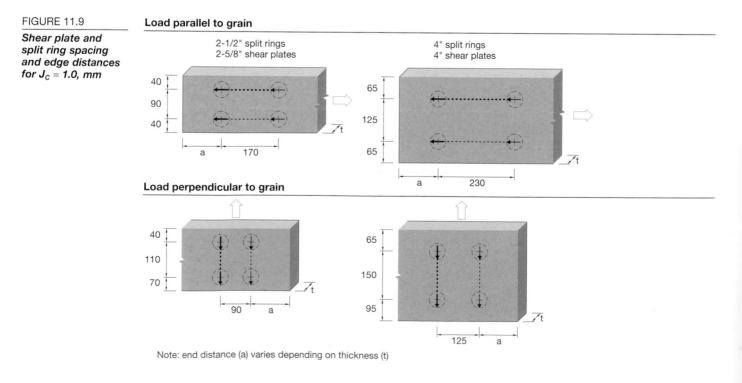

Note: end distance (a) varies depending on thickness (t)

FIGURE 11.10

***End grain
applications***

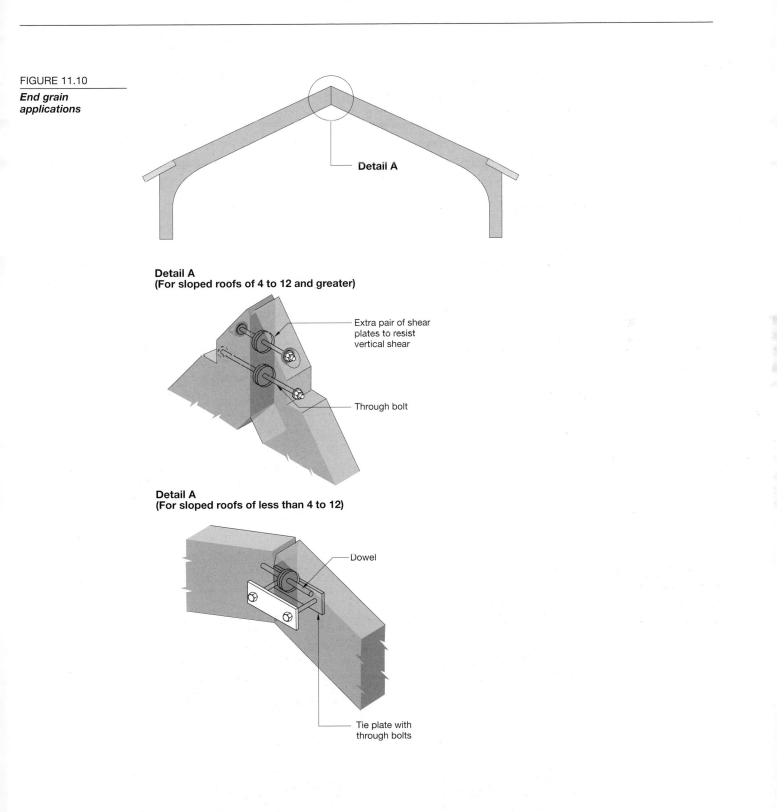

Detail A

**Detail A
(For sloped roofs of 4 to 12 and greater)**

Extra pair of shear
plates to resist
vertical shear

Through bolt

**Detail A
(For sloped roofs of less than 4 to 12)**

Dowel

Tie plate with
through bolts

EXAMPLE 11.2:
SPLIT RING – BEAM TO COLUMN

Two 130×304 mm Douglas fir glulam floor beams are attached to opposite sides of a 175×190 mm Douglas fir glulam column (Figure 11.11). The total reaction of 85 kN due to factored loads is transferred to the column by 4" diameter split rings on both sides, with a 3/4" diameter bolt holding the members together. Design the split ring connection.

Factored load on connection

$$Q_f = 85 \text{ kN}$$

Factored lateral strength resistance of 4" diameter split rings perpendicular to grain

$$Q_r = \phi \, Q_u \, n_F \, J_F$$

$$\begin{aligned} Q_u &= q_u \, (K_D \, K_{SF} \, K_T) \\ &= 42 \text{ kN} \,(1.0 \times 1.0 \times 1.0) \\ &= 42 \text{ kN} \end{aligned}$$

$$\begin{aligned} J_F &= J_G \, J_C \, J_T \, J_O \, J_P \\ &= 1.0 \times 1.0 \times 1.0 \times 1.0 \times 1.0 \\ &= 1.0 \end{aligned}$$

J_G and J_C are assumed to be 1.0, but should be verified once the number of split rings and joint configuration has been determined.

J_T = 1.0 (CSA O86 Table 10.3.4 since thickness > 76 mm)

J_O = 1.0 (since side grain installation)

J_P = 1.0 (since bolts are used and not lag screws)

$$\begin{aligned} Q_r &= 0.6 \times 42 \text{ kN} \times n_F \times 1.0 \\ &= 25.2 \, n_F \text{ (kN)} \end{aligned}$$

$$Q_r \geq Q_f$$

$$25.2 \, n_F \geq 85 \text{ kN}$$

$$n_F \geq 3.37$$

FIGURE 11.11

Beam to column connection using split rings

Plan

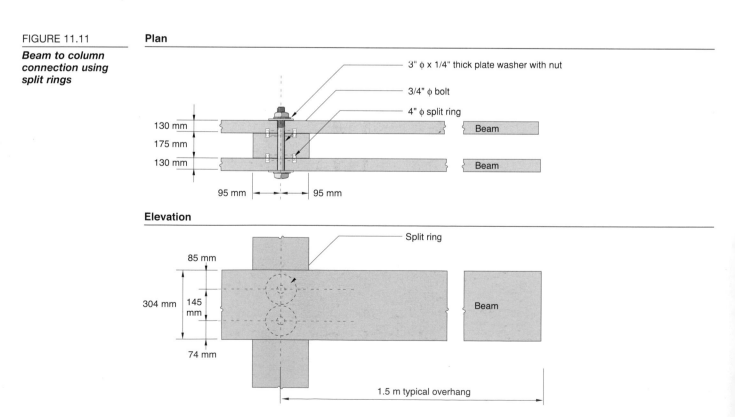

Elevation

Therefore use four, 4" diameter split rings in two rows as shown

J_G = 1.0 (since two fasteners per row)

Adjust J_C so that n_F = 4.0 and Q_r = 85 kN

J_C = 3.37/4.0

= 0.84

Angle of load to grain

θ = 90°

Angle of connector row to grain

β = 90°

Minimum loaded edge distance

= 72 mm
(linearly interpolating from
CSA O86 Table 10.3.3A)

Minimum unloaded edge distance

= 65 mm (as specified in Figure 11.9
for load perpendicular to grain)

Minimum spacing between connectors for J_C = 0.84 is, by interpolation (CSA O86 Table 10.3.3C)

$$125 + \left[\frac{0.84 - 0.75}{1.0 - 0.75}\right] \times [150 - 125] = 134 \, mm$$

Therefore use the following:

Loaded edge distance

85 mm > 72 mm *(Acceptable)*

Unloaded edge distance

74 mm > 65 mm *(Acceptable)*

Spacing between connectors

145 mm > 134 mm *(Acceptable)*

Note that end distance is not checked since the split rings are placed far away from the ends of the beams.

EXAMPLE 11.3:
SPLIT RING TENSION SPLICE

The bottom chord of a truss consists of two 89 × 286 mm S-P-F lumber members spaced at 306 mm on centre (Figure 11.12). A tension splice for the chord consists of 64 × 286 mm spruce lumber side plates on both sides of each member, with split rings between each member and side plate, and a filler to close up the connection. The truss members will be unseasoned when assembled but will be used in a dry service location.

Design a 4" diameter split ring connection for a tensile force of 160 kN due to factored dead and snow loads.

$$P_f = 160 \text{ kN}$$

Factored lateral strength resistance of 4" diameter split ring connection, parallel to grain, P_r, is given by:

$$P_r = \phi \, P_u \, n_F \, J_F$$

FIGURE 11.12

Tension splice connection using split rings

Plan

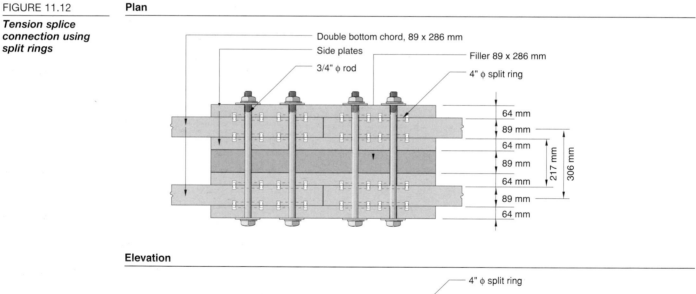

Elevation

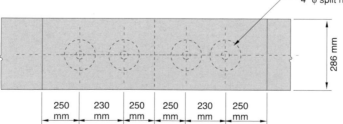

where

$$P_u = p_u (K_D K_{SF} K_T)$$
$$= 45 \text{ kN} (1.0 \times 0.80 \times 1.0)$$
$$= 36 \text{ kN}$$

$$J_F = J_G J_C J_T J_O J_P$$
$$= 1.0 \times 1.0 \times 1.0 \times 1.0 \times 1.0$$
$$= 1.0$$

(See Example 11.2 for table references for J factors.)

$$P_r = 0.6 \times 36 \text{ kN} \times n_F \times 1.0$$
$$= 21.6 \, n_F \text{ (kN)}$$

$$P_r \geq P_f$$

$$21.6 \times n_F \geq 160 \text{ kN}$$

$$n_F \geq 7.41$$

Therefore use eight, 4" split rings as shown

$$J_G = 1.0 \text{ (since two fasteners per row)}$$

Adjust J_C, so that

$$n_F = 8.0 \text{ and}$$
$$P_r = 160 \text{ kN}$$
$$J_C = 7.41/8.0$$
$$= 0.93$$

Angle of load to grain

$$\theta = 0°$$

Angle of connector row to grain

$$\beta = 0°$$

Minimum edge distance

$$= 65 \text{ mm (Figure 11.9 for load parallel to grain)}$$

Minimum end distance

$$= 245 \text{ mm for } J_C - 0.93$$
(CSA O86 Table 10.3.3B)

Minimum spacing between connectors for $J_C = 0.93$ is, by interpolation (CSA O86 Table 10.3.3C)

$$125 + \left[\frac{0.93 - 0.75}{1.00 - 0.75} \right] \times [230 - 125] = 201 \text{ mm}$$

Therefore use the following:

Edge distance

143 mm > 65 mm   *(Acceptable)*

End distance

250 mm > 245 mm   *(Acceptable)*

Spacing between connectors

230 mm > 201 mm   *(Acceptable)*

EXAMPLE 11.4:
SHEAR PLATE – BEAM TO GIRDER

A 130 × 342 mm Douglas fir glulam floor beam is supported by a hanger on a 175 × 608 mm Douglas fir glulam girder (Figure 11.13). The hanger is connected to the girder using shear plates, transferring specified dead and live loads of 7.5 kN and 22.5 kN respectively from the floor beam. Design the connection using 2-5/8" diameter shear plates.

Factored load from the beam

$$Q_f = 1.25\,D + 1.5\,L$$
$$= 1.25 \times 7.5 + 1.5 \times 22.5$$
$$= 43.1 \text{ kN}$$

Factored lateral strength resistance of 2-5/8" diameter shear plate perpendicular to grain,

$$Q_r = \phi\,Q_u\,n_F\,J_F$$

$$Q_u = q_u\,(K_D\,K_{SF}\,K_T)$$
$$= 23 \text{ kN } (1.0 \times 1.0 \times 1.0)$$
$$= 23 \text{ kN}$$

$$J_F = J_G\,J_C\,J_T\,J_O\,J_P$$
$$= 1.0 \times 1.0 \times 1.0 \times 1.0 \times 1.0$$
$$= 1.0$$

(See Example 11.2 for table references for J factors.)

FIGURE 11.13

Beam to girder connection using shear plates

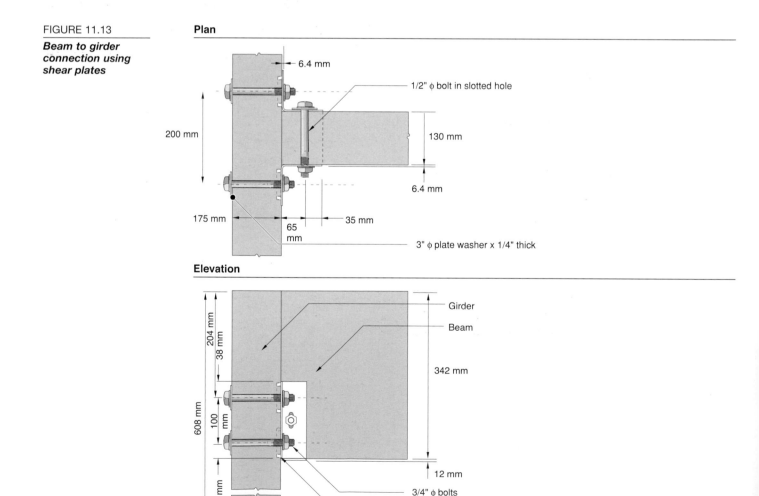

$Q_r = 0.6 \times 23 \times n_F \times 1.0$

$\quad = 13.8\, n_F \text{ (kN)}$

$Q_r \quad \geq Q_f$

$13.8\, n_F \geq 43.1 \text{ kN}$

$n_F \quad \geq 3.1$

Therefore use four, 2-5/8" diameter shear plates in two rows.

Factored load per shear plate

43.1 kN/4 = 10.8 kN

From CSA O86 Table 10.3.6C maximum factored strength resistance per shear plate is

18 kN > 10.8 kN   *(Acceptable)*

$J_G = 1.0$ (since two fasteners per row)

Adjust J_C so that $n_F = 4.0$ and $Q_r = 43.1$ kN

$J_C = 3.1/4$

$\quad = 0.78$

Angle of load to grain

$\theta \quad = 90°$

Angle of connector row to grain

$\beta \quad = 90°$

Minimum loaded edge distance

$\quad = 45 \text{ mm (for } J_C = 0.83,$
$\quad$ CSA O86 Table 10.3.3A)

Minimum unloaded edge distance

$\quad = 40 \text{ mm (Figure 11.9, Pg 11-16}$
$\quad$ for load perpendicular to grain)

Loaded edge distance is determined by the floor beam's depth

608 − 342 + 38 = 304 mm

Minimum spacing between connectors for $J_C = 0.78$ is, by interpolation (CSA O86 Table 10.3.3C)

$$90 + \left[\frac{0.78 - 0.75}{1.00 - 0.75}\right] \times \left[110 - 90\right] = 92 \text{ mm}$$

Therefore use the following:

Loaded edge distance

304 mm > 45 mm   *(Acceptable)*

Unloaded edge distance

204 mm > 40 mm   *(Acceptable)*

Spacing between connectors

100 mm > 92 mm   *(Acceptable)*

EXAMPLE 11.5:
SHEAR PLATE – ARCH PEAK

Two 175×418 mm Douglas fir glulam members form an arch at a slope of 30° from the horizontal (Figure 11.14). The arch peak is connected by shear plates used back to back in the end grain, with a 19 mm diameter threaded rod holding them together. If required, an additional pair of shear plates can be used above the first pair, centred on a 19 mm diameter dowel. The maximum vertical shear at the arch peak is 18 kN, due to factored snow plus dead loads. Design the connection using 2-5/8" diameter shear plates.

$$P_f = 18 \text{ kN}$$

Factored resistances of one 2-5/8" diameter shear plate parallel to grain, P_r and perpendicular to grain, Q_r are:

$$P_r = \phi P_u N_F J_F$$

$$P_u = p_u (K_D K_{SF} K_T)$$
$$= 27 \text{ kN} (1.0 \times 1.0 \times 1.0)$$
$$= 27 \text{ kN}$$

$$J_F = J_G J_C J_T J_O J_P$$
$$= 1.0 \times 1.0 \times 1.0 \times 0.67 \times 1.0$$
$$= 0.67$$

$$J_O = 0.67 \text{ (end grain installation)}$$

(See Example 11.2 for table references for other J factors)

$$P_r = 0.6 \times 27 \text{ kN} \times n_F \times 0.67$$
$$= 10.8 \ n_F \text{ (kN)}$$

$$Q_r = \phi Q_u n_F J_F$$

$$Q_u = q_u (K_D K_{SF} K_T)$$
$$= 23 \text{ kN} (1.0 \times 1.0 \times 1.0)$$
$$= 23 \text{ kN}$$

$$J_F = J_G J_C J_T J_O J_P$$
$$= 1.0 \times 1.0 \times 1.0 \times 0.67 \times 1.0$$
$$= 0.67$$

$$Q_r = 0.6 \times 23 \text{ kN} \times n_F \times 0.67$$
$$= 9.2 \ n_F \text{ (kN)}$$

FIGURE 11.14

Arch peak connection using shear plates

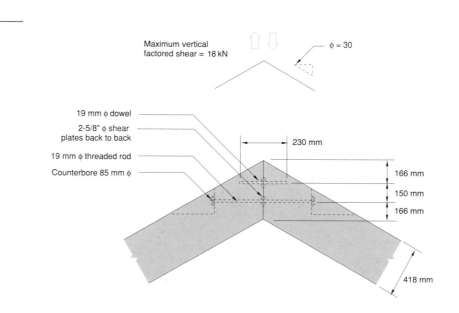

Maximum vertical factored shear = 18 kN

$\phi = 30$

19 mm ϕ dowel
2-5/8" ϕ shear plates back to back
19 mm ϕ threaded rod
Counterbore 85 mm ϕ

230 mm

166 mm
150 mm
166 mm

418 mm

Angle of load to grain

$$\theta \ = \ 60°$$

$$N_r \ = \ \frac{P_r Q_r}{P_r \sin^2\theta + Q_r \cos^2\theta}$$

$$= \ \frac{10.8 \times 9.2 \times n_F}{10.8(0.75) + 9.2(0.25)}$$

$$= \ 9.6 \, n_F \ (kN)$$

Therefore number of shear plates required

$$n_F \ = \ 18 \, / \, 9.6$$

$$n_F \ = \ 1.88$$

Therefore use two shear plates.

Factored load per shear plate

18 kN/2 = 9 kN

From CSA O86 Table 10.3.6C maximum factored strength resistance per shear plate is

18 kN > 9 kN   *(Acceptable)*

Angle of load to grain

$$\theta \ = \ 60°$$

Angle of connector row to grain

$$\beta \ = \ 60°$$

The arch dimensions are sufficiently large to provide edge and end distances and spacing such that $J_C = 1.0$.

Minimum loaded edge distance

= 70 mm CSA O86 Table 10.3.3A

Minimum unloaded edge distance

= 40 mm (Figure 11.9)

Minimum spacing between connectors

= 100 mm CSA O86 Table 10.3.3C

End distance does not apply to connections in end grain.

Therefore use the following:

Loaded edge distance

= 166 × cos 30°

= 144 mm > 70 mm   *(Acceptable)*

Unloaded edge distance

= member width/2

= 87.5 mm > 40 mm   *(Acceptable)*

Spacing between connectors

150 mm > 100 mm   *(Acceptable)*

11.4 Bolts and Dowels

Bolts are widely employed in wood construction, but the types used should not be confused with machine screws that are smaller and have finer threads.

Square-headed machine bolts are being replaced by finished hexagon bolts. This is due to the higher tensile strengths available in the hexagon bolts. However, higher strength is seldom needed in wood construction. Alternate types of heads are also available, such as countersunk heads which are used for flush surfaces. Carriage bolts can be tightened by turning the nut without holding the bolt since the shoulders under the head grip the wood.

The design requirements and data specified in CSA O86 apply to connections that use a metallic bolt or dowel whose material properties are referenced by a Canadian material design standard. Information on standard sizes, weights and lengths of hexagon bolts is provided in Tables 11.3 and 11.4.

Bolts can be dipped or plated, at additional cost, to provide resistance to corrosion. In exposed conditions, corrosion should be resisted by using hot dip galvanized or stainless steel bolts, washers and nuts. Frequent inspection in service is desirable to ensure that no corrosion ensues. Marine conditions are especially hazardous due to the presence of salt. Other exposed conditions include swimming pools, wood tanks, steam-producing plants, bridges and docks.

Bolted connections can be used with shop fabricated holes. Alternatively, bolt holes can be readily made on site using a portable drill.

Bolt holes must be accurately aligned and drilled no less than 1.0 mm and no more than 2.0 mm larger than the bolt hole.

APPLICATIONS

Bolts are widely used in wood construction. They are able to take moderately heavy loads with relatively few connectors.

Since bolts or dowels may be installed inside the wood member and the nuts and heads can be hidden, they are sometimes used for appearance reasons. Some typical applications for bolts include:

- purlin to beam connections
- beam to column connections
- column to base connections
- truss connections
- timber arches
- post and beam construction
- pole-frame construction
- bridges
- marine structures

LATERAL RESISTANCE

In CSA O86, the basic lateral resistance values for bolts parallel to grain, p_u, and perpendicular to grain, q_u, are based on a method of analysing dowel connections originally proposed by Johansen and subsequently refined by Larsen (1973) and Whale (1987).

Connections shall be designed to resist all possible yielding and brittle failure modes associated with the fasteners and material used. In CSA O86, the lateral design provisions for bolts and dowels address:

Yielding of the bolt or dowel (ductile failure modes, parallel to grain, perpendicular to grain and at an angle to grain), and

Wood failure mechanisms around the connection (brittle failure modes) including:

Row shear parallel to grain along each fastener row

Group tear-out of a connection with multiple rows of bolts loaded parallel to grain

Net tension of members loaded parallel to grain, and

Splitting of members loaded perpendicular to grain.

The potential failure modes are illustrated in Figure 11.15.

FIGURE 11.15

Potential failure modes

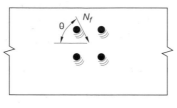

Yielding

(a) All loading directions

Notes

(1) A yielding failure can occur if the force is applied parallel to grain, perpendicular to grain, or at an angle to grain.

(2) Group tear-out and net tension failure need not be considered if the force is applied in such a way that the member is in compression.

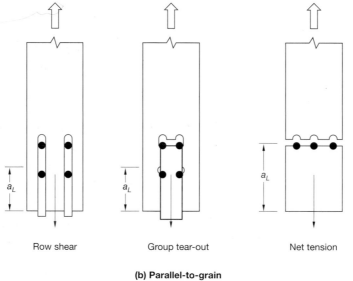

Row shear   Group tear-out   Net tension

(b) Parallel-to-grain

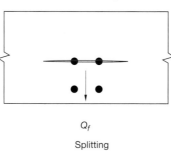

Q_f

Splitting

(c) Perpendicular-to-grain

The yielding resistances were derived from a method proposed originally by Johansen (1949) and subsequently refined by Larsen (1973) and Whale et. al. (1987). In this analysis, it is assumed that a bolt or dowel connection could fail by full bearing (crushing) in one or more wood members (for stocky bolts), or by bending of the bolt (for slender bolts) accompanied by local wood crushing near the member interfaces.

Row shear failure is the brittle fracture of a wood plug along a row of bolts or between bolts in a row loaded parallel to grain. Group tear-out failure is the fracture of a wood block around the outside of a connection with more than one row of bolts under tension loaded parallel to grain. Note that group tear-out failures modes do not occur where the member is loaded in compression. Tension parallel-to-grain resistance of wood members at the net cross section is checked to prevent net tension failure mode. Splitting failure is the fracture of wood across a connection with bolts loaded perpendicular to grain. Row shear, group tear-out, net tension and splitting are all brittle failure modes.

Different equations have been developed to describe the possible modes of failure. In analysing a particular connection, each of the appropriate equations are solved and the minimum resulting value is selected as the lateral resistance. The equations are presented in CSA O86 Clause 10.4.4.2 and shown below.

Factored Lateral Resistance

Connections shall be designed in accordance with the following requirements:

(a) $N_f \leq N_r$

where

N_f = factored load on the connection

N_r = factored lateral yielding resistance

(b) $P_f \leq P_r$

where

P_f = factored load parallel to grain

P_r = factored resistance parallel to grain

= the lesser of factored row shear resistance PR_{rT}, factored group tear-out resistance PG_{rT}, or factored net tension resistance TN_{rT}

(c) $Q_f \leq Q_r$

where

Q_f = factored load perpendicular to grain

Q_r = factored splitting resistance Q_{rT}

(d) For loading at an angle to grain, θ:

$$N_f \leq \frac{P_r Q_r}{P_r \sin^2\theta + Q_r \cos^2\theta}$$

where

θ = angle between the applied load and the grain

Yielding Resistance

The factored yielding resistance, N_r, of a group of fasteners in a joint due to yielding is a function of the number of shear planes in the connection and shall be greater than N_f.

$$N_r = \phi_y n_u n_s n_f$$

where

ϕ_y = resistance factor for yielding

= 0.8

n_u = unit lateral yielding resistance, N

n_s = number of shear planes

n_f = number of fasteners in the joint

Unit Lateral Yielding Resistance

The unit lateral yielding resistance, n_u (per shear plane), shall be taken as the smallest value calculated in accordance with items (a) to (g) as follows:

For two-member connections, only Items (a), (b) and (d) to (g) are considered valid.

For three-member connections, only Items (a), (c), (d) and (g) are considered valid.

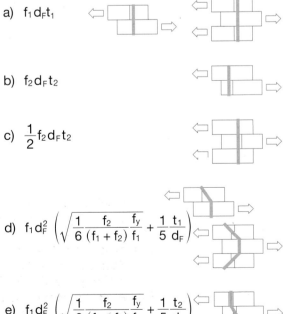

a) $f_1 d_F t_1$

b) $f_2 d_F t_2$

c) $\dfrac{1}{2} f_2 d_F t_2$

d) $f_1 d_F^2 \left(\sqrt{\dfrac{1}{6} \dfrac{f_2}{(f_1 + f_2)} \dfrac{f_y}{f_1}} + \dfrac{1}{5} \dfrac{t_1}{d_F} \right)$

e) $f_1 d_F^2 \left(\sqrt{\dfrac{1}{6} \dfrac{f_2}{(f_1 + f_2)} \dfrac{f_y}{f_1}} + \dfrac{1}{5} \dfrac{t_2}{d_F} \right)$

f) $f_1 d_F^2 \dfrac{1}{5} \left(\dfrac{t_1}{d_F} + \dfrac{f_2}{f_1} \dfrac{t_2}{d_F} \right)$

g) $f_1 d_F^2 \sqrt{\dfrac{2}{3} \dfrac{f_2}{(f_1 + f_2)} \dfrac{f_y}{f_1}}$

where

f_1, f_2 = embedment strength of members 1 and 2, where member 1 is the side member, MPa

d_F = diameter of the fastener

t_1, t_2 = member thickness or dowel bearing length

f_y = yield strength of fastener in bending

= 310 MPa for ASTM A307, SAE J429 Grade 2 bolts and dowels

For wood member embedment strength:

$$f_{i\theta} = \dfrac{f_{iP} f_{iQ}}{f_{iP}\sin^2\theta + f_{iQ}\cos^2\theta} K_D K_{SF} K_T$$

where

$f_{i\theta}$ = embedment strength of member i for a fastener bearing at angle θ relative to the grain, MPa

f_{iP} = embedment strength for a fastener bearing parallel to grain ($\theta=0°$)

= $50G(1-0.01d_F)$

f_{iQ} = embedment strength for a fastener bearing perpendicular to grain ($\theta=90°$)

= $22G(1-0.01)d_F$

G = mean relative density (CSA O86 Table A10.1)

K_D = load duration factor

K_{SF} = service condition factor

K_T = treatment factor

For non-wood based materials, the embedding strength, MPa, shall be taken as follows:

Steel: $3f_u (\phi_{steel}/\phi_y)$

Concrete or Masonry: 125 MP$_a$

where

f_u = ultimate strength of steel grade according to the appropriate material design Standard

ϕ_{steel} = 0.67 (resistance factor for metal member)

ϕ_y = 0.8 (resistance factor for yielding failures)

Parallel-to-grain Row Shear Resistance

The total factored parallel-to-grain shear resistance of a joint shall be calculated as the sum of the factored row shear resistance of the wood members resisting load, as follows:

$$P_{rT} = \Sigma(PR_{ri})$$

The total factored row shear resistance of fasteners in a wood member i shall be calculated as follows:

$$P_{ri} = \phi_w PR_{ij\,min} n_R (K_D K_{SF} K_T)$$

where

ϕ_w = 0.7

$PR_{ij\,min}$ = minimum row shear resistance of any row in the connection from PR_{i1} to PR_{inR}

n_R = number of fastener rows

PR_{ij} = shear resistance of fastener row j in member i, N

= $1.2 f_v K_{ls} t n_c a_{cr\,i}$

f_v = specified shear strength for member i, MPa

= CSA O86 Tables 5.3.1 A, 5.3.1 C, 5.3.1 D, and 6.3, or 0.6 x f_v in Table 5.3.1 B)

K_{ls} = 0.65 for side member

= 1.0 for internal member

t = member thickness

n_c = number of fasteners in row j of member i

a_{cri} = minimum of a_L and S_R for row j of member i, mm

The capacity of each member in the joint shall be checked separately for resistance to row shear failure.

Parallel-to-grain Group Tear-Out Resistance

The total factored group tear-out resistance of a joint shall be calculated as the sum of the factored group tear-out resistance of the wood members resisting load, as follows:

$$PG_{rT} = \Sigma(PG_{ri})$$

The total factored group tear-out resistance of fasteners in a wood member i with n_R rows shall be calculated as follows:

$$PG_{ri} = \phi_w \left[\frac{(PR_{i1} + PR_{inR})}{2} + \left[f_t(K_DK_{SF}K_T) A_{pGi} \right] \right]$$

where

ϕ_w = 0.7

PR_{i1} = 1.2 f_v ($K_D K_{SF} K_T$) K_{ls} t n_c $a_{cr\,1}$

    = shear resistance along row 1 of member i bounding the fastener group, N

PR_{inR} = 1.2 f_v ($K_D K_{SF} K_T$)K_{ls} t n_c $a_{cr\,nr}$

    = shear resistance along row n_R of member i bounding the fastener group, N

f_t = specified strength in tension of member i, MPa

    = CSA O86 Tables 5.3.1 A, 5.3.1 C, 5.3.1 D and 6.3, or 0.65 × f_t in Tables 5.3.1 B

A_{pGi} = critical perpendicular net area between rows 1 and n_R of member i, mm²

Group tear-out is not possible if the member end-distance is in compression. The capacity of each member shall be checked separately.

Net Tension Resistance

The total factored net tension resistance of the wood members loaded parallel to grain at a group of fasteners shall be calculated as follows:

$$T_{NrT} = \Sigma T_{Nri}$$

$T_{Nr\,i}$ of member i at a group of fasteners shall be determined using the method outlined in Chapter 9.1. The cross-sectional area deducted from the gross cross-section shall not be greater than 25% of the member gross area.

Perpendicular-to-Grain Splitting Resistance

The total factored splitting resistance of a joint shall be calculated as the sum of the splitting resistance of the wood members resisting the load and shall be the following:

$$QS_{rT} = \Sigma QS_{ri}$$

The factored perpendicular-to-grain splitting resistance of member i, N, shall be calculated as follows:

$$QS_{ri} = \phi_w QS_i (K_D K_{\mathcal{E}F} K_T)$$

where

ϕ_w = 0.7

QS_i = 14t $\sqrt{\dfrac{d_e}{1 - \dfrac{d_e}{d}}}$

t = member thickness, mm

d_e = d-e_p, effective member depth, mm

d = member depth, mm

e_p = unloaded edge distance, mm

The design process for bolts and dowels using CSA O86 is a trial and error process involving numerous equations. In order to assist the designer, Bolt and Dowel Selection Tables for typical connections are given in the *Wood Design Manual*, Section 7.4.

FIGURE 11.16

*Minimum spacing
for bolts loaded
parallel to grain*

Parallel to grain loading; rows in line

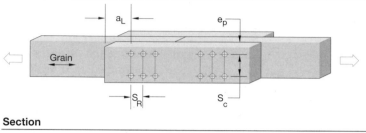

Section

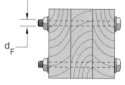

Edge Distance
$e \geq 1.5d_F$ or $S_c /2$ (whichever is greater)

End Distance
$a_L \geq 5d_F$ or 50 mm for members in tension
$a \geq 4d_F$ or 50 mm for members in compression

Proper end distance must also be provided for
centre members

Spacing in Rows
$S_R \geq 4d_F$

Spacing Between Rows
$S_c \geq 3d_F$
(When $S_c \geq 125$ mm, separate splice plates are used
for each row of fasteners.)

JOINT CONFIGURATION

Placement of bolts is important since it can
affect load carrying capacity. Factors that
must be considered in the geometry of a
bolted joint are:

- the angle of load to grain
- the thickness of the members to be joined
- the diameter of the bolt
- the distance between the bolt and the
  edge of the wood member measured
  perpendicular to the grain
- the distance between the bolt and the end
  of the wood member measured parallel to
  the grain
- the centre to centre spacing of bolts in a
  row measured parallel to the direction of
  the load

- the spacing between rows
- the number of bolts in a row
- the number of rows

Figures 11.16 and 11.17 illustrate minimum
spacing requirements for bolts loaded parallel to grain and bolts loaded perpendicular
to grain.

AXIAL RESISTANCE

Sometimes bolted connections are loaded
axially, but more often axial loading would
occur because of an axial component resulting from a load applied at an angle to the
axis of the bolt.

Washers, or plates used in lieu of washers
must be designed to carry any tensile load
component parallel to the axis of the bolt.

FIGURE 11.17

Minimum spacing for bolts loaded perpendicular to grain

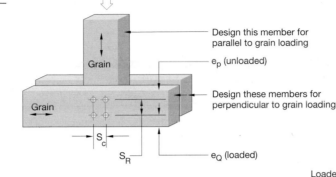

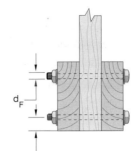

Loaded edge distance e_Q for outer members and end distance a for centre member.

Loaded edge distance
$e_Q \geq 4d_F$

Unloaded edge distance
$e_p \geq 1.5d_F$

End distance
$a \geq 4d_F$ but not less than 50 mm

Spacing in Rows
$S_R \geq 3d_F$

Spacing between Rows
$S_C \geq 3d_F$

Bearing stress of the wood under the washer or plate must not exceed the appropriate resistance values. Also, the tensile resistance of the bolt must not be exceeded.

EXAMPLE 11.6: BOLTS

Determine if two rows of 1/2" bolts are adequate for the attachment of the beam to the wooden tension member. The wood tension member consists of two 38 × 140 mm D.Fir-L No. 2 grade, untreated sawn lumber members. The beam is 89 × 140 mm D.Fir-L No. 2 grade, untreated sawn lumber. The total factored tension force is 20 kN. The load duration is standard, the material is seasoned and the service conditions are dry.

Yielding Resistance

Factored yielding resistance of a bolted connection, N_r, is given by:

$$N_r = \phi_y n_u n_s n_f$$

where

$\phi_y = 0.8$

n_u = unit lateral yielding resistance, N

$n_s = 2$

$n_f = 4$

Determine the unit lateral yielding resistance, n_u, for each shear plane of each bolt.

$d_F = 1/2$ inch (12.7 mm)

$f_y = 310$ MPa for ASTM A 307 bolts

$f_1 = f_{1P}K_D K_{SF} K_T$ for $\theta = 0°$ (parallel to grain loading)

where

$f_{1P} = 50G (1 - 0.01\ d_F)$

$G = 0.49$ (CSA O86, Table A.10.1)

$f_{1P} = 50 \times 0.49 \times (1 - 0.01 \times 12.7)$

$\quad = 21$ MPa

$f_1 = 21 \times 1.0 \times 1.0 \times 1.0$

$f_1 = 21$ MPa

$f_2 = f_{2Q}K_D K_{SF} K_T$ for $\theta = 90°$ (perpendicular to grain loading)

where

$f_{2Q} = 22G (1 - 0.01\ d_F)$

FIGURE 11.18

Beam to wooden tension member connection using bolts

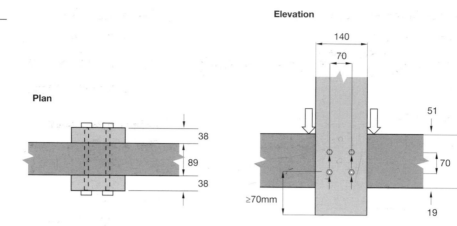

$$G = 0.49 \text{ (CSA O86, Table A.10.1)}$$

$$f_{2Q} = 22 \times 0.49 \times (1 - 0.01 \times 12.7)$$

$$= 9.4 \text{ MPa}$$

$$f_2 = 9.4 \times 1.0 \times 1.0 \times 1.0$$

$$f_2 = 9.4 \text{ MPa}$$

$$t_1 = 38 \text{ mm}$$

$$t_2 = 89 \text{ mm}$$

For a three member connection, n_u will be the minimum of the following equations:

(a) $n_u = f_1 d_F t_1$

$$= 21 \times 12.7 \times 38$$

$$= 10.3 \text{ kN}$$

(c) $n_u = \dfrac{1}{2} f_2 d_F t_2$

$$= 5.32 \text{ kN}$$

(d) $n_u = f_1 d_F^2 \left(\sqrt{\dfrac{1}{6} \dfrac{f_2}{(f_1 + f_2)} \dfrac{f_y}{f_1}} + \dfrac{1}{5} \dfrac{t_1}{d_F} \right)$

$$= 21 \times (12.7)^2 \times$$

$$\left(\sqrt{\dfrac{1}{6} \dfrac{9.4}{(21+9.4)} \dfrac{310}{21}} + \dfrac{1}{5} \left(\dfrac{38}{12.7} \right) \right)$$

$$= 5.03 \text{ kN}$$

g) $n_u = f_1 d_F^2 \sqrt{\dfrac{2}{3} \dfrac{f_2}{(f_1 + f_2)} \dfrac{f_y}{f_1}}$

$$= 21 \times (12.7)^2 \times$$

$$\left(\sqrt{\dfrac{2}{3} \dfrac{9.4}{(21 + 9.4)} \dfrac{310}{21}} \right)$$

$$= 5.93 \text{ kN}$$

$$N_r = 0.8 \times 5.03 \times 2 \times 4$$

$$N_r = 32.2 \text{ kN} > 20 \text{ kN} \qquad \textit{(Acceptable)}$$

Row Shear Resistance

$$PR_{r\,T} = \Sigma(PR_{ri})$$

$$PR_{r\,i} = \phi_w PR_{ij\,min} n_R (K_D K_{SF} K_T)$$

where

$$\phi_w = 0.7$$

$$n_R = 2$$

$$PR_{ij} = 1.2 f_v K_{ls} t n_c a_{cr\,i}$$

$$f_v = 1.9 \text{ MPa (CSA O86, Table A.5.3.1A)}$$

$$K_{ls} = 0.65$$

$$t = 38 \text{ mm}$$

$$n_c = 2$$

$$a_{cr\,i} = 70 \text{ mm}$$

$$PR_{r\,i} = 0.7 \times (1.2 \times 1.9 \times 0.65 \times 38 \times 2 \times 70)$$
$$\times 2 \times (1.0 \times 1.0 \times 1.0)$$

$$= 11.0 \text{ kN}$$

$$PR_{r\,T} = PR_{r1} + PR_{r2}$$

$$= 11.0 + 11.0$$

$$= 22.0 \text{ kN}$$

Group Tear-Out Resistance

$$PG_{rT} = \Sigma(PG_{ri})$$

$$PG_{ri} = \phi_w\left[\frac{(PR_{i1} + PR_{i2})}{2} + \left[f_t(K_D K_{SF} K_T) A_{pGi}\right]\right]$$

where

ϕ_w = 0.7

PR_{11} = $1.22 f_v(K_D K_{SF} K_T) K_{ls} t n_c a_{cr1}$

= $1.2 \times 1.9 \times (1.0 \times 1.0 \times 1.0) \times 0.65 \times 38 \times 2 \times 70$

= 7.88 kN

PR_{11} = $PR_{12} = PR_{21} = PR_{22} = 7.88$ kN

f_t = 5.8 MPa (CSA O86, Table A.5.3.1A)

A_{pGi} = $38 \times (70 - (12.7 + 2))$

= 2100 mm²

PG_{ri} = $0.7 \times$

$\left[\frac{(7880 + 7880)}{2} + \left[5.8 \times (1.0 \times 1.0 \times 1.0) \times 2100\right]\right]$

= 14.0 kN

PG_{rT} = $PG_{r1} + PG_{r2}$

= 14.0 + 14.0

= 28.0 kN

Net Tension Resistance

$$T_{NrT} = \Sigma T_{Nri}$$

$$T_{Nri} = \phi F_t A_n K_{Zt}$$

where

ϕ_w = 0.9

F_t = $f_t(K_D K_H K_{St} K_t)$

f_t = 5.8 MPa (CSA O86, Table A.5.3.1A)

A_n = $(140 - 2 \times (12.7 + 2)) \times 38$

= 4.20×10^3 mm²

$A_n \geq 0.75 A_g$ *(Acceptable)*

K_{Zt} = 1.3 (CSA O86, Table A.5.4.5)

T_{Nri} = $0.9 \times (5.8 \times 1.0 \times 1.0 \times 1.0 \times 1.0) \times 4.20 \times 10^3 \times 1.3$

T_{Nri} = 28.5 kN

T_{NrT} = $T_{Nr1} + T_{Nr2}$

= 57.0 kN

P_r = minimum of PR_{rT}, PG_{rT} or T_{Nrt}

P_r = 22 kN > 20 kN   *(Acceptable)*

Splitting Resistance

$$QS_{ri} = \phi_w QS_i (K_D K_{SF} K_t)$$

where

ϕ_w = 0.7

QS_i = $14t\sqrt{\dfrac{d_e}{1 - \dfrac{d_e}{d}}}$

where

t = 89 mm

d_e = $d - e_p$

d = 140 mm

e_p = 19

d_e = 140 − 19

= 121 mm

QS_{ri} = $0.7 \times 14 \times 89 \times \sqrt{\dfrac{121}{1 - \dfrac{121}{140}}}$

$\times (1.0 \times 1.0 \times 1.0)$

QS_{rT} = 26.0 kN

*Q_r = 26.0 kN > 20 kN   *(Acceptable)*

Note: The beam shear at the connection needs to be checked using the effective depth of the member, d_e.

Therefore four 1/2" bolts provide adequate lateral resistance.

Spacing Requirements

Load Applied Parallel to Grain (Outside Members)

Unloaded Edge Distance

$e_p \geq$ maximum of $1.5 d_F$ or $0.5 S_C$

e_p = 35 mm   *(Acceptable)*

Unloaded End Distance

$a \geq$ maximum of $4 d_F$ or 50mm

$a \geq 51$ mm   *(Acceptable)*

Loaded End Distance

$a_L \geq$ maximum of $5d_F$ or 50mm

$a_L \geq 70$ mm   *(Acceptable)*

Spacing in a Row

$S_R \geq 4d_F$

$S_R = 70$ mm   *(Acceptable)*

Spacing between Rows

$S_C \geq 3d_F$

$S_C = 70$ mm   *(Acceptable)*

Load perpendicular to grain (centre member):

Loaded Edge Distance

$e_Q \geq 4d_F$

$e_Q = 51$ mm   *(Acceptable)*

Unloaded Edge Distance

$e_Q \geq 1.5d_F$

$e_Q = 19$ mm   *(Acceptable)*

Spacing in a Row

$S_R \geq 3d_F$

$S_R = 70$ mm   *(Acceptable)*

Spacing between Rows

$S_C \geq 3d_F$

$S_C = 70$ mm   *(Acceptable)*

Therefore use four 1/2" bolts and the placement of bolts is shown in Figure 11.18.

11.5   Drift Pins

Drift pins are round steel dowels that do not have heads and are not threaded. The ends are tapered or shaped so that the pin may be easily driven into prebored holes with minimum damage to the wood. Unlike holes for split rings, shear plates or bolts, drift pin holes are prebored with the members aligned and held in place. With hole alignment thus assured, the hole diameter is slightly under-sized to give a tight fit when the pins are driven. This provides friction to draw the members tightly together during assembly. The holes must be between 0.8 mm and 1.0 mm smaller than the diameter of the drift pin.

Design information in CSA O86 is based on 16 mm (5/8") to 25 mm (1") diameter drift pins made from round mild steel conforming to ASTM Standard A307 or CSA G40.21.

APPLICATIONS

Drift pins are limited to applications where gravity or mechanical restraint prevents axial tension stress in the drift pins. CSA O86 provisions were developed for drift pins used to fasten timbers in cribwork. Drift pins may also be used to anchor beams and columns.

LATERAL RESISTANCE

The factored lateral resistance of a drift pin is equal to 60% of that for a bolt or dowel of the same diameter in single shear. At any shear plane between two overlapping members a maximum of two drift pins can be considered as resisting the shear force.

FIGURE 11.19

Drift pin connection

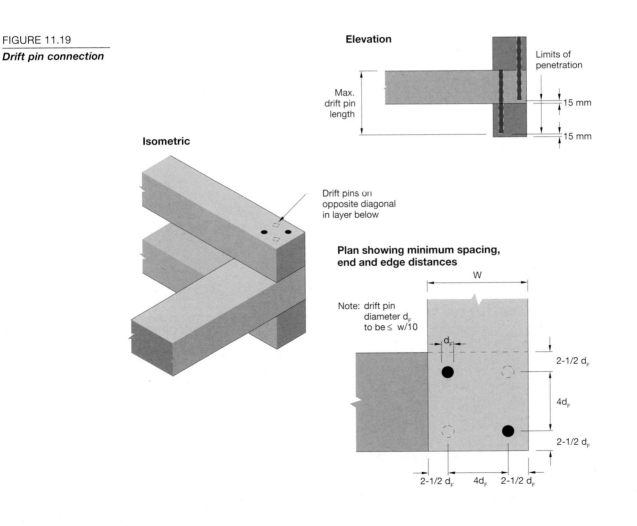

Factored Lateral Strength

The factored lateral strength of a drift pin connection, P_r, Q_r, or N_r shall be greater than or equal to the effects of the factored loads, as follows:

a) for parallel-to-grain loading, P_r shall be the lesser of $0.6\ PR_{r\,T}$, $0.6\ PG_{r\,T}$, or $0.6\ T_{Nr\,T}$;

b) for perpendicular-to-grain loading, Q_r shall be $0.6\ QS_{r\,T}$;

c) for yielding resistance, N_r shall be $0.6 N_r$; and

d) for loads at angle θ to grain, the factored load on the joint, N_f, shall be as follows:
$$N_f \leq \frac{P_r Q_r}{P_r \sin^2\theta + Q_r \cos^2\theta}$$

where

$PR_{r\,T}$ = factored row shear resistance

$P_{Gr\,T}$ = factored group tear out resistance

$T_{Nr\,T}$ = factored net tension resistance

$QS_{r\,T}$ = factored splitting resistance

N_r = factored lateral yielding resistance

JOINT CONFIGURATION

Drift pin size and spacing rules were developed from a 90° joint using four 20 mm pins to secure pairs of 200 mm wide timbers in a typical cribwork joint as shown in (Figure 19).

Factors that must be considered in the geometry of a drift pin joint are:

• the width of the members to be joined

• the thickness of the members to be joined

• the diameter of the drift pin

• the distance between the drift pin and the edge of the wood member measured perpendicular to the grain

• the distance between the drift pin and the end of the wood member measured parallel to the grain

• the centre to centre spacing of drift pins in a row measured parallel to the direction of the load

• the spacing between rows

In order to minimize splitting during driving, the diameter of the drift pin cannot be greater than 1/10 of the width of the timbers to be connected.

Drift pins must be slightly shorter than the combined depth of each pair of members to be pinned. This prevents interference between the pins in successive layers as they are tightened together.

EXAMPLE 11.7: DRIFT PINS

A timber crib used in a marine wharf is made of 191 × 191 mm, seasoned, preservative treated, No.2 Grade Douglas-fir members and connected with drift pins at each corner. The timbers and connections must resist the lateral pressure from the rock fill. Determine the maximum shear load that can be resisted at each connection.

Maximum diameter of drift pin which can be used

$d_F \leq$ 191/10

$\leq$ 19.1

Therefore, use 19 mm (3/4") drift pins.

Maximum number of pins per shear plane:

n_F = 2

Factored Lateral Strength

Minimum end and edge distances:

2.5 d_F = 47.5 mm

Minimum spacing between drift pins:

4 d_F = 76 mm

To optimize the connection, use 57 mm end and edge distances and 77 mm spacing between pins.

Determine the values of $PR_{r\,T}$, $PG_{r\,T}$, $T_{Nr\,T}$, Q_r and N_r from the equations used in bolt design:

Yielding Resistance

N_r = $\phi_y n_u n_s n_f$

where

ϕ_y = 0.8

n_u = unit lateral yielding resistance, N

n_s = 1

n_f = 2

Unit Lateral Yielding Resistance

The yield equations for bolts are also used for drift pin connections. The unit lateral yielding resistance, n_u (per shear plane), for a two member connection, shall be taken as the smallest value calculated in accordance with bolt yield equations (a), (b) and (d) to (g).

G = 0.49 (CSA O86, Table A.10.1)

d_F = 19 mm

f_{iP} = 50 × 0.49 × (1 − (0.01 × 19))

f_{iP} = 19.8 MPa

f_{iQ} = 22 × 0.49 × (1 − (0.01 × 19))

f_{iQ} = 8.73 MPa

θ = 45°

$f_1, f_2 = f_{i\theta} = \dfrac{19.8 \times 8.73}{19.8 \sin^2(45) + 8.73 \cos^2(45)}$
$\times 0.65 \times 0.67 \times 1.0$

$f_1, f_2 = f_{i\theta} = 5.28$ MPa

t_1 = 191 − 15

= 176 mm

t_2 = 191 mm

f_y = 310 MPa for ASTM A 307 bolts

(a) $f_1 d_F t_1$

= 5.28 × 19 × 176

= 17.7 kN

(b) $f_2 d_F t_2$

= 5.28 × 19 × 191

= 19.2 kN

(d) $f_1 d_F^2 \left(\sqrt{\dfrac{1}{6} \dfrac{f_2}{(f_1 + f_2)} \dfrac{f_y}{f_1}} + \dfrac{1}{5} \dfrac{t_1}{d_F} \right)$

= 5.28 × 19² ×

$\left(\sqrt{\dfrac{1}{6} \times \dfrac{5.28}{(5.28 + 5.28)} \times \dfrac{310}{5.28}} + \dfrac{1}{5}\left(\dfrac{176}{19}\right) \right)$

= 7.75 kN

(e) $f_1 d_F^2 \left(\sqrt{\dfrac{1}{6} \dfrac{f_2}{(f_1 + f_2)} \dfrac{f_y}{f_1}} + \dfrac{1}{5} \dfrac{t_2}{d_F} \right)$

= 5.28 × 19² ×

$\left(\sqrt{\dfrac{1}{6} \times \dfrac{5.28}{(5.28 + 5.28)} \times \dfrac{310}{5.28}} + \dfrac{1}{5}\left(\dfrac{191}{19}\right) \right)$

= 8.05 kN

(f) $f_1 d_F^2 \dfrac{1}{5}\left(\dfrac{t_1}{d_F} + \dfrac{f_2}{f_1} \dfrac{t_2}{d_F} \right)$

= 5.28 × 19² x

$\dfrac{1}{5}\left(\dfrac{176}{19} + \left(\dfrac{5.28}{5.28} \times \dfrac{191}{19}\right) \right)$

= 7.36 kN   (Governs)

(g) $f_1 d_F^2 \sqrt{\dfrac{2}{3} \dfrac{f_2}{(f_1 + f_2)} \dfrac{f_y}{f_1}}$

= 5.28 × 19² $\sqrt{\dfrac{2}{3} \dfrac{5.28}{(5.28 + 5.28)} \dfrac{310}{5.28}}$

= 8.43 kN

Therefore, based on the above unit lateral yield equations, n_u = 7.36 kN.

$N_r = \phi_y n_u n_s n_f$

= 0.8 × 7.36 × 1 × 2

= 11.8 kN

Row Shear Resistance

$PR_{ri} = \phi_w PR_{ij\,min} n_R (K_D K_{SF} K_T)$

where

ϕ_w = 0.7

n_R = 2

PR_{ij} = $1.2 f_v K_{ls} t n_c a_{cr\,i}$

f_v = 1.5 MPa (CSA O86, Table A.5.3.1D)

K_{ls} = 0.65

t = 191 − 15 = 176 mm

n_c = 1

$a_{cr\,i}$ = 57 mm

$PR_{r\,T}$ = 0.7 × (1.2 × 1.5 × 0.65 × 176 × 1 × 57) × 2 × (0.65 × 0.67 × 1.0)

= 7.16 kN

Group Tear-Out Resistance

$$PG_{r\,i} = \phi_w\left[\frac{(PR_{i1} + PR_{i2})}{2} + \left[f_t(K_D K_{SF} K_T)A_{pGi}\right]\right]$$

where

ϕ_w = 0.7

PR_{i1} = $1.2f_v(K_D\ K_{SF}\ K_T)K_{ls}\ tn_c a_{cr\,1}$

= 1.2 × 1.5 × (0.65 × 0.67 × 1.0) × 0.65 × 176 × 1 × 57

= 5.11 kN

PR_{i2} = $1.2f_v(K_D K_{SF} K_T)\ K_{ls}\ tn_c a_{cr\,2}$

= 1.2 × 1.5 × (0.65 × 0.67 × 1.0) × 0.65 × 176 × 1 × 77

= 6.90 kN

f_t = 3.8 MPa (CSA O86, Table A.5.3.1D)

A_{pGi} = (77 − 19) × 191

= 11100 mm²

$PG_{r\,T}$= 0.7 ×

$$\left[\frac{(5110 + 6900)}{2} + \left[3.8 \times (0.65 \times 0.67 \times 1.0) \times 11100\right]\right]$$

= 17.1 kN

Net Tension Resistance

T_r = $\phi F_t A_n K_{Zt}$

where

ϕ_w = 0.9

F_t = $f_t(K_D\ K_H\ K_{St}K_T)$

f_t = 3.8 MPa (CSA O86, Table A.5.3.1D)

A_n = (191 − 19 × 2) × 191

= 29.2 × 10³ mm²

A_n ≥ 0.75A_g (Acceptable)

K_{Zt} = 1.2 (CSA O86, Table A.5.4.5)

T_r = 0.9 × (3.8 × 0.65 × 1.0 × 1.0 × 1.0) × 29.2 × 10³ × 1.2

T_{Nrt} = 78.0 kN

Splitting Resistance

$QS_{r\,i}$= $\phi_w QS_i\,(K_D\ K_{SF}K_T)$

where

ϕ_w = 0.7

$$QS_i = 14t\sqrt{\frac{d_e}{1-\dfrac{d_e}{d}}}$$

where

t = 191 mm

d_e = $d − e_p$

where

d = 191 mm

e_p = 57

$QS_{r\,i}$ = $0.7 \times 14 \times 191 \times \sqrt{\dfrac{\frac{134}{191}}{1-\frac{134}{191}}}$

$\times (0.65 \times 0.67 \times 1.0)$

$QS_{r\,T}$ = 17.3 kN

Parallel-to-grain resistance, P_r, shall be the lesser of 0.6 $PR_{r\,T}$, 0.6 $PG_{r\,T}$ or $0.6T_{Nr\,T}$.

Therefore:

P_r = 0.6×7.16

= 4.30 kN

Perpendicular-to-grain resistance, Q_r, shall be 0.6 $QS_{r\,T}$:

Q_r = 0.6×17.3

= 10.4 kN

Resistance to yielding failures, N_r, in drift pin connections shall be 0.6 N_r:

N_r = 0.6×11.8

= 7.08 kN

The factored load on the joint, N_f, at an angle, $\theta=45°$, to the grain shall be:

$N_f \leq \dfrac{P_r Q_r}{P_r \sin^2\theta + Q_r \cos^2\theta}$

$= \dfrac{4.30 \times 10.4}{4.30 \sin^2(45) + 10.4\cos^2(45)}$

= 6.08 kN   *(Governs)*

Spacing Requirements

Minimum end and edge distances
(Figure 11.19)

= 2.5 × diameter

= 2.5 (19 mm)

= 47.5 mm

Maximum length of drift pin
(Figure 11.19)

= 2 × member depth – 15 mm

= 2 × 191 mm – 15 mm

= 367 mm

Minimum spacing between rows and spacing between pins in a row (Figure 11.19)

= 4 × diameter

= 4 (19 mm)

= 76 mm

Therefore use the following:

End and edge distances

57 mm > 47.5 mm   *(Acceptable)*

Drift pin length

367 mm   *(Acceptable)*

Spacing between rows and spacing between pins in a row

77 mm > 76 mm   *(Acceptable)*

11.6 Lag Screws

Lag screws (lag bolts), which are larger than wood screws, are installed through one face of a connection into the adjoining wood member. Design values in CSA O86 are based on the use of lag screws conforming to the requirements of ANSI/ASME Standard B18.2.1.

Usually lag screws are manufactured with regular square heads and cone points, but they can be obtained with hexagon heads and gimlet points. A typical lag screw joint is shown in Figure 11.19.

Lag screws are normally available in imperial sizes. Typical sizes range from 3" to 12" in length and from 1/4" to 1" in diameter. The availability of long lengths should be confirmed before specifying. Table 11.5 contains information on standard lag screw dimensions.

Lag screw holes consisting of a lead hole for the threaded portion and a counterbore for the unthreaded portion, must be accurately drilled to the dimensions shown in Table 11.6. The screw must be turned with a wrench, not driven with a hammer. Soap, wax or a non-petroleum-based lubricant can be used to make turning easier. These installation procedures must be strictly followed, or the load carrying capacity of the joint will be seriously reduced.

APPLICATIONS

Lag screws are used to anchor metal or wood to wood in places where through bolts are undesirable or impractical. They may be loaded laterally or in withdrawal. They are suited to inaccessible areas where a nut cannot be fixed on the end, or where an especially long bolt would be needed to fully penetrate a joint to allow a nut to be used.

Lag screws may also be used to hold timber connectors in place, in lieu of bolts, for wood construction. In general however, it is better to use bolts wherever possible.

Lag screws are often used in situations where withdrawal resistance is required. Withdrawal resistance in the end grain of wood is variable and especially sensitive to changes in the moisture content of the wood in the connection. The use of lag screws, loaded in the end grain of wood, should be avoided where possible.

FIGURE 11.20

Typical lag screw joint

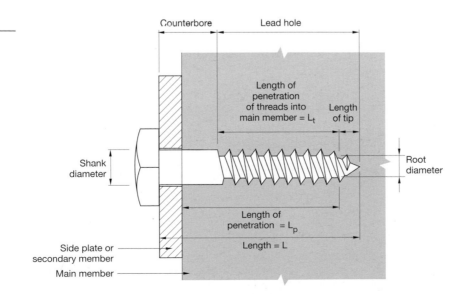

LATERAL RESISTANCE

In CSA O86 the European Yield Model is used to describe the ultimate strength of a lag screw connection loaded laterally in the side grain of a wood member. The same yield equations are used for lag screws and bolts. Lag screws are only considered for single shear connections and the equations are presented accordingly. The wood embedding strengths are the same as for bolts. The ϕ value for lag screws is 0.6 compared to a ϕ value of 0.8 for bolts. Therefore the steel embedding strength used in lag screw designs is:

f_1 = embedding strength of steel side plate, MPa

$f_1 = 3.75 \times f_u (\phi_{steel}/\phi_{wood})$

where

f_u = ultimate tensile strength of steel

= 400 MPa for A36/A 36M steel

= 450 MPa for CSA G40.21 steel, Grades 300W and 350W

ϕ_{steel} = 0.67

ϕ_{wood} = 0.60

The lag screw yield strengths is dependent on diameter such that higher yield strengths are applicable to smaller diameter lag screws.

The design process for lag screws using CSA O86 is a trial and error process involving numerous equations. In order to assist the designer, Lag Screw Selection Tables for typical connections are given in the *Wood Design Manual*, Section 7.6.

Factored Lateral Strength Resistance

Factored lateral strength resistance parallel to the grain is calculated as

$P_r = \phi P_u n_F J_G J_{PL}$

Factored lateral strength resistance perpendicular to the grain is calculated as

$Q_r = \phi Q_u n_F J_G J_{PL}$

Loads at an angle θ to the grain are calculated as

$$N_r = \frac{P_r Q_r}{P_r \sin^2\theta + Q_r \cos^2\theta}$$

where

ϕ = 0.6

$P_u = p_u (K_D K_{SF} K_T)$

$Q_u = q_u (K_D K_{SF} K_T)$

J_G = factor for group of fasteners

J_{PL} = factor for reduced penetration

= 0.625 for penetration of 5d

= 1.0 for penetration of 8d or greater

Parameters p_u and q_u are determined in accordance with Clause 10.6.6.1.2 of CSA O86 in a manner similar to that used for bolts.

The resistances outlined above are for members laterally loaded in side grain. Lag screws may also be laterally loaded in end grain. For this configuration, the resistance will be 2/3 of the lateral side grain resistance for perpendicular to grain loading in the main member if wood side plates are used. If steel side plates are used, the resistance will be 1/2 of the lateral resistance for perpendicular to grain loading in the main member.

WITHDRAWAL RESISTANCE

The resistance values in CSA O86 were developed empirically from load tests. The tests showed that withdrawal resistance was a function of the lag screw diameter, the specific gravity of the wood and the length of penetration of the lag screw. Resistance to withdrawal loads is provided by the mechanical bearing of the threads against the sides of the lead hole. Therefore, the effective length in withdrawal, L_t, is equal to the threaded length less the length of the point.

When designing a lag screw joint in withdrawal, it is important to check the resistance of the lag screw itself. The tensile resistance of the lag screw must be checked using the cross sectional area corresponding to the root diameter. Steel resistance values to be used are the same as those for ASTM A307 bolts.

Factored withdrawal resistance in side grain is calculated as

$$P_{rw} = \phi \, Y_w \, L_t \, n_F \, J_E$$

where

ϕ = 0.6

Y_w = $y_w \, (K_D \, K_{SF} \, K_T)$

y_w = basic withdrawal resistance per millimeter of penetration, N/mm (CSA O86 Table 10.6.5.1)

K_D = load duration factor

K_{SF} = service condition factor

K_T = fire-retardant treatment factor

L_t = length of penetration of the threaded portion of the lag screw into the main member, mm

n_F = number of lag screws

J_E = factor for lag screws in end grain

= 0.75 for lag screws installed in end grain

= 1.0 for all other cases

JOINT CONFIGURATION

The location of lag screws is important since it affects resistance. Sufficient end and edge distance must be provided to prevent splitting and provide sufficient shear and area resistance.

Adequate space between screws is also needed to develop the potential strength of the connection. The spacing requirements for lag screws are generally the same as bolted connections. Exceptions are:

- For parallel to grain loading, minimum spacing between rows, S_C, may be 2 d_F, and
- For perpendicular to grain loading, minimum spacing between rows is :
  - $S_C \geq 2.5 d_F$ for L/d_F of 2 or less
  - $S_C \geq 5 d_F$ for L/d_F of 6 or greater

  Interpolation may be used for L/d_F ratios between 2 and 6

Lag screw holes, where drilled in place with proper lead holes, do not present the same lack-of-fit problems as bolt holes drilled prior to assembly. The fastener diameter, d_F, for a lag screw is equal to the lag screw shank diameter.

EXAMPLE 11.8: LAG SCREWS

Two 140 × 292 mm lumber purlins are anchored against wind uplift force by a metal framing connection to a 175 × 912 mm spruce glulam beam (Figure 11.20). Lag screws in the beam must be designed to resist withdrawal loading. Net uplift force on the connection due to factored loads is 28 kN. Design the connection using 19 mm diameter lag screws.

Factored withdrawal load

$P_{fw} = 28$ kN

Try four, 3/4 inch (19 mm) diameter lag screws.

Factored withdrawal resistance

$P_{rw} = \phi\, Y_w\, L_t\, n_F\, J_E$

$Y_w = y_w\, (K_D\, K_{SF}\, K_T)$

$\quad = 140$ N/mm $\times (1.15 \times 1.0 \times 1.0)$

$\quad = 161$ N/mm

$P_{rw} = 0.6 \times 161 \times 4 \times 1 \times L_t$

$\quad = 386.4\, L_t$ N/mm

$P_{rw} \geq P_{fw}$

$386.4 \times L_t \geq 28\ 000$

$L_t \geq 72$ mm

Depth Hole – Depth C.B. ≥ 72 mm (Table 11.6)

Try 6 inch (150 mm) long lag screws:

141 mm – 64 mm = 77 mm   *(Acceptable)*

Note: Steel strength of lag screw in tension must be checked.

Therefore use four 3/4 inch (19 mm) diameter × 6 inch (150 mm) long lag screws.

FIGURE 11.21

Uplift connection using lag screws

Plan

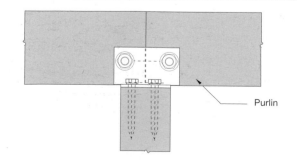

Purlin

Lag screw

Beam

Elevation

Purlin

11.7   Timber Rivets

Timber rivets, formerly known as glulam rivets, are high strength fasteners, shaped somewhat like cut nails. Various cross-sectional shapes were tested to arrive at the optimum oval shape. This shape improves strength, stiffness, and resistance to splitting of the joint.

Timber rivets are commonly available in lengths of 40, 65 and 90 mm. The rivets are galvanized and made from a high yield-point, high ultimate-strength steel, but are soft enough to provide ductility and corrosion resistance for most service conditions. Under extreme corrosion conditions where water combined with salts or acid can fall on the connection, or where steam is present, timber rivets should not be used.

Rivets must be used with steel side plates conforming to either CSA G40.21 or ASTM Standard A 36/A 36M. Side plates must be at least 3.2 mm thick and must be hot-dip galvanized for use in wet service conditions. Steel plates are generally predrilled (sometimes punched) with 6.7 to 7 mm diameter holes to accommodate the rivets.

Timber rivets are driven until the tapered head is firmly seated in the pre-drilled steel side plate while maintaining a minimum 2 mm head projection above the plate (Figure 11.21). Either a standard or pneumatic hammer may be used to drive the rivet.

When properly driven through the predrilled plate and into the timber beyond, the tapered heads deform the holes and wedge tightly. This prevents any movement of the heads within the plate, thus increasing both strength and stiffness of the joint.

When driving timber rivets, safety glasses should be worn because particles of the galvanizing or the hardened steel of the rivets may break off when struck. Rivets must be installed so the flat face is parallel to grain regardless of loading conditions.

Timber rivets have become a favoured connection for glulam members because of their many advantages. These include:

- Timber rivets are much stiffer and transfer greater loads for a given connector area than any other timber fastener.

- The wood members need not be drilled, bored or grooved. This simplifies fabrication, As well, member design can be based on gross cross-sectional area resulting in smaller member sizes.

- The typically smaller connection is often favoured for aesthetic reasons.

- Timber rivet connections can be readily inspected in the field.

FIGURE 11.22

Timber rivet

Elevation

Section

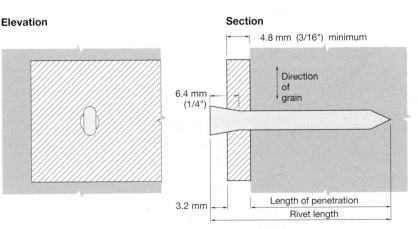

Assembly of timber rivet joints in place, however, can be time consuming and costly in situations where rivets are difficult to drive. Care should be taken to design these joints so the rivets can be driven easily. Furthermore, adjustments are difficult once rivets are in place.

If possible, each job should use only one length of timber rivet to avoid using the wrong length in a particular location.

APPLICATIONS

Typical applications include:

- truss connections
- purlin to beam connections
- beam to column connections
- column to base connections
- arch to base connections

Timber rivets are especially suited to field fabrication where plates are attached to members on the ground before erection. For example, purlins may be set into metal framing connections that are rivetted to the beam before setting it in place. Usually timber rivet connections are not assembled in the plant because the connection could be damaged or knocked out of alignment during transportation to the job site.

Timber rivets can also be used in lieu of lag screws since neither penetrate completely through the member. Timber rivets are more easily applied than lag screws since lead holes are not needed and driving is quicker than turning the screws home. This advantage may be offset by the greater number of rivets required for the joint.

Design values for rivets loaded in withdrawal are also provided in CSA O86.

LATERAL RESISTANCE

Design of timber rivet joints is based primarily on resistance formulations developed by Foschi and Longworth (1975). Their work describes and quantifies various modes of failure for timber rivet connections. The ultimate capacity of the connection can be limited by either the yielding strength of the rivets or the strength of the wood surrounding the connection. The type of failure depends on the direction of loading and the configuration of the connection.

For timber rivet connections loaded parallel to the grain, three types of failures are considered:

1. Rivet yield accompanied by local crushing of the wood.

2. The wood fails in tension parallel to grain at the edge of the connection.

3. The wood fails in a plug shear mode around the rivets.

For timber rivet connections loaded perpendicular to the grain two types of failures are considered:

1. Rivet yield accompanied by local crushing of the wood.

2. Wood failure in tension perpendicular to grain at the edge of the connection.

CSA O86 Appendix A10.7.2.3 gives formulations for the various failure modes. Using these formulas, design would be a trial-and-checking process of choosing a connection configuration and then determining the limiting resistance. In order to simplify the process, basic resistance values are tabulated for typical design configurations. For joint designs outside of the table, the appendix formulations may be used.

More recent research was used to develop design values for timber rivets used in material other than Douglas fir glulam. Rivet tests in spruce-pine glulam (Karakabeyl and Fraser, 1989) and solid sawn timbers (Karacabeyli, Fraser and Duncan, 1995) were used to develop the material factor, H used in timber rivet design. To obtain design values for alternate wood members, the basic design values for Douglas fir glulam are multiplied by the material factor, H.

For each connection the resistance of the rivets in yielding and the resistance of the wood around the connection must be assessed. The lower resistance forms the basis of the design.

Factored lateral resistance parallel to the grain per rivet joint is calculated as

$$P_r = \phi P_u H$$

Factored lateral resistance perpendicular to the grain per rivet joint is calculated as

$$Q_r = \phi Q_u H$$

where

P_u = lesser of P_y and P_w

P_y = $(1.09 L_p^{0.32} n_R n_C) J_Y K_{SF} K_T$ for rivet capacity

P_w = $p_w K_D K_{SF} K_T$ for wood capacity

Q_u = lesser of Q_y and Q_w

Q_y = $(0.62 L_p^{0.32} n_R n_C) J_Y K_{SF} K_T$ for rivet capacity

Q_w = $(q_w L_p^{0.8} C_t) K_D K_{SF} K_T$ for wood capacity

n_R = number of rows of rivets

n_C = number of rivets per row

L_p = length of penetration of the rivet

= overall rivet length − 10mm

p_w = lateral wood resistance parallel to grain (CSA O86 Table 10.7.2.3)

q_w = unit wood resistance value for perpendicular to grain loading (CSA O86 Table 10.7.2.5A)

C_t = factor relating to edge distance (CSA O86 Table 10.7.2.5B)

K_D = load duration factor

K_{SF} = service condition factor

K_T = fire-retardant treatment factor

J_Y = side plate factor

= 0.8 for side plates between 3.2 mm and 4.7 mm in thickness

= 0.90 for plates between 4.8 mm and 6.3 mm in thickness

= 1.00 for side plates 6.3 mm and more in thickness

H = material factor

= 1.0 for Douglas Fir-Larch glulam

= 0.8 for Spruce-Pine glulam

= 0.5 for Douglas Fir Larch sawn timber

= 0.45 for Hem-Fir Sawn timber

= 0.40 for Spruce-Pine-Fir sawn timber

= 0.35 for Northern Species sawn timber

JOINT CONFIGURATION

The resistance of a timber rivet joint is dependent on the number of rivets in a connection and the placement of the rivets. Tables 11.7 and 11.8 summarize minimum dimensions for glulam rivet connections. Refer to Figure 11.22 for an illustration of terms.

WITHDRAWAL RESISTANCE

Withdrawal resistance values for timber rivets are also included in CSA O86. The resistance values are limited to connections in dry material for short or standard term load durations.

FIGURE 11.23

Timber rivet dimensions

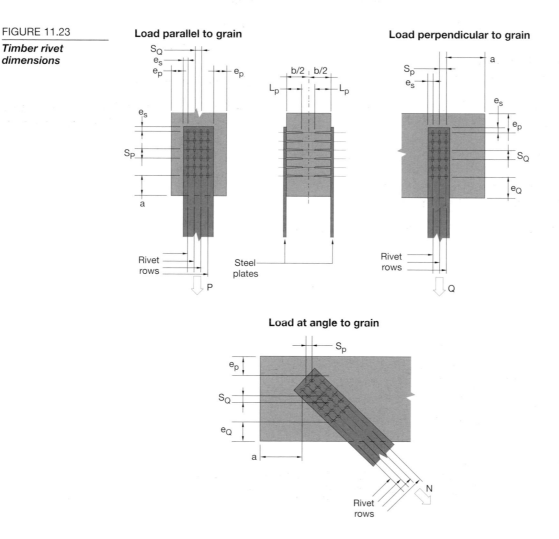

Withdrawal resistance is calculated as

$$P_{rw} = \phi Y_w L_p n_R n_C$$

where

$$\phi = 0.6$$

$$Y_w = y_w K_{SF} K_T$$

$$y_w = 13 \text{ N/mm for glulam}$$

$$= 7 \text{ N/mm for sawn lumber}$$

$L_p n_R n_C$ are as defined for lateral loading.

EXAMPLE 11.9:
GLULAM RIVETS – BEAM HANGER

A 130 × 304 mm Douglas fir glulam floor beam is supported on a hanger connected to a 175 × 608 mm Douglas fir glulam girder (Figure 11.23). The factored reaction from the beam is 41.125 kN. Design the timber rivet connection between the hanger and the girder. Use 90 mm rivets.

Orientation of load is perpendicular to grain

$$Q_f = 41.125 \text{ kN}$$

$$Q_r = \phi Q_u H$$

Consider rivet capacity per rivet

$$J_Y = 1.0 \text{ (assuming side plate thickness} \geq 6.3 \text{ mm)}$$

$$Q_y = (0.62 \times n_F L_P^{0.32}) J_Y K_{SF} K_T$$

$$= (0.62 \times n_F (90-10)^{0.32}) \times 1.0 \times 1.0 \times 1.0$$

$$= 2.52 \, n_F$$

Try four rows of seven 90 mm rivets arranged in two groups as shown.

$$Q_y = 2.52 \times 4 \times 7$$

$$= 70.56 \text{ kN}$$

Check for wood capacity

Note Q_w is capacity of each group, i.e. of two rows of rivets with seven rivets in each row.

$$Q_w = q_w I_P^{0.8} (K_D K_{SF} K_T) C_t$$

FIGURE 11.24

Beam hanger connection using timber rivets

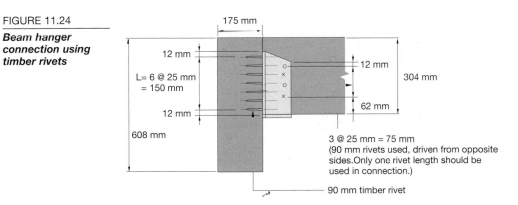

175 mm

12 mm

L= 6 @ 25 mm
= 150 mm

12 mm

608 mm

12 mm

12 mm

304 mm

62 mm

3 @ 25 mm = 75 mm
(90 mm rivets used, driven from opposite sides. Only one rivet length should be used in connection.)

90 mm timber rivet

Modification factors and parameters

e_P = 142 mm Free edge distance,
(Figure 11.22 for load perpendicular
to grain)

n_c = 7 rivets per row

S_Q = 25 mm spacing perpendicular
to grain,

$$\frac{e_P}{[n_c - 1]S_Q} = \frac{142}{6 \times 25} = 0.95 \approx 1.0$$

C_t = 1.20 (from CSA O86 Table 10.7.2.5B)

K_D = 1.0 (standard load duration)

K_{SF} = 1.0 (dry fabrication and dry
service condition)

K_T = 1.0 (untreated)

q_w = 0.90 (from CSA O86 Table 10.7.2.5A)

Q_w = $q_w L_P^{0.8} (K_D K_{SF} K_T) C_t \times 2$

   = $0.90 (90 - 10)^{0.8} \times (1 \times 1 \times 1) \times 1.2 \times 2$

   = 71.9 kN

Q_y governs

Q_r = $0.6 \times 70.56 \times 1$

   = 42.3 kN > 41.1 kN   *(Acceptable)*

**Therefore, use two groups of two rows
of seven 90 mm rivets each (28 rivets
in total).**

EXAMPLE 11.10:
TIMBER RIVETS – ARCH BASE

A shoe is designed to transfer a factored horizontal thrust of 55.0 kN from a 130×418 mm Douglas fir glulam arch leg to a 175×532 mm Douglas fir glulam floor beam through timber rivets in the 6.4 mm base plate (Figure 11.24). Loads include dead plus snow loads. Design the rivet connection.

Orientation of load is parallel to grain

Try 3 rows of 65 mm rivets with 8 rivets in each row and

S_P = 40 mm

S_Q = 25 mm

P_r = $\phi P_u H$

Consider rivet capacity

P_y = $(1.09 L_p^{0.32} n_R n_C) J_Y K_{SF} K_T$

L_p = 65 mm – 10 mm

   = 55 mm

P_y = $(1.09 (55)^{0.32} \times 3 \times 8) \times 1.0 \times 1.0 \times 1.0$

   = 94.3 kN

Consider wood capacity

P_w = $p_w K_D K_{SF} K_T$

p_w = 150 kN (linearly interpolating from
CSA O86 Table 10.7.2.3)

P_y governs

P_r = $0.6 \times 94.3 \times 1$

   = 57 kN > 55 kN   *(Acceptable)*

**Therefore, use three rows of eight
65 mm rivets.**

FIGURE 11.25

*Arch base
to support
connection*

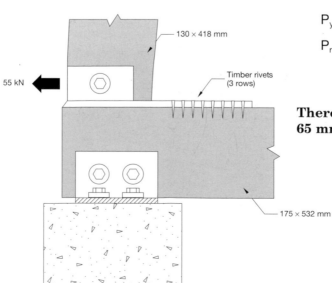

130 × 418 mm

Timber rivets
(3 rows)

55 kN

175 × 532 mm

11.8 Truss Plates

Truss plates are fasteners used to assemble pieces of dimension lumber into roof and floor trusses. They are produced by punching light gauge galvanized steel (normally 16, 18 or 20 gauge) so that teeth protrude from one side (Figure 11.25). The pattern of the teeth in the plate varies from manufacturer to manufacturer. There are a number of different plate manufacturers in Canada and each has developed its own set of proprietary tooth patterns.

Truss plates must be produced from galvanized sheet steel meeting the requirements of Clause 14.4 of CSA O86. Because the sheet steel used for truss plates is relatively thin, any corrosion of the plates can cause significant strength loss. Therefore, truss plates cannot be designed or specified for use in corrosive environments and, in particular, they cannot be used in the highly corrosive environment where fire retardant treated wood is exposed to moisture.

Truss plates are installed at every joint of a light frame wood truss. Plate sizes vary considerably depending on the loads that must be transferred at the connection. Truss fabrication is carried out at a fabricator's plant where the truss plates are embedded into the lumber with either a hydraulic press or a roller. In order to meet the design requirements of CSA O86, the plates must be installed in the following manner:

- The joints must be tight fitting with identical truss plates placed on opposite faces so that each plate is directly opposite the other.
- The truss plates must not be deformed during installation.
- The teeth must be normal to the surface of the lumber.
- The teeth must be fully embedded in the wood so that the plate is tight to the wood surface. However, the plate must not be embedded into the lumber deeper than half of the plate thickness.
- The lumber below the truss plate must comply with Appendix G of TPIC-2007.

APPLICATIONS

The structural use of truss plates is limited almost exclusively to light frame wood trusses. The stringent installation requirements would limit their use in most other applications. Furthermore, truss plates and their corresponding design values are proprietary and not readily available to the general design or construction community.

FIGURE 11.26

Typical truss plate

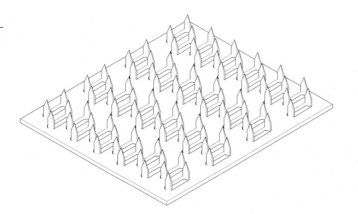

RESISTANCE

Unlike most fasteners in CSA O86, specific resistance values for truss plates are not given. Instead, CSA O86 outlines procedures for deriving resistance values based on required tests. The resulting resistance values are normally used by the truss plate manufacturer who usually has the responsibility for truss design.

Truss plates are called upon to transfer forces in tension or shear or both. Those forces may act in various directions depending on the geometry of the joint. Truss plates are used in compression joints, but mainly to keep the truss together and in alignment during handling and erecting and for stress reversal situations. The main compression forces are transferred by wood-to-wood bearing for which tightly fitted joints are essential.

With truss plate joints that are relatively short in the direction of the load, failure occurs when the teeth yield and then withdraw from the wood. Failures of this type are resisted by the lateral resistance of the teeth. With longer plates, the failure mode changes to tension failure across the most critical net section of the plate. This failure mode is resisted by the tensile resistance of the plates. A third failure mode involves shear of the plate, usually indicated by diagonal buckling of the plate followed by tooth withdrawal or tensile tearing of the steel along the shear line. This is resisted by the shear resistance of the plate.

Truss plates must be tested in accordance with CSA Standard S347 *Method of Test for Truss Plates used in Lumber Joints*. Test results for commercially used plates are listed in the *Manual of Evaluation Reports* published by the Canadian Construction Materials Centre (CCMC) Institute for Research in Construction, Ottawa, Ontario. The evaluation reports also include resistance values derived from the tests.

CSA Standard S347 calls for four types of tests: lateral resistance of the teeth, tensile resistance of the plates, ultimate tensile strength of the steel from which the plates are stamped and shear resistance of the plates. To determine lateral resistance of the teeth, plates are tested with the primary axis of the plate oriented parallel and perpendicular to the direction of load, and loaded parallel and perpendicular to the grain for a total of four different test configurations.

CSA O86 gives procedures for converting the test results into design resistance values. Truss plates must be designed so that the following criteria are satisfied:

1. Factored ultimate lateral resistance of the teeth, N_r > factored lateral load, N_f

2. Factored tensile resistance of the plate T_r > factored tensile force, T_f

3. Factored shear resistance of the plates V_r > factored shear force, V_f

4. Factored lateral slip resistance N_{rs} > specified lateral load, N_s

11.9   Nails and Spikes

Nails and spikes are manufactured in many lengths, diameters, styles, materials, finishes and coatings, each designed for a specific purpose (Figure 11.26).

In Canada, nails are usually specified by the type and length (inches). Nails are made in lengths from 1" to 6", and spikes 4" to 14". Nail diameter is specified by gauge number (British Imperial standard) and is the same as the wire diameter used in manufacture.

Gauges vary according to nail type and length. The equivalent diameter of a spiral nail is defined as the projected lateral area of a given length of the spiral nail divided by the given length.

In the US, the length of nails is designated by penny (abbreviated d). For example twenty-penny (20d) common wire nails, spikes and spiral nails have lengths of 4". The diameter of a nail depends upon its type; 4" (20d) common wire nails, spikes and spiral nails have diameters of 4.88 mm (0.192"), 5.72 mm (0.225") and 4.50 mm (0.177") respectively.

The corresponding Canadian nails have diameters of 4.88 mm, 6.40 mm and 4.33 mm. The design data in Clause 10 of CSA O86 apply only to nails conforming to Canadian Standards Association Standard B111, *Wire Nails, Spikes and Staples*.

Spikes are usually longer and sturdier than nails. A short spike, for example, has a larger cross-sectional area than an equivalent length common nail.

Many different shapes of nail heads are manufactured. Sometimes a choice of head shapes is available for a single type of nail. Nails with flat heads or square shoulders under the head are measured from the end of the points to just below the heads, while nails with brad or countersunk heads are measured over their total length.

T-shaped and D-shaped heads are often used to manufacture nails for pneumatic nailing guns; the nails are lightly attached to each other or collated with plastic, allowing quick loading of clips of nails.

Nail shanks are made smooth or deformed. The deformed shank is usually spiral (or helical) or ringed, but variations of these such as barbed and fluted nails are available. Spiral deformations are usually formed by threading while drawing the wire, but sometimes are threaded after drawing.

Spiral nails are available in many sizes and designs. They can provide greater withdrawal resistance than smooth shank nails. They reduce wood splitting and are particularly effective against shock loads.

Ring-threaded nails have very high holding power, created through the keying action of displaced fibres against the nail grooves. Resistance drops sharply after an initial slip; as the nail withdraws, the threads tear the wood. For this reason, ring threads are not recommended against shock loads.

There are five basic types of points: diamond, blunt diamond, long diamond, duckbill and conical. The most widely used nail point is the diamond. It is fairly easy to drive and gives good holding power. Use of the blunt diamond point reduces splitting, but also reduces holding power; a slight taper helps maintain withdrawal resistance.

Splitting can also be reduced by purposely blunting the point of the nail before driving. The long diamond point is easiest to drive, but may tend to split the harder wood species. Duckbill points are not as common but are occasionally used for clinching, to increase resistance.

Nails are normally made of low – or medium – carbon steels or aluminum (Table 11.9). Medium-carbon steels can be hardened by heat treating and quenching, to increase toughness. Nails of copper, brass, bronze, stainless steel, monel and other special metals are available if specially ordered.

FIGURE 11.27

Types of nails

Type of nail	Head	Shank	Point	Material	Finishes and coatings	Common lengths mm	in.
Common (Spike)	F	C, S	D	S, E	B	100 to 350 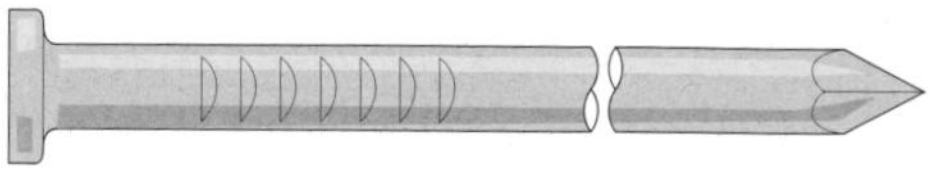	4 to 14
Eavestrough (Spike)	Cs, F	C, S	D, N	S	B, Ghd	125 to 250 	5 to 10
Standard or Common	F	C, R, S	D	A, S, E	B, Ge	25 to 150 	1 to 6
Box	F, Lf	C, R, S	D	S	B, Pt, Ghd	19 to 125 	3/4 to 5
Finishing	Bd	C, S	D	S	B, Bl	25 to 100 	1 to 4
Flooring and Casing	Cs	C, S	Bt, D	S	B, Bl, Ht	28 to 80 	1-1/8 to 3-1/4
Concrete	Cs	S	Con, Bt, D	Sc	Ht	13 to 75 	1/2 to 3
Cladding and Decking	F, O	C, S	D	A, S	B, Ghd	50 to 63 	2 to 2-1/2
Clinch	F, Lf	C, S	Db	S	B	19 to 63 	3/4 to 2-1/2

FIGURE 11.27
continued

Types of nails

Type of nail	Head	Shank	Point	Material	Finishes and coatings	Common lengths mm	in.
Hardwood Flooring	Cs	S	Bt	S	B, Ht	38 to 63 	1-1/2 to 2-1/2
Gypsum Wallboard	Dw, F	C, R, S	D, N	S	B, Bl, Ge	28 to 50 	1-1/8 to 2
Underlay and Underlay Subfloor	F, Cs	C, R	D	S	B, Ht	19 to 50 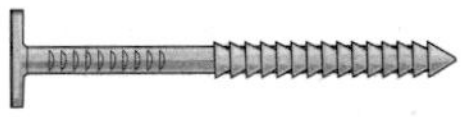	3/4 to 2
Roundwire Sash Pins		C	D	S	B	19 to 50 	3/4 to 2
Roofing	Lf, F	C, R, S	D	A, S	B, Ghd	19 to 50 	3/4 to 2
Wood Shingle	F	C, R, S	D	A, S	B, Ghd	31 to 44 	1-1/4 to 1-3/4
Gypsum Lath	F	C, S	D, N	S	B, Bl, Ge	31 	1-1/4
Wood Lath	F	C, S	D	S	Bl	25 to 28 	1 to 1-1/8

FIGURE 11.27
continued

Nail heads, shanks and points

Type		Abbr.	Remarks	
Heads	Flat Counter-Sink	Cs	For nail concealment, light construction flooring, and interior trim.	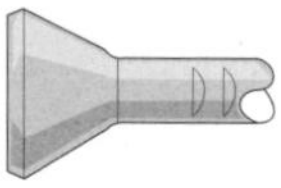
	Gypsum Wallboard	Dw	For gypsum wallboard.	
	Finishing	Bd	For nail concealment; cabinetwork, furniture.	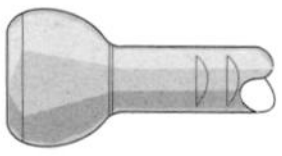
	Flat	F	For general construction.	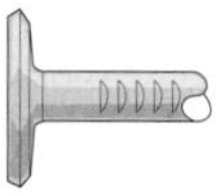
	Large Flat	Lf	For tear resistance; roofing paper.	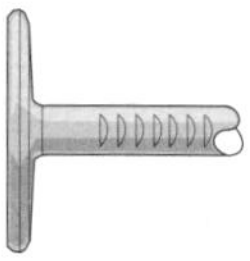
	Oval	O	For special effects; cladding and decking.	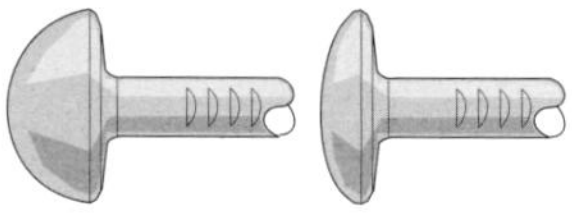
Shanks	Smooth	C	For normal holding power; temporary fastening. 	
	Spiral or Helical	S	For greater holding power; permanent fastening. 	
	Ringed	R	For highest holding power; permanent fastening. 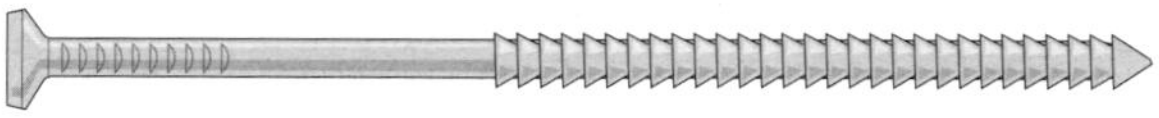	
Points	Diamond	D	For general use, 35° angle; length about 1.5 × diameter.	
	Blunt Diamond	Bt	For harder wood species to reduce splitting, 45° angle.	
	Long Diamond	N	For fast driving, 25° angle; may tend to split harder species.	
	Duckbill	Db	For ease of clinching.	
	Conical	Con	For use in masonry; penetrates better than diamond.	

Uncoated steel nails, used in exterior applications such as siding, react with extractives in the wood. For example, uncoated steel nails will cause black stains on western red cedar siding. In such cases, it is best to use nails made of non-corrosive material, or finished with non-corrosive material such as galvanized zinc. Copper nails, or blued or electrogalvanized steel wire nails, should not be used with cedars.

APPLICATIONS

Nails are used extensively in all types of wood construction. Because they are so commonplace, they are sometimes overlooked as structural fastenings – particularly in structures designed to meet the Part 4 requirements of the *National Building Code of Canada*. In fact, research and practice has shown that nails are a viable connection for wood structures with light to moderate loads. They are particularly useful in locations where a ductile connection is required such as may occur under seismic loads. Typical structural applications for nailed connections include:

- wood frame construction
- post and beam construction
- heavy timber construction
- shearwalls and diaphragms
- nailed gussets for wood truss construction
- wood panel assemblies

LATERAL RESISTANCE

The modes of failure for a nailed joint have been described and quantified by Johansen and subsequently modified by Larsen (1977). The theory, similar to that for bolts, estimates the ultimate strength of a joint based on the yielding moment of the nail and the embedding strength of the wood. In order to find the resistance of a connection, all failure modes are examined and the weakest one is assumed to govern the design. For a two-member connection, four different failure modes are identified:

- wood crushing in both members before the nail yields (stiff nail, thin members)
- wood failure in only the thinner member
- a combination of wood failure in both members with nail yielding in the thicker member
- a failure that is governed by nail yielding and wood failures in both members

For nails or spikes installed in the side grain, resistance of the connection is assumed to be the same whether loaded parallel or perpendicular to the grain. When nails are installed in the end grain, only 67% of the side grain resistance is obtained, J_E. Toe-nails are partially resisted in the end grain of the wood. Therefore, they have only 83% of the lateral resistance of a connection installed in the side grain, J_A.

There are two other factors specific to nail and spike connections: J_B for nail clinching and J_D for diaphragm construction. In a two member wood connection, lateral resistance may be increased by 60% if the nail is clinched on the far side (Crandall, 1959). The factor for nail clinching does not apply to three member connections since it is already covered by the n_s factor.

The tabular values in CSA O86 are near minimum resistance values. In diaphragm construction, many nails are used and the effects of variability of ultimate resistance are reduced. Therefore the resistance of nails used in diaphragms may be increased by 30%.

Factored lateral strength resistance is calculated as

$$N_r = \phi N_u n_F n_s J_F$$

where

ϕ = 0.8

N_u = $n_u(K_D K_{SF} K_T)$

n_u = unit lateral strength resistance per nail or spike, N

K_D = load duration factor

K_{SF} = service condition factor

K_T = fire retardant treatment factor

n_F = number of fasteners in the connection

n_s = number of shear planes per nail or spike

J_F = $J_E J_A J_B J_D$

J_E = factor for nailing into end grain

J_A = factor for toe nailing

J_B = factor for nail clinching

J_D = factor for diaphragm construction

Unit Lateral Strength Resistance

The unit lateral yielding resistance, n_u (per shear plane), shall be taken as the smallest value calculated in accordance with items (a) to (g) as follows:

For two-member connections, only Items (a), (b) and (d) to (g) are considered valid.

For three-member connections, where nails penetrate all three members and meet the minimum penetration requirements, only Items (a), (c), (d) and (g) are considered valid.

(a) $f_1 d_F t_1$

(b) $f_2 d_F t_2$

(c) $\dfrac{1}{2} f_2 d_F t_2$

(d) $f_1 d_F{}^2 \left(\sqrt{\dfrac{1}{6} \dfrac{f_3}{(f_1 + f_3)} \dfrac{f_y}{f_1}} + \dfrac{1}{5} \dfrac{t_1}{d_F} \right)$

(e) $f_1 d_F{}^2 \left(\sqrt{\dfrac{1}{6} \dfrac{f_3}{(f_1 + f_3)} \dfrac{f_y}{f_1}} + \dfrac{1}{5} \dfrac{t_2}{d_F} \right)$

(f) $f_1 d_F{}^2 \dfrac{1}{5} \left(\dfrac{t_1}{d_f} + \dfrac{f_2}{f_1} \dfrac{t_2}{d_F} \right)$

(g) $f_1 d_F{}^2 \sqrt{\dfrac{2}{3} \dfrac{f_3}{(f_1 + f_3)} \dfrac{f_y}{f_1}}$

where

t_1 = head side member thickness for two member connections, mm

= minimum side plate thickness for three member connections, mm

d_F = nail or spike diameter, mm

f_1 = embedding strength of head side member, MPa

= $50G(1 - 0.01d_F)$

f_2 = embedding strength of main member, MPa

= $50G(1 - 0.01d_F)$

G = mean relative density

t_2 = length of penetration into point side member for two member connections, mm

= centre member thickness for three member connections, mm

f_3 = embedding strength of main member where failure is fastener yielding, MPa

= $110G^{1.8}(1 - 0.01d_F)$

f_y = nail or spike yield strength, MPa

= $50(16 - d_F)$

For lumber side plates:

f_1 = embedding strength, MPa

= $50G(1 - 0.01d_F)$

For structural panel side plates:

f_1 = embedding strength, MPa

= $104G(1 - 0.1d_F)$

where

G = 0.49 for DFP

= 0.42 for CSP and OSB

For steel side plates:

f_1 = embedding strength of steel side plate, MPa

= $K_{sp} (\phi_{steel}/\phi_{wood}) f_u$

where

K_{sp}= 3.0 for mild steel meeting the requirements of

CSA G40.21 or ASTM A 36/A 36M

= 2.7 for light gauge steel

ϕ_{steel} = resistance factor for steel member in nail connection

= 0.67 for mild steel meeting the requirements of

CSA G40.21 or ASTM A 36/A 36M

= 0.4 for light gauge steel

ϕ_{wood} = resistance factor for wood member in nail connection

= 0.8

f_u = ultimate tensile strength of steel

= 400 MPa for ASTM A 36/A 36M

= 450 MPa for CSA G40.21, Grades 300W and 350W

= 310 MPa for light gauge steel, Grade SQ230 and higher

Serviceability requirements for nails and spikes have not been included in the body of CSA O86. Instead, a formulation for estimating the deflection of a nailed connection has been included in Appendix CSA O86 A10.9.3.2. This permits designers to estimate the in-service deformation of nailed joints. The formula is limited to specified loads up to 1/3 of the ultimate. Designers are advised to use this in cases where stiffness must be estimated for analysis, or where stiffness should be controlled.

WITHDRAWAL RESISTANCE

The driving of a nail jams bent or broken wood fibres between the nail and other fibres. Other fibres are forced aside as the nail enters the wood, exerting a squeezing action on the nail. It used to be commonly accepted that most of the withdrawal resistance of a nail was due to the jamming and wedging action of bent or broken fibres. Research now indicates that nail holding characteristics are totally dependent on the squeezing effect of displaced fibres. Frictional withdrawal resistance depends on the bearing of these fibres on the nail surface.

Research has shown that the withdrawal resistance of a nail is a function of the length of penetration into the main member, the diameter of the nail and the specific gravity of the wood. With time, the displaced fibres around a driven nail relax and the withdrawal resistance is greatly reduced. This effect is more pronounced for nail connections subject to long term loads and changing moisture conditions. Therefore, withdrawal loading for nails is only permitted for short duration loads (wind and earthquake).

Nails driven into the end grain cannot be considered to resist any loads in withdrawal. Toe-nails are partially resisted in the end grain of the wood. Therefore, they have only 67% of the withdrawal resistance of a connection installed in the side grain.

When nails are clinched, withdrawal resistance will be increased because of the bearing of the clinched portion on the member. A 60% increase in the withdrawal resistance is allowed for clinched nails.

Factored lateral withdrawal resistance is calculated as

$$P_{rw} = \phi\, Y_w\, L_p\, n_F\, J_A\, J_B$$

where

ϕ = 0.6

Y_w = $y_w\, (K_{SF}\, K_T)$

y_w = withdrawal resistance per mm of penetration, N/mm

= $(16.4)(d_F)^{0.82}(G)^{2.2}$

Note: y_w values for sawn lumber are given in CSA O86 Table 10.9.5.2

d_F = nail or spike diameter, mm

G = mean relative density (CSA O86 Table A10.1)

K_{SF} = service condition factor

K_T = fire-retardant treatment factor

L_p = penetration length in main member, mm

n_F = number of nails or spikes

J_A = factor for toe nailing

J_B = factor for nail clinching

JOINT CONFIGURATION

Placement of nails or spikes is important since it can affect load carrying capacity. Factors which must be considered in the geometry of a nailed joint are:

- the thickness of the members to be joined
- the diameter of the nail or spike
- the distance between the nail and the edge of the wood member measured perpendicular to the grain
- the distance between the nail and the end of the wood member measured parallel to the grain
- the centre to centre spacing of nails measured parallel to the grain
- the centre to centre spacing of nails measured perpendicular to the grain

Wood Design Manual Figure 7.4 gives the minimum spacing, end, and edge distances for nails and spikes. The spacing requirements have been established based on the work by Ramos (1960) and, Lau and Tardiff (1987). These minimum requirements have been established to reduce strength reductions as a result of splitting of the wood.

Some species of wood are more prone to splitting and therefore, spacing requirements for them are more stringent.

Very dry wood has a greater tendency to split when nails are driven into it. Therefore, these spacing requirements for nails and spikes are limited to wood which is greater than 10% moisture content when nailed. When nailed connections are used in very dry wood the holes should be pre-drilled to prevent splitting.

For single shear connections, the thickness of the head side member must be 3 nail diameters (d_F) or greater and the penetration into the point side member must be $5d_F$ or greater.

For double shear connections, the thickness of the head side member must be $3d_F$ or greater; the thickness of the centre member must be $8d_F$ or greater and penetration into the point side member must be $5d_F$ or greater.

Minimum thickness of steel side plates is 0.9 mm.

EXAMPLE 11.11: NAILS

The roof over a garage of a residence is to be constructed using tied rafters at 600 mm on centre (Figure 11.28). The effects of dead and snow loads produce a total factored tensile force of 2500 N in the two 38 × 235 mm members which act as a tie in addition to providing support for the garage ceiling and the attic floor. The two 38 × 235 mm members and the

FIGURE 11.28

Rafter-joist assembly

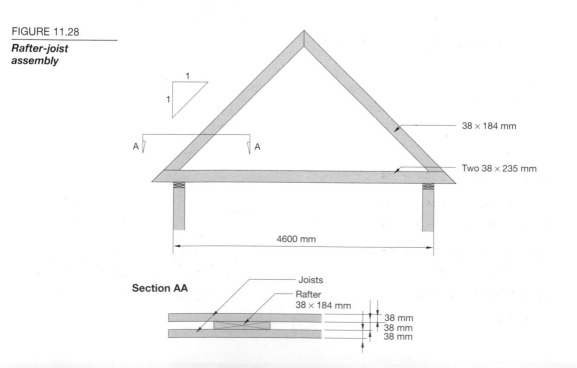

Section AA

38 × 184 mm sloping rafters are untreated and belong to the Spruce-Pine-Fir group. They will be seasoned and the service conditions will be dry.

Design the heel joint between the 38 × 184 mm and two 38 × 235 mm members using nails.

Heel Connection

Try 3in (76 mm) long common round wire nails

diameter = 3.66 mm

Required penetration in the head side member is $3d_F$.

$3 \times 3.66 = 11$ mm < 38 mm

Required penetration in the point side member is $5d_F$.

$5 \times 3.66 = 18$ mm < 38 mm

Design for lateral strength resistance

Factored tensile force, N_f

$N_f = 2500$ N

Factored resistance, N_r

$N_r = \phi N_u n_F n_s J_F$

where

$\phi = 0.8$

$N_u = n_u(K_D K_{SF} K_T)$

n_u = unit lateral strength resistance per nail or spike, N

n_F = number of fasteners in the connection

$n_s = 1$ (nails are in single shear)

$J_F = J_E J_A J_B J_D$

$J_E = 1.0$ (nails are driven into side grain)

$J_A = 1.0$ (nails are not toe nailed)

$J_B = 1.0$ (nails are not clinched)

$J_D = 1.0$ (not used in diaphragm construction)

$J_F = 1.0 \times 1.0 \times 1.0 \times 1.0$

$= 1.0$

Unit Lateral Strength Resistance

The penetration depth of the nail is 76 mm (3 inch), therefore this is a two member wood to wood connection.

For two-member connections, only Items (a), (b) and (d) to (g) of the yield equations are considered valid.

where

$t_1 = 38$ mm

$d_F = 3.66$ mm

$f_2 = 50G(1 - 0.01d_F)$

$= 50 \times 0.42 \times (1 - 0.01 \times 3.66)$

$= 20$ MPa

$G = 0.42$ (CSA O86, Table A. 10.1)

$t_2 = 38$ mm

$f_3 = 110G^{1.8}(1 - 0.01d_F)$

$= 110 \times 0.42^{1.8} \times (1 - 0.01 \times 3.66)$

$= 22$ MPa

$f_y = 50(16 - d_F)$

$= 50 \times (16 - 3.66)$

$= 617$ MPa

For lumber side plates:

$f_1 = 50G(1 - 0.01d_F)$

$= 20$ MPa

(a) $f_1 d_F t_1$

$= 20 \times 3.66 \times 38$

$= 2814$ N

(b) $f_2 d_F t_2$

$= 20 \times 3.66 \times 38$

$= 2714$ N

(d) $f_1 d_F^2 \left(\sqrt{\dfrac{1}{6} \dfrac{f_3}{(f_1 + f_3)} \dfrac{f_y}{f_1}} + \dfrac{1}{5} \dfrac{t_1}{d_F} \right)$

$= 20 \times 3.66^2 \times$

$\left(\sqrt{\dfrac{1}{6} \times \dfrac{22}{(20 + 22)} \times \dfrac{617}{20}} + \dfrac{1}{5} \times \dfrac{38}{3.66} \right)$

$= 996$ N

(e) $f_1 d_F^2 \left(\sqrt{\dfrac{1}{6} \dfrac{f_3}{(f_1 + f_3)} \dfrac{f_y}{f_1}} + \dfrac{1}{5} \dfrac{t_2}{d_F} \right)$

$\quad = 20 \times 3.66^2 \times$

$\left(\sqrt{\dfrac{1}{6} \times \dfrac{22}{(20 + 22)} \times \dfrac{617}{20}} + \dfrac{1}{5} \times \dfrac{38}{3.66} \right)$

$\quad = 996 \text{ N}$

(f) $f_1 d_F^2 \dfrac{1}{5} \left(\dfrac{t_1}{d_F} + \dfrac{f_2}{f_1} \dfrac{t_2}{d_F} \right)$

$\quad = \dfrac{1}{5} \times 20 \times 3.66^2 \times$

$\quad \left(\dfrac{38}{3.66} + \dfrac{20}{20} \times \dfrac{38}{3.66} \right)$

$\quad = 1113 \text{ N}$

(g) $f_1 d_F^2 \sqrt{\dfrac{2}{3} \dfrac{f_3}{(f_1 + f_3)} \dfrac{f_y}{f_1}}$

$\quad = 20 \times 3.66^2 \times$

$\quad \sqrt{\dfrac{2}{3} \times \dfrac{22}{(20 + 22)} \times \dfrac{617}{20}}$

$\quad = 879 \text{ N} \qquad \qquad (Governs)$

Therefore, based on the above unit yield equations, $n_u = 879$ N.

$N_u = n_u (K_D K_{SF} K_T)$

$\quad = 879 \times (1.0 \times 1.0 \times 1.0)$

$\quad = 879 \text{ N}$

$N_r = \phi N_u n_f n_s J_F$

$\quad = 0.8 \times 879 \times n_F \times 1\ 1.0$

$\quad = 703\ n_F \text{ (N)}$

$N_r \quad \geq N_f$

$703 n_F \geq 2500 \text{ N}$

$n_F \quad \geq 3.6$

Use four 3 inch nails.

Joint Configuration

Spacing parallel to grain

$\quad 16\ d_F = 16\ (3.66)$

$\quad \quad \quad = 59 \text{ mm}$

Spacing perpendicular to grain

$\quad 8\ d_F = 30 \text{ mm}$

*Loaded and unloaded end distance

$\quad 15\ d_F = 55 \text{ mm}$

Edge distance

$\quad 4\ d_F = 15 \text{ mm}$

*Although CSA O86 allows shorter end distances in some cases, it is recommended where possible to use end distances of $15 d_F$ or more, to prevent splitting.

Therefore, use two 3 inch nails from each side (Figure 11.29).

FIGURE 11.29

Heel connection

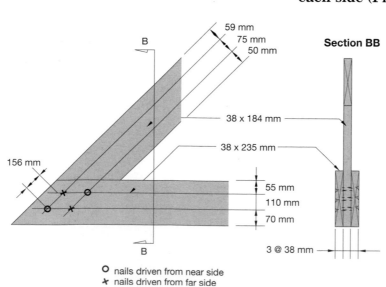

156 mm

59 mm
75 mm
50 mm

Section BB

38 x 184 mm

38 x 235 mm

55 mm
110 mm
70 mm

3 @ 38 mm

O nails driven from near side
✗ nails driven from far side

11.10   Joist Hangers

Joist hangers are produced by a number of manufacturers, each having their own proprietary designs. They are generally fabricated from 20, 18 or 16 gauge galvanized steel. Most joist hangers are the face-mount type, but top-mount hangers are available for heavier loads. Special hangers for wood I-joists and structural composite lumber are also readily available.

INSTALLATION

Joist hangers are to be installed in accordance with the manufacturer's installation requirements. Where specifying a joist hanger, designers must ensure that the following conditions are satisfied:

- The hanger is at least half the depth of the joist and is capable of providing lateral support for the joist. If lateral support is not provided by the joist hanger, twisting must be prevented by some other means.

- The hanger is fastened to both the header and joist and nails or bolts used in the header and joist are sized and installed in accordance with the manufacturer's literature.

- Hangers used to support prefabricated wood I-joists are deep enough to provide lateral stability to the top flange of the joist. If the joist hanger does not provide lateral support, bearing stiffeners may be required.

- Backer blocks are provided between the web and face mount hangers where prefabricated I-joists are used as the header.

- Where a wood I-joist is supporting a top mount hanger, filler blocks are used between the top and bottom flange of the I-joist. The blocks are to be tight to the bottom of the top flange.

RESISTANCE

Since joist hangers are proprietary, CSA O86 provides a method for determining design values but does not provide the design values. Instead it requires that joist hangers be tested in accordance with ASTM Standard D 1761 *Standard Test Methods for Mechanical Fasteners in Wood*. Test results are listed in the *Manual of Evaluation Reports* published by the Canadian Construction Materials Centre (CCMC), Institute for Research in Construction, Ottawa, Ontario. The evaluation report also includes resistance values derived from the test results.

Design values for joist hangers are published by the manufacturer. CSA O86 gives design procedures and formulae for joist hangers and requires the effect of the factored loads to be less than or equal to the factored resistance of the hanger.

The factored resistance of joist hangers is calculated from the following formula:

$$N_r = \phi \, N_u$$

where

ϕ = 0.6

$N_u = n_u \, (K_D \, K_{SF} \, K_T)$

n_u = ultimate resistance of the hanger. The value of n_u is taken from the CCMC evaluation report.

11.11   Wood Screws

Wood screws are manufactured in many different lengths, diameters and styles. Screws are usually specified by gauge number, length, head style, material and finish. Design provisions in CSA O86 are limited to 6, 8, 10 and 12 gauge screws and are applicable only for wood screws that meet the requirements of ASME B18.6.1 *Wood Screws*. For wood screw diameters greater than gauge 12, design should be in accordance with lag screw requirements. Screw lengths between 1 inch and 2 ¾ inch lengths are manufactured in ¼ inch intervals, whereas screws 3 inches and longer, are manufactured in ½ inch intervals. Designers should check with suppliers to determine availability. Table 11.10 shows the wood screw gauges and diameters that are considered under CSA O86, along with their respective minimum yield strengths.

Wood screws are used in general construction. Screws have better withdrawal resistance than nails. The length of the threaded portion of the screw is approximately two-thirds of the screw length. Where the wood relative density is equal to or greater than 0.5, lead holes, at least the length of the threaded portion of the shank, are required as per Table 10.11.2.1 of CSA O86. In order to reduce the occurrence of splitting, pre-drilled holes are recommended for all screw connections.

LATERAL RESISTANCE

The lateral resistance of wood screws is based on the same European Yield Model equation design approach used for bolts, lag screws and nails. This theory estimates the ultimate lateral resistance of a joint based on the yielding moment of the screw and the embedment strength of the wood. All failure modes are examined and the weakest one is assumed to govern the design. Failure of the screw connection is defined by the wood crushing, the screw yielding or a combination of both crushing and yielding. The embedment strength is higher where the failure mode involves fastener yielding (f_3), compared to where the failure mode is limited to wood crushing (f_2).

For wood screws installed in the side grain, resistance of the connection is assumed to be the same whether loaded parallel or perpendicular to the grain. When screws are installed in the end grain, only 67% of the side grain resistance is obtained. Toe-screws are partially resisted in the end grain of the wood. Toe-screwing must be started at approximately one-third the screw length from the end of the piece and at an angle of about 30° to the grain. Toe-screws have only 83% of the lateral resistance of a connection installed in the side grain.

For two- or three-member joints, the factored lateral strength resistance, N_r, of a wood screw connection is based on the same yield equation used for nail design. Yield strength values for wood screws are provided in Table 11.10

N_r = $\phi N_u n_s n_f J_A J_E$

ϕ = 0.8

N_u = $n_u(K_D K_{SF} K_T)$

n_u = unit lateral strength resistance, N

K_D = load duration factor

K_{SF} = service condition factor

K_T = fire retardant treatment factor

n_s = number of shear planes per screw

n_f = number of fasteners in the connection

J_A = toe screwing factor

J_E = factor for fastening into end grain

WITHDRAWAL RESISTANCE

Withdrawal resistance design for wood screws, applies only to short-term wind or earthquake loading, similar to nails. The withdrawal resistance is higher for wood screws than nails, reflecting the superior holding capacity of wood screws loaded in withdrawal.

Wood screw design also includes a requirement to check the head pull-through failure mode. This can occur when the force on the screw head exceeds the resistance of the steel, structural wood panel or lumber side plate. The comparatively low resistance factors for withdrawal ($\phi = 0.6$) and head pull-through ($\phi = 0.4$) resistance of wood screws reflects the high variance of these failure modes.

The factored withdrawal resistance shall be equal to the lesser of the factored screw withdrawal resistance of the main member or the factored head pull-through resistance of the side member.

For a two-member joint connected with wood screws, the factored withdrawal resistance, P_{rw}, of the main member shall be taken as follows:

$$P_{rw} = \phi Y_w L_{pt} n_F$$

where

ϕ = 0.6

Y_w = $y_w(K_T K_{SF})$

y_w = basic withdrawal resistance per millimetre of the threaded shank penetration in main member, N/mm

= $68 d_F^{0.82} G^{1.77}$

K_{SF} = service condition factor

K_T = fire retardant treatment factor

d_F = nominal wood screw diameter, mm

G = mean relative density of main member

L_{pt} = threaded length penetration in the main member, mm

n_F = number of wood screws in the connection

For a connection with three members, the threaded length penetration shall be the maximum threaded length within any member other than the head-side member.

For connections with light gauge steel side plates, the factored head pull-through resistance, P_{pt}, shall be taken as follows:

$$P_{pt} = 1.5 \phi t_1 d_w f_u n_F$$

For connections with lumber or structural panel side plates, the factored head pull-through resistance shall be taken as follows:

$$P_{pt} = 75 \phi t_1 n_F$$

where

ϕ = 0.4

t_1 = side plate thickness, mm

d_w = diameter of screw head, mm

f_u = ultimate tensile strength of steel, MPa

= 400 MPa for ASTM A 36/A 36M steel

= 450 MPa for CSA G40.21 steel, Grade 300W

= 310 MPa for light gauge steel, Grades SQ230 and higher

n_F = number of wood screws in the connection

Connection Configuration

The joint configurations of screwed connections, including spacing, edge and end distances, are identical to the requirements for nails and spikes and are shown in the *Wood Design Manual* as Figure 7.4. Screw penetration lengths, locations, and member thickness provisions for wood-to-wood and steel-to-wood connections are also identical to nail and spike requirements

EXAMPLE 11.12: WOOD SCREWS

Determine the size and number of screws required for the OSB tension splice shown below (dimensions in mm). The lumber members and kiln dried, untreated 38 x 140 mm S-P-F and the OSB is 11 mm construction sheathing OSB. The factored load is 8 kN due to dead load plus snow loads. Service conditions are dry.

Try 6 gauge, 2" long screws, driven from alternate sides of the main member.

diameter = 3.50 mm

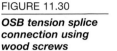

FIGURE 11.30

OSB tension splice connection using wood screws

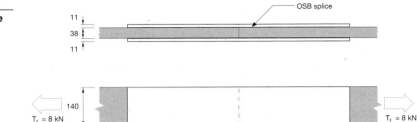

Lateral Strength Resistance

Factored tensile force, T_f

$\quad T_f \quad = \quad 8 \text{ kN}$

Factored lateral resistance, N_r

$\quad N_r \quad = \quad \phi N_u n_s n_f J_A J_E$

where

$\quad \phi \quad = \quad 0.8$

$\quad N_u \quad = \quad n_u(1.0 \times 1.0 \times 1.0)$

$\quad n_u \quad = \quad$ unit lateral strength resistance, N

$\quad n_s \quad = \quad 1$

$\quad n_f \quad = \quad$ number of fasteners

$\quad J_A \quad = \quad 1.0$ (not toe screwed)

$\quad J_E \quad = \quad 1.0$ (nailed in side grain)

Determine the unit lateral yielding resistance, n_u, for each shear plane of each bolt.

for two-member connections, only items (a), (b) and (d) to (g) of the yield equations are considered valid.

$\quad d_F \quad = \quad 3.50 \text{ mm}$

$\quad f_1 \quad = \quad 104G(1 - 0.1d_F)$

where

$\quad G \quad = \quad 0.42$

$\quad f_1 \quad = \quad 104 \times 0.42 \times (1 - 0.1 \times 3.50)$

$\quad\quad = \quad 28 \text{ MPa}$

$\quad f_2 \quad = \quad 50G (1 - 0.01d_F)$

$\quad G \quad = \quad 0.42$ (CSA 086, Table A. 10.1)

$\quad f_2 \quad = \quad 50 \times 0.42 \times (1 - 0.01 \times 3.50)$

$\quad\quad = \quad 20 \text{ MPa}$

$f_3 \quad = \quad 110G^{1.8}(1 - 0.01d_F)$

$G \quad = \quad 0.42$ (CSA 086, Table A. 10.1)

$f_3 \quad = \quad 110 \times 0.42^{1.8} \times (1 - 0.01 \times 3.50)$

$\quad = \quad 22 \text{ MPa}$

$f_y \quad = \quad 690 \text{ MPa}$ (CSA 086, Table 10.11.1)

$t_1 \quad = \quad 11 \text{ mm}$

$t_2 \quad = \quad 38 \text{ mm}$

a) $f_1 d_F t_1$

$\quad = \quad 28 \times 3.50 \times 11$

$\quad = \quad 1078 \text{ N}$

b) $f_2 d_F t_2$

$\quad = \quad 20 \times 3.50 \times 38$

$\quad = \quad 2660 \text{ N}$

d) $f_1 d_F{}^2 \left(\sqrt{\dfrac{1}{6} \dfrac{f_3}{(f_1 + f_3)} \dfrac{f_y}{f_1}} + \dfrac{1}{5} \dfrac{t_1}{d_F} \right)$

$\quad = \quad 28 \times 3.50^2 \times$

$\left(\sqrt{\dfrac{1}{6} \times \dfrac{22}{(28 + 22)} \times \dfrac{690}{28}} + \dfrac{1}{5} \times \dfrac{11}{3.50} \right)$

$\quad = \quad 677 \text{ N} \quad\quad\quad\quad$ *(Governs)*

e) $f_1 d_F{}^2 \left(\sqrt{\dfrac{1}{6} \dfrac{f_3}{(f_1 + f_3)} \dfrac{f_y}{f_1}} + \dfrac{1}{5} \dfrac{t_2}{d_F} \right)$

$\quad = \quad 28 \times 3.50^2 \times$

$\left(\sqrt{\dfrac{1}{6} \times \dfrac{22}{(28 + 22)} \times \dfrac{690}{28}} + \dfrac{1}{5} \times \dfrac{38}{3.50} \right)$

$\quad = \quad 1206 \text{ N}$

f) $\dfrac{1}{5} f_1 d_F{}^2 \left(\dfrac{t_1}{d_F} + \dfrac{f_2}{f_1} \dfrac{t_2}{d_F} \right)$

$\quad = \quad \dfrac{1}{5} \times 28 \times 3.50^2 \times \left(\dfrac{11}{3.50} + \dfrac{20}{28} \times \dfrac{38}{3.50} \right)$

$\quad = \quad 748 \text{ N}$

g) $f_1 d_F^2 \sqrt{\dfrac{2}{3} \dfrac{f_3}{(f_1 + f_3)} \dfrac{f_y}{f_1}}$

$= 28 \times 3.50^2 \times \sqrt{\dfrac{2}{3} \times \dfrac{22}{(28 + 22)} \times \dfrac{690}{28}}$

$= 922$ N

Therefore, based on the above unit lateral yield equations, $n_u = 677$ N.

$N_u = n_u (K_D K_{SF} K_T)$

$\quad = 677 \times (1.0 \times 1.0 \times 1.0)$

$\quad = 677$ N

$N_r = \phi N_u n_s n_f J_A J_E$

$\quad = 0.8 \times 677 \times 1.0 \times n_F \times 1.0 \times 1.0$

$\quad = 542 \, n_F$ (N)

$N_r \geq T_f$

$542 \, n_F \geq 8000$ N

$n_F \geq 14.8$

For symmetry, use sixteen 6 gauge, 2 inch screws.

Joint Configuration

Determine the minimum spacing requirements as per Figure 10.9.2.1 from CSA O86:

   Minimum spacing perpendicular to grain c = 28 mm

   Minimum edge distance d = 14 mm

Therefore, use three rows of screws, spaced vertically at 35 mm.

   Minimum spacing parallel to grain a = 56 mm

   Minimum end distance b = 42 mm

The final connection geometry is shown below as Figure 11.31 (dimensions in mm).

Note that the tensile strength of OSB and lumber members should also be checked.

FIGURE 11.31

OSB tension splice joint configuration

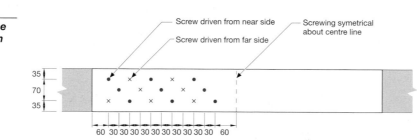

11.12 Tables

TABLE 11.1

Washer dimensions and mass

Type of washer	Rod or bolt diam mm	Hole diam mm	Outside dimension mm	Bearing area mm²	Thickness mm	Mass per 100 pieces kg	Pieces per 100 kg
Malleable iron	12	16	64	2970	6	7.71	1300
	16	20	70	3350	8	10.4	960
	20	22	76	4000	11	14.1	720
	22	26	89	5680	11	16.8	600
	24	29	102	7480	13	28.1	360
Cut	12	14	35	840	3	1.75	5700
	16	18	45	1290	4	3.49	2900
	20	21	51	1680	4	4.54	2200
	22	24	57	2130	4	6.49	1550
	24	29	64	2520	4	7.94	1260
Round plate[1]	12	14	64	2970	5	10.9	920
	20	21	76	4190	6	20.4	500
	22	24	83	4900	8	30.4	320
Square plate	12	14	64	3870	5	14.1	720
	16	18	70	4650	6	22.7	450
	20	21	76	5480	6	26.8	380
	22	24	83	6390	8	39.5	255
	24	29	89	7290	10	53.5	190
Ogee[2]	12	14	64	2970	13	15.9	630
	16	18	76	3550	16	29.0	345
	20	22	89	3810	19	48.5	206
	22	24	102	6580	22	66.7	150
	24	30	102	7480	25	84.8	118

Notes:

1. For use with timber connectors. These washers are larger than cut washers and are necessary for drawing up a number of connectors on a single bolt without cupping and damage of the washer. They are often preferred to square plate washers for more pleasing appearance.

2. These washers, because of their thickness, resist cupping better than malleable iron washers.

TABLE 11.2

Area removed for shear plate and split ring joints (mm² × 10³)

Connector	Size in.	Bolt size in.	Number of faces with connector	Member thickness mm 38	64	80	89	130	140	175	191	215	241
Split rings	2-1/2	1/2	1	1.11	1.48	1.71	1.84	2.43	2.57	3.07	3.30	3.64	4.02
			2	1.68	2.05	2.28	2.41	3.00	3.14	3.64	3.87	4.21	4.58
	4	3/4	1	1.97	2.51	2.84	3.02	3.87	4.07	4.79	5.12	5.62	6.15
			2	3.16	3.70	4.02	4.21	5.06	5.26	5.98	6.31	6.81	7.34
Shear plates	2-5/8	3/4	1	1.31	1.85	2.18	2.36	3.20	3.41	4.13	4.46	4.96	5.49
			2	1.84	2.37	2.70	2.89	3.73	3.94	4.66	4.99	5.50	6.02
	4	3/4	1	2.12	2.65	2.98	3.17	4.01	4.22	4.94	5.27	5.76	6.30
			2	–	3.99	4.32	4.50	5.34	5.55	6.27	6.60	7.10	7.63
	4	7/8	1	2.19	2.80	3.18	3.40	4.38	4.61	5.45	5.83	6.40	7.02
			2	–	4.09	4.47	4.68	5.66	5.89	6.73	7.11	7.68	8.30

TABLE 11.3

Machine bolt and nut dimensions

Bolt diameter in.	Hex bolts height		Width across	
	Head mm	Nut mm	Flats mm	Corner mm
1/2	8	12	19	22
5/8	10	14	24	28
3/4	12	17	29	33
7/8	14	19	34	39
1	16	22	38	44
1-1/8	18	25	43	50
1-1/4	20	27	48	55
1-1/2	24	33	58	66
1-3/4	28	38	67	77
2	31	44	77	88

TABLE 11.4

Machine bolts and nuts – threaded length and mass

Finished hex bolts

Minimum thread length (T) and mass (M) per 100, without nuts

ASTM A307 Bolt Diameter (in.)

Bolt length under head in.	1/2		5/8		3/4		7/8		1	
	T mm	M kg	T mm	M kg	T mm	M kg	T mm	M kg	T mm	M kg
4	32	11.5	38	18.2	44	27.2	51	38.4	57	51.3
4-1/2	32	12.8	38	20.2	44	30.0	51	42.3	57	56.4
5	32	14.0	38	22.1	44	32.9	51	46.1	57	61.4
6	32	16.6	38	26.1	44	38.6	51	53.9	57	71.5
6-1/2	38	17.8	44	28.1	51	41.4	57	57.7	63	76.6
7	38	19.1	44	30.0	51	44.2	57	61.6	63	81.6
8	38	21.6	44	34.0	51	49.9	57	69.3	63	91.7
9	38	24.1	44	37.9	51	55.6	57	77.1	63	102
10	38	26.7	44	41.9	51	61.3	57	84.8	63	112
11	38	29.2	44	45.8	51	67.0	57	92.5	63	122
12	38	31.7	44	49.8	51	72.6	57	100	63	132
13	38	34.2	44	53.7	51	78.3	57	108	63	142
14	38	36.8	44	57.7	51	84.0	57	115	63	152
15	38	39.3	44	61.6	51	89.7	57	124	63	162
Hex nuts	–	1.7	–	13.3	–	15.4	–	18.6	–	12.8

TABLE 11.5

Lag screw dimensions

Nominal length of lag screw (L) in.	Item	Dimensions of lag screws (mm), with nominal diameter (in.)				
		1/4	3/8	1/2	5/8	3/4
All lengths	Shank dia.	6.4	10	13	16	19
	Root dia.	4.4	6.7	9.4	11.9	14.7
	Unthread. tip len.	4.8	6.4	7.9	9.5	11.1
	Head height	4.4	6.4	8.3	10.7	12.7
	Head width	9.5	14.3	19.1	23.8	28.6

TABLE 11.6

Lag screw hole dimensions

Length in.	C.B.[1] dia.	Dimensions for lag screw holes, mm				
		6.4	10	13	16	19
All lengths	L.H.[2] dia. D.Fir-L	5	6.7	10	12	15
	L.H. dia. Hem-Fir	3	6	9	10	13
	L.H. dia. S-P-F	3	6	9	10	13
	L.H. dia. Northern	3	6	9	10	13
3	Depth Hole	72	70	68	67	65
	Depth C.B.	26	26	26	26	26
3-1/2	Depth Hole	84	83	81	79	78
	Depth C.B.	32	32	32	32	32
4	Depth Hole	97	95	94	92	90
	Depth C.B.	38	38	38	38	38
4-1/2	Depth Hole		108	107	105	103
	Depth C.B.		45	45	45	45
5	Depth Hole		120	119	117	116
	Depth C.B.		51	51	51	51
6	Depth Hole		146	145	143	141
	Depth C.B.		64	64	64	64
7	Depth Hole		171	170	168	167
	Depth C.B.		77	77	77	77
8	Depth Hole		196	195	194	192
	Depth C.B.		89	89	89	89
9	Depth Hole		222	221	219	217
	Depth C.B.		102	102	102	102
10	Depth Hole		248	246	244	243
	Depth C.B.		114	114	114	114
11	Depth Hole			271	270	268
	Depth C.B.			127	127	127
12	Depth Hole			297	295	294
	Depth C.B.			153	153	153

Notes:

1. C.B. = counterbore

2. L.H. = lead hole

TABLE 11.7

Minimum dimensions for timber rivet connections

Limitation	Description	Dimension mm
S_P	Spacing parallel to grain	25
S_Q	Spacing perpendicular to grain	15
e_s	Edge distance for steel plate	12
a	End distance in wood	varies
e	Edge distance in wood	varies
e_P	Free edge distance in wood	25
e_Q	Loaded edge distance in wood	50

TABLE 11.8

Minimum end distances for glulam rivet joints

Number of rivet rows, n_R	Minimum end distance, a (mm)	
	Load parallel to grain	Load perpendicular to grain
1, 2	75	50
3 to 8	75	75
9, 10	100	80
11, 12	125	100
13, 14	150	120
15, 16	175	140
17 and greater	200	160

TABLE 11.9

Nail materials, finishes and coatings

Type		Abbr.	Remarks
Material	Aluminum	A	For improved appearance and long life; increased stain and corrosion resistance.
	Steel-mild	S	For general construction.
	Steel-high-carbon hardened	Sc	For special driving conditions; improved impact resistance.
	Stainless steel, copper and silicon-bronze	E	For superior corrosion resistance; more expensive than hot-dip galvanizing.
Finish & Coatings	Bright	B	For general construction; normal finish; not recommended for exposure to weather.
	Blued	Bl	For increased holding power in hardwood; thin oxide finish produced by heat treatment.
	Heat treated	Ht	For increased stiffness and holding power; black oxide finish.
	Phoscoated	Pt	For increased holding power; not corrosion resistant.
	Electrogalvanized	Ge	For limited corrosion resistance; thin zinc plating; smooth surface; for interior use.
	Hot-dip galvanized	Ghd	For improved corrosion resistance; thick zinc coating; rough surface; for exterior use.

TABLE 11.10

Diameter and minimum yield strength of wood screws

	Gauge number			
	6	8	10	12
Diameter, mm*	3.50	4.16	4.82	5.48
Minimum yield strength, MPa†	690	620	550	550

* For wood screw diameters greater than gauge 12, design in accordance with lag screw requirements.
† Linear interpolation for yield strength may be used.

Lateral Load Resisting Systems

12.1 General Information

Buildings are subjected to lateral loading due to earthquakes and wind forces, which cause the structure to sway sideways. In order for the building to remain stable, it must have a vertical bracing system that is capable of transferring the horizontal loading to the foundation (see Figure 12.1).

Following are some common vertical bracing systems used in wood buildings (see Figure 12.2):

- Rigid frames such as glulam arches are designed to carry the gravity loading as well as the lateral loads. The lateral forces cause bending in the legs of the frames.

- Knee-bracing between the columns and the roof framing is a common method of bracing farm buildings. With this system the columns are subjected to bending as well as axial loading.

- Pole-framed buildings with columns embedded in concrete piers are often used in farm buildings in combination with knee-bracing. The columns act as cantilevered bending members to resist the lateral loads.

- Cross-braces between columns act in tension and compression to transfer the lateral loads to the foundation.

- Shearwalls act as vertical cantilever beams to resist lateral loading. This is a widely used bracing system in woodframe buildings.

FIGURE 12.1

Function of vertical bracing system

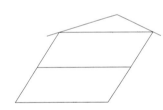
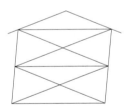

Wind forces on a building.

Without vertical bracing, the building will sway excessively and become unstable.

With vertical bracing, the building sway will be minimized and wind forces are transferred to the foundation.

FIGURE 12.2

Vertical bracing systems

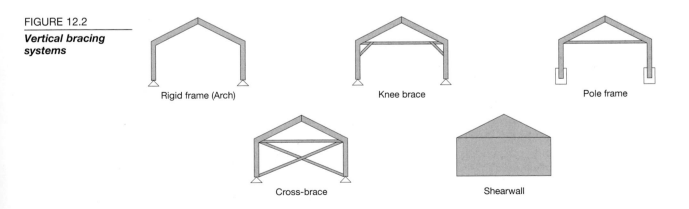

Rigid frame (Arch) Knee brace Pole frame

Cross-brace Shearwall

Rigid frame, pole frame, and knee braced buildings typically have horizontal wall framing to transfer the lateral loads to the bracing frames.

Cross-bracing frames and shearwalls may only be located at the exterior walls of the building. In larger buildings, interior walls may also be designed to resist lateral loads. A horizontal bracing system must be provided to transfer the lateral loads to the vertical bracing locations. This is usually achieved in one of two ways (Figure 12.3):

- Horizontal cross-bracing acts as a truss to transfer the lateral loads to the vertical cross bracing.

- Horizontal roof and floor diaphragms are detailed to act as a deep beams to carry lateral loads to the shearwalls.

The choice of the bracing system has an impact on the magnitude of earthquake forces that are used in the building design. As described in Chapter 3, the NBCC prescribes a base shear force that is calculated using a Ductility Related Force Modification Factor, R_d and an Overstrength Related Force Modification Factor, R_o. R_d reflects the capability of a lateral resisting system to dissipate energy through inelastic behaviour and R_o accounts for the dependable portion of reserve strength in a structure. Base shear is a function of $1/(R_d R_o)$ so systems with higher R_d and R_o values will have a lower base shear.

For wood structures designed and detailed according to CSA O86, R_d ranges from 1.0 to 3.0 and R_o ranges from 1.0 to 1.7. The highest values – $R_d = 3.0$ and $R_o = 1.7$ – are assigned to nailed shearwalls using wood based panels. As a result, wood-based shearwalls are a very efficient system where the design of the bracing is governed by earthquake forces.

Shearwalls and diaphragms are a very common and practical bracing solution for wood buildings. Typically the sheathing that is specified for the gravity loading can also act as the bracing system once additional connection details are provided. This means that the sheathing serves a number of purposes including distributing loads to the framing, bracing beams and studs from buckling out of plane, and providing the overall bracing for the building.

CSA O86 also provides design information for shearwalls constructed from gypsum wallboard in combination with wood based panels. Where gypsum wallboard is used in combination with wood based panels to resist earthquake loading, R_d is 2.0 and R_o is 1.7.

The remainder of this chapter will focus on the design and detailing of shearwalls and diaphragms.

FIGURE 12.3

Horizontal bracing systems

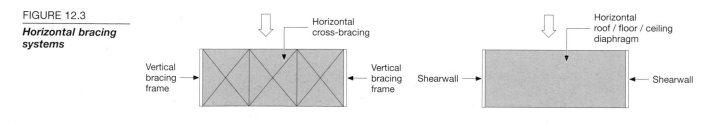

Plan view of building

12.2   Shearwall and Diaphragm Action

A shearwall or diaphragm is a plate-type structural element designed to transmit force in its own plane. Generally the term diaphragm is applied to horizontal elements such as floors and roofs. The term shearwall is applied to vertical elements such as walls.

Diaphragms do not have to be flat. As shown in Figure 12.4, sloped roofs, hip roofs and curved roofs can also be used as diaphragms. Also, the diaphragm sheathing need not be limited to the upper surface of the roof. Ceiling diaphragms are common in industrial and farm buildings where wood panels are placed on the underside of roof trusses allowing a direct tie-in to the exterior walls.

The action of shearwalls and diaphragms in bracing a simple box-like building subjected to wind load is illustrated in Figure 12.5. The sidewalls, laterally supported by the roof diaphragm and the foundation, transfer half of the wind load to the roof level. The roof diaphragm, acting as a horizontal beam, transmits the load to the end shearwalls, which in turn transfer the load to the foundations.

Figure 12.6 illustrates the flow of forces within the shearwall and diaphragm due to the applied lateral loading. The diaphragm is assumed to behave similar to a deep I-beam, where the sheathing acts as a web to carry the shear forces. Chord members at the perimeter of the beam must be provided to carry the axial tension and compression forces that result due to the applied bending

moment (similar to the flanges of an I-beam). The reaction at the ends of the diaphragm must be transferred to the shearwalls below.

The shearwall is assumed to act as a cantilevered beam with the sheathing carrying all of the shear, and chord members at each edge carrying tension and compression. The tension, compression and shear forces at the bottom of the shearwall are transferred to the foundation. Typically, the chords have a hold-down connection to transfer the tension. Anchor bolting of the wall plate transfers the shear to the foundation.

The shear capacity of shearwalls and diaphragms may be limited by the shear capacity of the sheathing or the capacity of the connections between the sheathing and framing. Thicker sheathing used in combination with larger nails will have greater shear capacity than thinner sheathing with smaller nails. Increasing the number of nails and/or the density of the framing material will increase shear resistance due to the greater connection capacity.

Strut members are required to transfer the shear from the diaphragm to the shearwall. Struts that bridge over openings in the attached shearwall are called drag struts and are used to transfer the diaphragm shear to the adjacent wall sections. Drag struts are designed to carry shear plus tension and compression forces.

FIGURE 12.4

Typical shearwalls and diaphragms

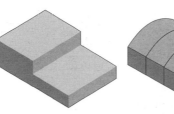

Vertical shearwalls and horizontal diaphragms

Vertical shearwalls and curved diaphragms

Combination sloping shearwall diaphragms

Hip roof diaphragm and shearwalls

FIGURE 12.5

Shearwall and diaphragm action

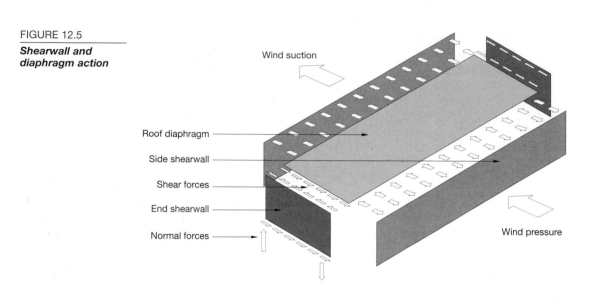

Wind suction

Roof diaphragm

Side shearwall

Shear forces

End shearwall

Normal forces

Wind pressure

FIGURE 12.6

Free body diagram of a shearwall and diaphragm

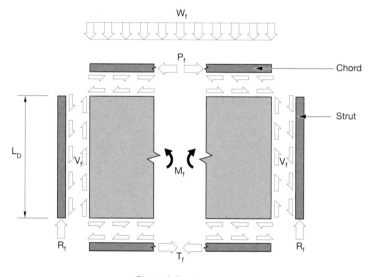

W_f

P_f

Chord

Strut

L_D

V_f M_f V_f

R_f R_f

T_f

Plan of diaphragm

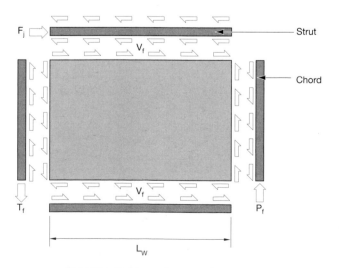

F_j Strut

V_f

Chord

V_f

T_f P_f

L_W

Elevation of shearwall segment

12.3   Analysis Considerations

DISTRIBUTION OF LATERAL LOADS TO THE SHEARWALLS

The previous sections showed a simple bracing system with a single diaphragm connected to shearwalls at the ends only. Often a building has shearwalls at the ends and at intermediate locations. In this case, determining the distribution of load to each shearwall is less straightforward.

Figure 12.7 illustrates the problem as follows:

- In Case 1 the building has an infinitely rigid diaphragm and four non-rigid shearwalls of equal stiffness. The rigid diaphragm causes each shearwall to deform equally, resulting in an equal force being applied to each shearwall.

- In Case 2 the interior shearwalls are constructed the same as the exterior walls, but are more flexible because they

are shorter. The rigid diaphragm again forces each shearwall to deflect equally. Since the deformation of the walls is proportional to the applied load, each wall receives a load based on its relative stiffness. In this case the interior walls are half as stiff and therefore receive half the load of the exterior walls.

- In Case 3 the diaphragm is very flexible and the shearwalls are infinitely rigid. This means that the diaphragm is in effect simply supported between shearwalls. The shearwall will receive load based on its tributary area.

- In Case 4 the diaphragm and shearwalls are both semi-rigid, which is the most realistic situation. In this case the diaphragm behaves like a beam on elastic supports and the solution is statically indeterminate.

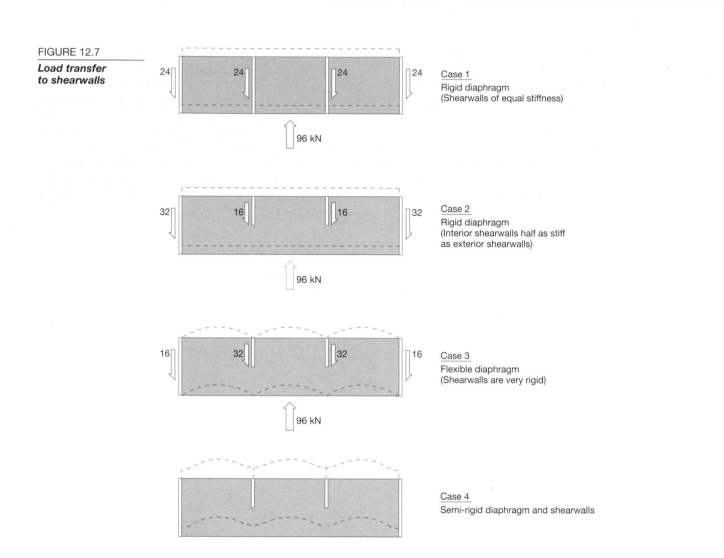

FIGURE 12.7

*Load transfer
to shearwalls*

In practice, most wood buildings can be designed successfully using simplifying but rational assumptions. Typically the assumption is made that the diaphragm is much more flexible than the shearwalls, allowing the loads to be distributed based on tributary area. This is referred to as flexible diaphragm analysis and has been the traditional approach used in the analysis of wood structures. Increasingly, designers are considering rigid analysis of wood diaphragms. A rigid diaphragm is assumed to act as a multiple span continuous bending member. For rigid diaphragms the lateral loads are assumed to be distributed based on the relative stiffness of the shearwalls.

Torsional effects may also need to be considered in the design of wood structures. Torsion is introduced by eccentricity between the centres of mass and resistance, and due to accidental eccentricities. Refer to Chapter 3 for the determination of torsional moments.

Further discussion on lateral load distribution to shearwalls can be found in the Clause 9 Commentary to CSA O86 in the *Wood Design Manual*.

OPENINGS IN SHEARWALLS

Figure 12.8 shows the endwall of a building with two large wall sections available to resist the total diaphragm shear. Since the two shearwall sections are tied together, they are forced to deflect equally. This means that the diaphragm force resisted by each shearwall section is proportional to its stiffness. To simplify the analysis, the stiffness of each shearwall section has traditionally been assumed to be proportional to its length.

This results in the shear force distribution shown in Figure 12.8 (b), where the diaphragm shear is uniformly distributed along the top of the wall including the header over the opening. The header acts as a drag strut to accumulate the shear and transfer an axial force to the end of each shearwall section. The resulting unit shear at the bottom of each shearwall section is equal to the total diaphragm shear divided by the total length of the shearwall sections.

FIGURE 12.8

Endwall with openings

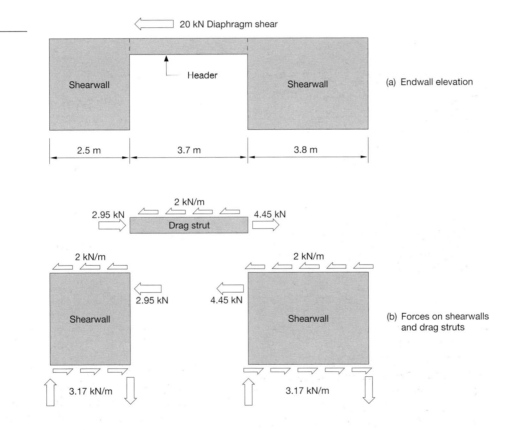

(a) Endwall elevation

(b) Forces on shearwalls and drag struts

Traditionally the two shearwall sections shown in Figure 12.8 would be designed as separate walls with hold-downs at the ends of each wall (four total). CSA O86 allows the designer to consider eliminating some or all of the hold-down connections. The strength of this arrangement is usually lower than the traditional separate shearwall design, but may be adequate for many buildings.

A shearwall is designed to resist the sum of factored shear forces from upper storey shearwalls and diaphragms. Where materials or construction details vary between shearwall segments, the capacity of the shearwall may be conservatively estimated based on the minimum segment capacity. Alternatively, the total factored shear force may be distributed to each of the segments based on the relative strength of each segment or more accurately, by the relative stiffness of each segment.

12.4   Construction

WOOD-BASED PANEL SHEATHING

CSA O86 provides specified shear strengths for the following types of wood-based panels:

- Douglas fir plywood conforming to CSA O121

- Canadian softwood plywood conforming to CSA O151

- OSB construction sheathing produced to meet the requirements of CSA O325.0

CSA O86 provides diaphragm and shearwall design values that are applicable to all of these panels. However, the shear-through-thickness rigidity of the different types of sheathing vary slightly, which means that the deflection of the system will depend on the type of panel used.

Plywood has been used for wall, floor and roof sheathing for many years and is widely available. The most commonly available OSB product is the construction sheathing panel manufactured to CSA O325. The CSA O325 standard sets performance ratings for specific end uses. Since the diaphragm and shear wall tables are based on panel thickness, CSA O86 Table 9.5.3 provides an equivalent norminal thickness for the various panel marks.

All panels must be at least 1200 × 2400 mm, except near boundaries and changes in framing where two short or narrow panels may be used. Both square-edge or tongue-and-groove edge panels are acceptable. Generally the choice of edge will depend on the particular application. Roof and floor sheathing usually require edge support for gravity loading and tongue-and-groove edges are often used to satisfy this requirement.

In past editions of CSA O86, the design values for shearwalls assumed solid blocking at all panel edges. CSA O86 permits the use of unblocked shearwalls by the incorporation of a strength adjustment factor for this application (CSA O86 Table 9.4.4). This application is limited to horizontally laid panels on shearwalls no higher than 4880 mm.

GYPSUM WALLBOARD

CSA O86 provides design information for shearwalls sheathed with Type X (fire-rated) gypsum wallboard conforming to ASTM Standard C36 subject to the following conditions:

- Gypsum wallboard shearwalls are only used to resist short-term loads under dry service conditions only.
- Gypsum wallboard is used in platform frame construction where the storey height does not exceed 3600 mm.
- Gypsum wallboard is used in combination with wood-based panels.
- The percentage of the shear force on any storey that may be resisted by the gypsum wallboard is limited to the values given in Table 9.5.4 of CSA O86. Depending on the location in a building, the percentage of the shear force that may be resisted by gypsum ranges from 40 to 80% and the remainder of the shear force has to be resisted by wood-based panels.

These provisions allow designers to take advantage of the typical wall configuration of wood-based panels on the exterior surface and gypsum wallboard on the interior. However, the use of gypsum wallboard as part of the lateral load resisting system in high seismic areas may not be an advantage since an R_d of 2 must be used for earthquake design, which increases the design force by 50%.

LUMBER SHEATHING AND PLANK DECKING

Lumber sheathing typically consists of 19 mm thick boards with tongue-and-groove or square edges. While less common today, this product can be used to sheath roof, floors and walls with framing members spaced at 610 mm or less on centre.

Tongue-and-groove plank decking is available in 38, 64 and 89 mm thicknesses and can span much larger distances than lumber sheathing.

When lumber sheathing and 38 mm plank decking is laid perpendicular to the framing, it is difficult to achieve significant diaphragm action. Since there is no connection between the individual boards, the shear transfer can only be achieved through the resistance of the two nails where each board crosses a framing member. The two nails create a moment couple to resist shear (Figure 12.9a). Since the distance between the nails is quite small, the resulting shear resistance is very low. Also, the flexibility of this system is quite high.

Significant diaphragm resistance is generated when the decking is laid diagonally across the framing. In this case a bracing-like system is created where boards act in axial tension or compression to resist the applied shear (Figure 12.9b). The boards transfer the axial force to the perimeter members through the edge nailing, which creates bending forces in the perimeter members.

CSA O86 provides additional guidance on how to address forces at boundary members and at corners of boundary elements in single-layer lumber shearwalls and diaphragms. These forces occur in the boundary members parallel to the interior framing members (studs in shearwalls or joists in diaphragms). The normal load component, acting perpendicular to the boundary member, creates a moment that must be accounted for in design of the boundary member. The boundary load component also causes the corners of the shearwall or diaphragm to separate. And therefore the boundary frame members in single-layer diagonally sheathed shearwalls and diaphragms shall be designed to resist the separation force.

The bending forces on the perimeter members can be eliminated by using two layers of diagonal sheathing laid at right angles to one another to create a truss-like system. In this case one layer acts in tension and the other in compression. Each layer is assumed to carry an equal share 0of the shear force and the resultant nail force is parallel to the perimeter members (Figure 12.9c).

It should be noted that the diagonal lay-up increases the span of the deck, which increases the bending stress due to gravity loading. Where a diagonal lay-up is not desirable, significant diaphragm action can

FIGURE 12.9

Sheathing resistance to applied shear

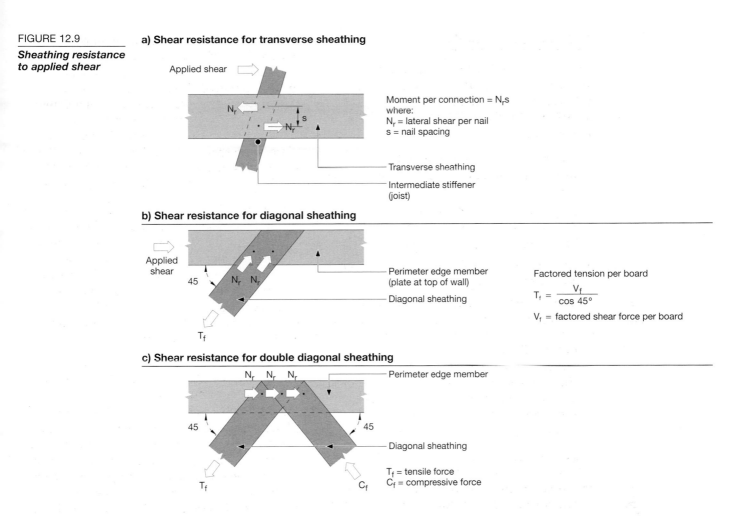

a) Shear resistance for transverse sheathing

Applied shear

N_r

N_r

s

Moment per connection = $N_r s$
where:
N_r = lateral shear per nail
s = nail spacing

Transverse sheathing

Intermediate stiffener (joist)

b) Shear resistance for diagonal sheathing

Applied shear

45

N_r N_r

T_f

Perimeter edge member (plate at top of wall)

Diagonal sheathing

Factored tension per board

$$T_f = \frac{V_f}{\cos 45°}$$

V_f = factored shear force per board

c) Shear resistance for double diagonal sheathing

N_r N_r N_r

Perimeter edge member

45   45

Diagonal sheathing

T_f C_f

T_f = tensile force
C_f = compressive force

be created by adding a layer of plywood or OSB over top of the deck, as long as minimum nail penetration (in the framing) is satisfied.

MULTIPLE LAYERS OF PANEL SHEATHING

Shearwalls may be constructed with the following combinations of sheathing:

- wood-based panels on both sides;
- Wood-based panels on one side and gypsum wallboard panels on the opposite side.

CSA O86 allows the factored shear resistance of panels on opposite sides of the same shearwall to be added together. Where a wood structural panel is applied over 12.7 mm or 15.9 mm thick gypsum wallboard, the shear resistance of the wood-based panel may be considered in the shearwall design, provided minimum nail penetration requirements are met. In all other cases, where two panels are applied on the same side of the shearwall, the capacity is determined using the inside panel.

12.5   Design Procedures

DIAPHRAGM DESIGN

Figure 12.10 shows a typical horizontal diaphragm subjected to a uniformly distributed load with supporting shearwalls at each end. In this situation the diaphragm is assumed to act like a simply supported beam and the chord members act as the flanges of the beam to resist the applied bending moment. The factored axial force in the chord members may be calculated as follows:

$$P_f \text{ and } T_f = \frac{M_f}{h}$$

Where:

P_f = maximum factored compressive force

T_f = maximum factored tension force

M_f = maximum factored bending moment

$$= \frac{w_f L^2}{8}$$

h = centre to centre distance between chords

w_f = factored loading

L = diaphragm length

= dimension perpendicular to the applied load

The shear force in the diaphragm is carried by the sheathing and has a maximum value at the supports equal to the following:

$$V_f = \frac{w_f L}{2}$$

Where:

V_f = maximum factored shear force

W_f = factored loading

L = diaphragm length

FIGURE 12.10

Diaphragm design

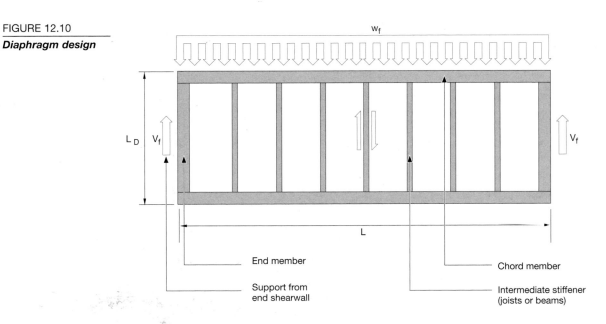

Chords

Often the double top plate of the wood stud wall is used as the chord member. The plate members are usually lapped with staggered end joints and connected together by nailing or bolting (Figure 12.11). Alternatively, the rim joist can be designed to act as the chord with the end joints connected together with nailed or bolted steel or wood splice plates.

The chord members are designed as tension and compression members in accordance with Clause 5 of CSA O86. The splice connections are designed using the fastening information in Clause 10 of CSA O86, however, many prefabricated steel straps are available for this application. Design values for these proprietary straps are published by the manufacturer.

Struts

Strut members are required to transfer the shear from the diaphragm to the shearwall. Generally the member that acts as the chord for lateral loading perpendicular to the wall becomes the strut when the loading is parallel to the wall. Therefore the struts (including splices) should be designed to carry the most critical of the strut force or chord force.

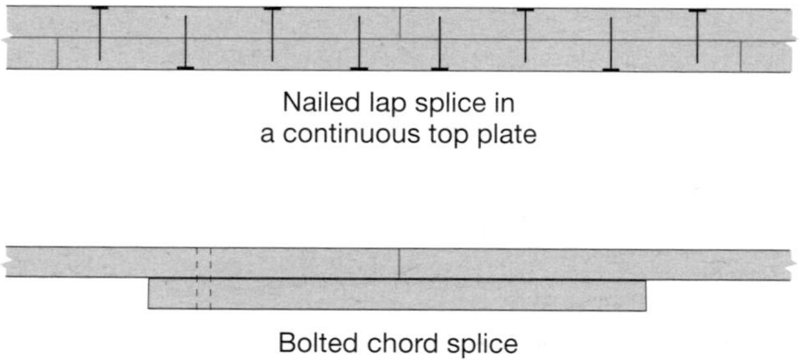

FIGURE 12.11

Chord splice details

Nailed lap splice in
a continuous top plate

Bolted chord splice

Wood-based Panel Sheathing

The factored resistance of nailed diaphragms with wood-based panels is calculated as follows:

$$V_r = \phi\, v_d\, K_D\, K_{SF}\, J_{sp}\, L_D$$

Where:

ϕ = resistance factor

= 0.7

v_d = specified shear strength for diaphragms with plywood, OSB or waferboard sheathing, kN/m (CSA O86 Table 9.5.2)

K_D = load duration factor

K_{SF} = service condition factor for fastenings (CSA O86 Table 10.2.1.5)

J_{sp} = species factor for framing material (CSA O86 Table 9.4.3)

L_D = dimension of diaphragm parallel to the direction of the factored load, m

Specified strengths are given in CSA O86 Table 9.5.2 for diaphragms with and without solid blocking at the panel edges. Blocked diaphragms have higher unit resistance values. Sometimes it is feasible to specify blocking only in the high shear areas at the ends of the diaphragm and eliminate blocking in the middle of the diaphragm in order to provide an economical design.

Diagonal Lumber Sheathing

Clause 9.5.5 of CSA O86 outlines design procedures to determine the shear capacity of diagonally sheathed diaphragms. For a single layer of diagonal sheathing, the axial forces in the diagonal sheathing create load components acting both parallel and perpendicular to the boundary framing members. As a result the boundary members must be designed for the out-of-plane bending in addition to the axial forces. The span of the perimeter member is taken as the distance between framing members of the diaphragm such as the joists, studs or blocking.

Where double diagonal sheathing is used, the tension and compression layers are assumed to equally share the applied shear force. At the diaphragm boundary the tension and compression forces result in a force that acts parallel to the perimeter member as shown in Figure 12.9c. As a result, the perimeter members only need be designed for axial forces, similar to diaphragms constructed with panel sheathing.

Deflection of Diaphragms

In accordance with Clause 9.7.2 of CSA O86-09, the following formula may be used to estimate the lateral static deflection at mid-span, Δ_d, mm, of a simply supported blocked diaphragm:

$$\Delta_d = \frac{5v_s L^3}{96EAL_D} + \frac{vL}{4B_v} + 0.000614Le_n + \frac{\sum(\Delta_c x)}{2L_D}$$

Where:

Δ_d = lateral deflection at mid-span (mm)

v = maximum shear force per unit length due to specified lateral loads (N/mm)

L = diaphragm span perpendicular to the direction of the load (mm)

A = cross-sectional area of chord members (mm²)

E = modulus of elasticity of chords (MPa)

L_D = depth of diaphragm parallel to the direction of the load (mm)

B_v = shear-through-thickness rigidity (N/mm) (refer to Tables 7.3A, 7.3B and 7.3C of CSA O86)

e_n = nail deformation for a particular load per nail (mm) (Table 12.1)

$\sum(\Delta_c x)$ = sum of the individual chord-splice slip values, Δ_c, on both sides of the diaphragm, each multiplied by its distance x to the nearest support

Openings in the Sheathing

Most diaphragms have openings for pipes, ductwork, elevators, stairwells and skylights. Openings in high shear areas may have to be reinforced with additional framing members and connections to transfer the forces around the opening (Figure 12.12A).

TABLE 12.1

Deformation e_n for shearwall and diaphragm calculations[2]

Load per nail[1] N		Deformation, e_n mm		
	Nail length (in.)	2	2-1/2	3
	Gauge	11-3/4	10	9
	Diameter (mm)	2.84	3.25	3.66
300		0.46	0.29	0.23
400		0.76	0.46	0.35
500		1.20	0.64	0.49
600		1.89	0.88	0.66
700		2.97	1.21	0.86
800			1.70	1.13
900			2.33	1.48
1000				1.95

Notes:

1. Load per nail = v_s s
   where:
   v_s = maximum specified shear force per unit length along the diaphragm boundary or the top of shearwall
   s = nail spacing along the boundary of an interior panel

2. Multiply values by 2 for unseasoned lumber.

3. Adapted from the Uniform Building Code (International Conference of Building Officials, Whittier, California).

DIAPHRAGM CONNECTIONS

All of the components of the shearwall and diaphragm system must be adequately fastened together so that the structure acts as an effective unit. The following connections are suggested for wood-frame construction. For anchorage to concrete or masonry shearwalls, refer to CSA O86 Sections 9.3.5.1 and 9.3.5.2.

Sheathing to Chord

Where the sheathing is not directly attached to the chord, a path for the transfer of shear forces is necessary in order for the chord to develop its axial force. The shear flow q_f between the sheathing and the chord may be calculated as:

$$q_f = \frac{V_f}{h}$$

Where:

V_f = factored shear force in the sheathing

h = centre to centre distance between chords

The shear flow is maximum at the support and follows the shape of the shear force diagram.

For wood frame walls with the top plate acting as the chord, this connection may be made by nailing to the header, which in turn is toe-nailed to the top plates or connected by a framing anchor as shown in Figure 12.12B. This connection also provides diaphragm to shearwall anchorage for lateral loading parallel to the wall.

Sidewall–to–diaphragm (Walls Perpendicular to Lateral Loads)

The lateral wind forces perpendicular to the wall must be transferred from the wall studs to the diaphragm. In wood frame walls, the studs are either end-nailed or toe-nailed to the top plate. Where the joists are perpendicular to the wall, the joists may either be toe-nailed to the top plate or connected with a framing anchor (Figure 12.12B). Where the joists are parallel to the wall, blocking is toe-nailed or anchored to the top plate and the sheathing is nailed to the blocking (Figure 12.12B).

Where the diaphragm sheathing is laid over wood trusses, it is necessary to provide cross-bracing to transfer the lateral forces from the perpendicular walls to the roof sheathing (Figure 12.12C).

Diaphragm-to-shearwall (Walls Parallel to Lateral Loads)

At the diaphragm edge, the plywood is nailed to a joist (or blocking), which in turn must be connected to the top plate of the shear wall. This may be accomplished by toe-nailing the blocking or rim joist to the wall plate, or by fastening with metal framing anchors (Figure 12.12B).

Corner Connections

The perimeter members should be connected at the corners of the diaphragm. Where the top plate of the wall acts as the perimeter member, this may be done by lapping and nailing the plates.

FIGURE 12.12A

Typical connection details: framing at an opening

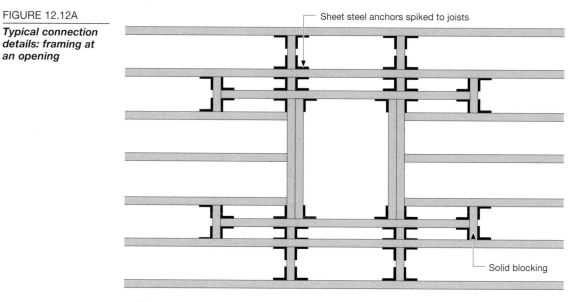

Sheet steel anchors spiked to joists

Solid blocking

Note
This suggested layout can be used where diaphragms with openings are unavoidable. Other means of reinforcing the openings can be developed.

FIGURE 12.12B

Typical connection details: joists on shearwall

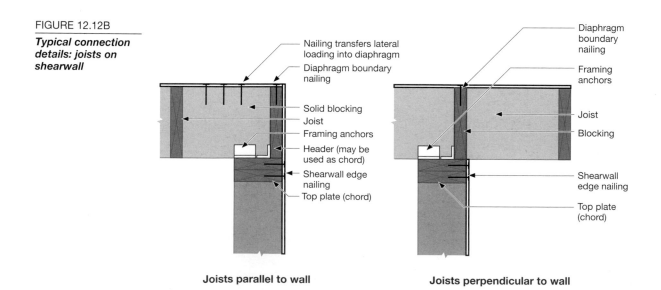

Nailing transfers lateral loading into diaphragm

Diaphragm boundary nailing

Solid blocking

Joist

Framing anchors

Header (may be used as chord)

Shearwall edge nailing

Top plate (chord)

Diaphragm boundary nailing

Framing anchors

Joist

Blocking

Shearwall edge nailing

Top plate (chord)

Joists parallel to wall   **Joists perpendicular to wall**

FIGURE 12.12C

Typical connection details: trusses on shearwall

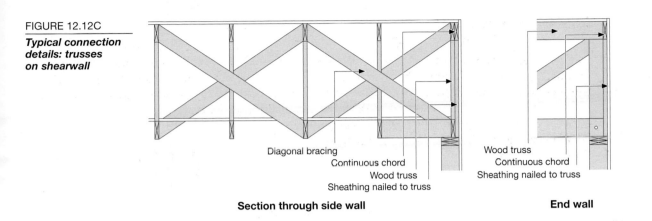

Diagonal bracing
Continuous chord
Wood truss
Sheathing nailed to truss

Wood truss
Continuous chord
Sheathing nailed to truss

Section through side wall

End wall

SHEARWALL DESIGN

Figure 12.13 shows a typical single storey shearwall segment subjected to a factored shear force at the top edge and supported by a foundation at the bottom. The shearwall segment is assumed to act like a cantilevered beam with the end posts acting as the chords. This shear force is considered to be uniformly distributed along the length of the shearwall segment. The resulting factored unit shear force is:

$$v_{fs} = \frac{V_{fs}}{L_s}$$

Where:

V_{fs} = factored unit shear force

L_s = length of the shearwall segment parallel to the direction of the factored load.

Chords

Generally the chord is a post built up from wood studs that are designed as tension and compression members in accordance with Clause 5 of CSA O86. Resistance to overturning is provided by shearwall chord members at the ends of the shearwall segments. The chord members must be designed so that the factored compression and tensile resistance is greater than or equal to maximum factored axial load. For the tension case, the factored dead load tributary to the post may be used to reduce the net force. Since the dead load is resisting overturning, the factored dead load is 0.9D for wind load design. When shearwalls are designed to resist earthquake loads, the factored dead load is 1.0D. The axial chord forces need to include the chord forces from upper storeys. In some situations, shearwall chord members also resist snow and live loads. In this case, the factored snow and live loads resisted by the chords must be added to the overturning compression force P_f.

$$P_f = \frac{M}{h} + 1.25P_D, \text{ for wind load design}$$

$$= \frac{M}{h} + P_D, \text{ for seismic design}$$

$$T_f = \frac{M}{h} - 0.9P_D, \text{ for wind load design}$$

$$= \frac{M}{h} - P_D, \text{ for seismic design}$$

At the top storey, n, M is calculated as $M_n = V_{fsn} \times (H_{sn} + d_n)$

In lower storeys, the factored overturning moment at a particular storey, i, is calculated as the sum of the overturning moments from storey i to storey n calculated as follows:

FIGURE 12.13

Shearwall design

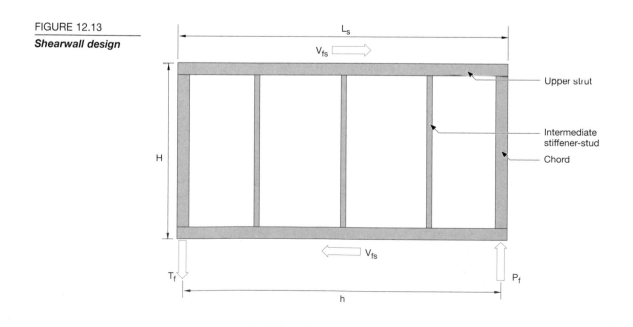

$$M_i = \sum_{j=i}^{n} (V_{fsj}(H_{sj} + d_j))$$

$$P_{Di} = \sum_{j=i}^{n} P_{Dj}$$

Where:

n is the total number of storeys in the structure

i is the storey being considered

j is a storey between storey i and storey n

V_{fsj} = factored shear force on the shearwall segment at level j (kN)

H_{sj} = the height of the shearwall segment at storey j (m)

d_j = depth of the roof or floor framing at the top of the shearwall segment at storey j.

h = centre-to-centre distance between chord members (m).

And

P_{Dj} = specified dead load on the chord of the shearwall segment at storey j (kN)

Wood-based Panel sheathing

The factored resistance of nailed shearwall segments with wood-based panels is calculated as follows:

$$V_{rs} = \phi v_d K_D K_{SF} J_{ub} J_{sp} J_{hd} L_s$$

Where:

ϕ = resistance factor

  = 0.7

v_d = specified shear strength for shearwalls with plywood, OSB or waferboard sheathing, kN/m (CSA O86 Table 9.5.1A)

K_D = load duration factor

K_{SF} = service condition factor for fastenings (CSA O86 Table 10.2.1.5)

J_{ub} = strength adjustment factor for unblocked shearwalls (CSA O86 Table 9.4.4)

J_{sp} = species factor for framing material (CSA O86 Table 9.4.3)

J_{hd} = hold-down effect factor for shearwall segment (CSA O86 Clause 9.4.5)

L_s = length of the shearwall segment parallel to the direction of the factored load, m.

The hold-down factor is applicable to a shearwall consisting of segments separated by openings in which there are not hold-down anchors at each side of the openings. The *Wood Design Manual* provides a detailed explanation of the design procedures required for this application.

Diagonal Lumber Sheathing

Clause 9.5.5 of CSA O86 outlines design procedures to determine the shear capacity of diagonally sheathed shearwalls. For a single layer of diagonal sheathing, the axial forces in the diagonal sheathing create load components acting both parallel and perpendicular to the boundary framing members. As a result, the boundary members must be designed for the out-of-plane bending in addition to the axial forces.

Where double diagonal sheathing is used, the tension and compression layers are assumed to equally share the applied shear force. At the shearwall boundary the tension and compression forces result in a force that acts parallel to the member. As a result, the perimeter members only need be designed for axial forces, similar to shearwalls constructed with panel sheathing.

Gypsum Wallboard

The factored resistance for a shearwall segment sheathed with Type X gypsum wallboard is calculated as follows:

$$V_{rs} = \phi\, v_d\, J_{hd}\, L_s$$

Where:

ϕ = resistance factor

= 0.7

v_d = specified shear strength for shearwalls with gypsum wallboard, kN/m (CSA O86 Table 9.5.1B)

J_{hd} = hold-down effect factor for shearwall segment (CSA O86 Clause 9.4.5)

L_s = length of the shearwall segment parallel to the direction of the factored load, m.

Deflection of Shearwalls

Clause 9.7.1 of CSA O86, provides an equation for the static deflection at the top of the wall, Δ_{sw}, mm, of a blocked, single storey, shearwall segment with wood-based panels constructed in accordance with Clauses 9.5.3 to 9.5.5:

$$\Delta_{sw} = \frac{2vH_s^3}{3EAL_s} + \frac{vH_s}{B_v} + 0.0025H_s e_n + \frac{H_s}{L_s}d_a$$

where:

Δ_{sw} = horizontal in-plane deflection of the top of the shearwall segment

v = maximum shear force per unit length due to specified lateral loads (N/mm)

H_s = shearwall segment height (mm)

E = modulus of elasticity of chords (MPa)

A = cross-sectional area of chord members (mm²)

L_s = length of shearwall segment (mm)

B_v = shear-through-thickness rigidity, (N/mm) (see Table 7.3A, 7.3B and 7.3C of CSA O86)

e_n = nail deformation for a particular load per nail (mm) (See Table 8.2 of Wood Design Manual)

d_a = total vertical elongation of the wall anchorage system (including fastener slip, device elongation, anchor or rod elongation, etc.) at the induced shear load

For shearwall segments without hold-downs, the total vertical elongation, d_a, may be taken as follows:

$$d_a = 2.5d_F K_m \left[\frac{(vH_s - P_{ij})\frac{S_n}{L_s}}{n_u} \right]^{1.7}$$

Note: This equation is an approximation.

Where:

d_F = nail diameter (mm)

K_m = service creep factor (CSA O86 Table A.10.9.3.2)

P_{ij} = specified uplift restraint force for storey i at the bottom of the end stud of a shearwall segment j (N)

s_n = nail spacing around panel edge (mm)

n_u = unit lateral nail strength resistance, N (CSA O86 Clause 10.9.4)

For unblocked shearwall segments with wood-based panels, Δ_{ub} may be calculated as

$$\frac{\Delta_{sw}}{J_{ub}}$$

Where:

Δ_{sw} is the deflection calculated based on blocked shearwall segments with 600 mm stud spacing and nails spaced at 150 mm at panel edges and 300 mm spacing along intermediate studs

J_{ub} is the adjustment factor for unblocked shearwall segment (CSA O86 Table 9.4.4)

SHEARWALL CONNECTIONS

Hold-down Connections

Hold-down connections are used to anchor the shearwall chords to the foundation wall or shearwall below. Figure 12.14 shows some example connections. Usually a bracket is bolted to the chord that has an anchor bolt or rod running vertically to the structure below. Prefabricated hold-down brackets are widely available from lumber connector suppliers.

Shear Transfer Connections

The shear force in the bottom plate of the wall must be transferred to the structure below. Where the shearwall sits directly on a foundation wall, this is accomplished with anchor bolts designed in accordance with CSA O86 Section 10.4. Where the shearwall sits on a wood floor in a multi-storey building,

FIGURE 12.14

Typical hold-down details: shearwall to foundation and shearwall to shearwall

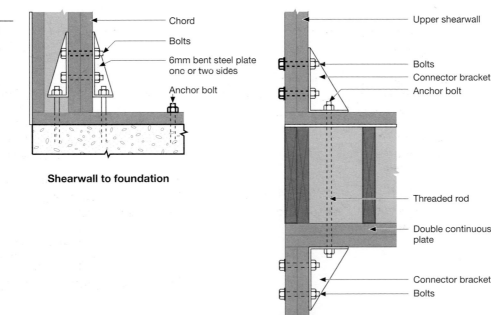

Shearwall to foundation

Chord
Bolts
6mm bent steel plate one or two sides
Anchor bolt

Upper shearwall
Bolts
Connector bracket
Anchor bolt
Threaded rod
Double continuous plate
Connector bracket
Bolts
Lower shearwall

Shearwall to shearwall

the bottom plate can be nailed through to the rim joist. The rim joist must then be fastened to the lower shearwall to transfer both the shear force from the upper shearwall and the shear from the floor diaphragm. The fastening could be toe-nails or framing anchors like those shown in Figure 12.12B.

In some situations, wood-based panel sheathing may be used to lap the upper and lower sheathing over the face of the rim joist to provide a direct shear transfer. In this case, a space must be left between the upper and lower panels to allow for shrinkage of the rim joist and the nails should also be staggered to avoid splitting the rim joist.

12.6   Examples

EXAMPLE 12.1: DIAPHRAGM DESIGN

Design the roof diaphragm for the warehouse building shown in Figure 12.15. The warehouse is to be 15 m × 42 m × 6.3 m high. The roof is to be constructed of joists, 38 × 184 mm spaced 600 mm on centre supported on the top of D. Fir-L glulam beams spaced at 3 m on centre supported by columns set in wood stud walls. The studs are to be 38 × 184 mm spaced 400 mm on centre. The framing lumber is S-P-F No.2 grade.

The specified wind pressure load, calculated using $I_w = 1.0$, on the main part of the long side of the building is 0.72 kN/m², with the higher wind load for the end zone = 1.08 kN/m². Thus the factored wind force at the eave line = 1.4 [0.72 (6.3/2)] = 3.18 kN/m (and 4.76 kN/m on the end portion from the end wall to the first beam, 3 m away).

The moments and shears on the diaphragm are shown in Fig 12.16. The tension and compression force which the chords must resist are found by assuming the diaphragm acts like a deep horizontal beam, with bending resistance from axial forces in the chords and shear only taken by the web, or sheathing.

Thus the resisting moment

$$M_r = T_r\,h \geq M_{f\,(max)}$$

where

h	=	centre-to-centre distance between chords
	=	15 − 0.1
	=	14.9 m

Therefore,

$$
\begin{aligned}
T_r &= M_{f\,(max)} / h \\
&= 704 / 14.9 \\
&= 47.4 \text{ kN}
\end{aligned}
$$

Design of chord members

Try using the 38 × 184 rim joist as the chord

$$f_t = 5.5 \text{ MPa}$$

Tensile resistance parallel to grain

$$
\begin{aligned}
T_r &= \phi\,f_t\,(K_D\,K_H\,K_{St}\,K_T)\,A_n\,K_{Zt} \\
&= 0.9 \times 5.5 \times 1.15 \times 1 \times 1 \times 1 \times A_n \times 1.2 \\
&= 6.83\,A_n
\end{aligned}
$$

Assume two staggered rows of 1 inch bolts will be used for the splice.

Thus the net area per chord member

$$
\begin{aligned}
A_n &= 38\,(184 - 27.4) \\
&= 5950 \text{ mm}^2
\end{aligned}
$$

Number of chord members required

$$
\begin{aligned}
&= 47400 / (6.83 \times 5950) \\
&= 1.17
\end{aligned}
$$

Use two 38 × 184 mm No.2 grade S-P-F lumber chord members.

FIGURE 12.15

Warehouse building roof diaphragm

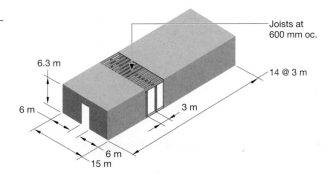

Design of Sheathing

Try panel sheathing on the 38×184 mm joists spaced 600 mm on centre.

Factored shear force

$$V_f = 71.4 \text{ kN}$$

Maximum shear along edge of diaphragm

$$v_f = V_f / L_D$$
$$= 71.4 / 15$$
$$= 4.76 \text{ kN/m}$$

The factored shear resistance of nailed shear panels

$$V_r = \phi \, v_d \, (K_D \, K_{SF}) \, J_{sp} \, L_D$$

For S-P-F framing

$$J_{sp} = 0.8$$

For wind load

$$K_D = 1.15$$

For construction with S-Dry lumber

$$K_{SF} = 1.0$$

Using these factors the required specified shear strength is:

$$v_d = \frac{4.76}{0.7 \times 1.15 \times 1.0 \times 0.8}$$
$$= 7.39 \text{ kN/m}$$

From CSA O86 Table 9.5.2, select 15.5 mm thick panels with 3.66 mm diameter nails spaced at 150 mm at diaphragm boundaries and spaced at 150 mm at other panel edges. The specified shear strength:

$$v_d = 8.7 \text{ kN/m}$$

Use 15.5 mm panels with 3.6 mm diameter (3 in. common) nails spaced at 150 mm at diaphragm boundaries and at 150 mm at other panel edges.

Note: The specified strength of this arrangement is 5.9 kN/m when the blocking is removed. Therefore, the designer only needs to specify blocking in the end two bays of the building.

FIGURE 12.16

Moments and shears on the roof diaphragm

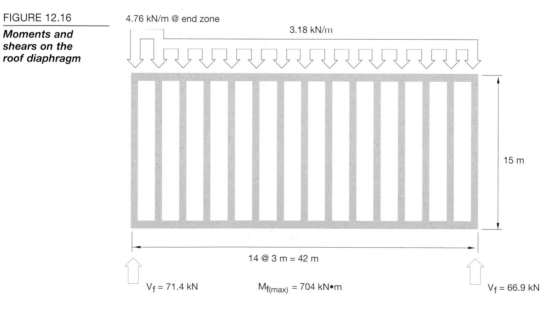

4.76 kN/m @ end zone

3.18 kN/m

15 m

14 @ 3 m = 42 m

$V_f = 71.4$ kN $M_{f(max)} = 704$ kN•m $V_f = 66.9$ kN

EXAMPLE 12.2: SHEARWALL DESIGN

The two storey (plus basement) 44-unit motel shown in Figure 12.17 is to be built in Calgary, Alberta. It is required to be designed for lateral stability using shear-walls (and diaphragms) to resist wind loads. Other aspects of the design have already been completed.

Structural Design Criteria – Climatic Information

Wind pressures

$$q = 0.48 \text{ kN/m}^2$$

Wind Loads

External wind pressure for strength

$$I_w = 1.0$$

$$C_e = 1.0$$

$$\begin{aligned} p &= I_w \, q \, C_e \, C_g \, C_p \\ &= 1.0 \times 0.48 \times 1.0 \times C_g \, C_p \\ &= 0.48 \, C_g \, C_p \text{ (kN/m}^2) \end{aligned}$$

Note that internal pressures do not contribute to the overall lateral loading on the building and do not need to be considered.

FIGURE 12.17

Two-storey motel example

Plan of ground floor

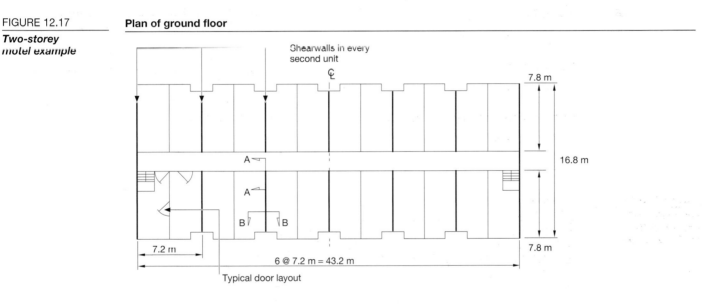

Shearwalls in every second unit

7.8 m

16.8 m

7.8 m

7.2 m

6 @ 7.2 m = 43.2 m

Typical door layout

Elevation

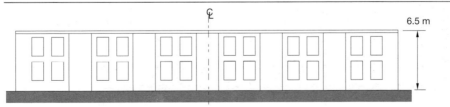

6.5 m

Using Figure 3.4, the wind pressures to be considered are shown below for two important areas for this type of building.

The shaded zone near the corner under consideration is subject to higher wind loads than the area away from the corner or the corners at the other end of the building.

Specified wind pressure loads are shown in Figure 12.18.

For strength under lateral load from wind, consider two cases:

1. Near the corner in the end effect zone

$$Q_f = 1.4 \times 0.936$$
$$= 1.31 \text{ kN/m}^2$$

2. For the rest of the wall

$$Q_f = 1.4 \times 0.624$$
$$= 0.874 \text{ kN/m}^2$$

It is assumed that the floor and roof diaphragms are relatively flexible in their own plane, so that the load on the shearwalls is proportional to the tributary width, which is taken as 7.2 m (Figure 12.17). (Note that 7.2 m is also the length of the end zone as shown in Figure 12.18.)

The shearwall elements consist of framing lumber sheathed with wood panels. Each shearwall element acts as an individual shearwall in resisting factored wind load. The lower shearwalls must also resist the load transferred from the element above.

Due to the end effect, the first shearwall from each end of the building is subject to both the higher loading from the end bay, and the lower loading from the next bay toward the centre of the building.

Factored loads for the different members in shearwalls A and B are shown in Figure 12.19.

Design of Chord Members

Consider the chord members in shearwall B. Use No.2 grade Spruce-Pine-Fir, S-Dry lumber for framing. Try 38 × 89 mm.

Tension force to be resisted (Figure 12.19)

$$T_f = 0.994 \text{ kN}$$

Check tension parallel to grain resistance

$$T_r = \phi \, f_t \, (K_D \, K_H \, K_{St} \, K_T) \, A_n \, K_{Zt}$$
$$= 0.9 \times 5.5 \times 1.15 \times 1 \times 1 \times 1 \times A_n \times 1.5$$
$$= 8.54 \, A_n \text{ (N)}$$

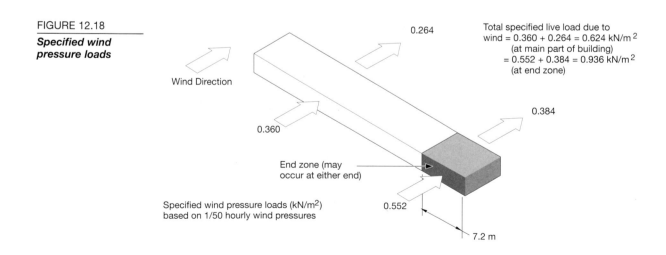

FIGURE 12.18

Specified wind pressure loads

0.264

Total specified live load due to wind = 0.360 + 0.264 = 0.624 kN/m^2 (at main part of building) = 0.552 + 0.384 = 0.936 kN/m^2 (at end zone)

Wind Direction

0.360

0.384

End zone (may occur at either end)

Specified wind pressure loads (kN/m^2) based on 1/50 hourly wind pressures

0.552

7.2 m

Assume that 12.5 mm bolts will be used for the tie-down connection. Thus:

$$A_n = 38 \times (89 - 14.5)$$
$$= 2830 \text{ mm}^2$$

Number of studs required

$$= 994 / (8.54 \times 2830)$$
$$= 0.041$$

The factored compression force to be resisted:

$$P_f = 18.9 \text{ kN}$$

The factored compressive resistance parallel to grain:

$$P_r = \phi F_c A K_{Zc} K_c$$
$$F_C = f_c(K_D K_H K_{Sc} K_T)$$
$$= 11.5 \times (1.15 \times 1 \times 1 \times 1)$$
$$= 13.2$$

$$K_{Zc} = 6.3(dL_d)^{-0.13}$$
$$= 6.3 (89 \times 2600)^{0.13}$$
$$= 1.26$$
$$C_{cd} = \frac{2600}{89} = 29.2$$

$$K_c = \left[1.0 + \frac{F_C K_{Zc} C_C^3}{35 E_{05} K_{SE} K_T} \right]^{-1}$$

$$= \left[1.0 + \frac{13.2 \times 1.26 \times 29.2^3}{35 \times 6500 \times 1 \times 1} \right]^{-1}$$

$$= 0.353$$

$$P_r = \phi F_c A K_{Zc} K_c$$
$$= 0.8 \times 13.2 \times A \times 1.26 \times 0.353 = 4.72A$$

Number of studs required:

$$n = \frac{18900}{4.72 \times (38 \times 89)} = 1.18$$

Use two pieces of 38 × 89 mm No. 2 grade S-P-F lumber.

FIGURE 12.19

Wind forces on first shearwall from each end of the building

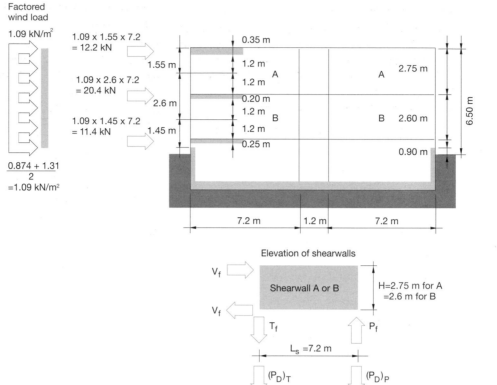

Factored
wind load

1.09 kN/m²

$\dfrac{0.874 + 1.31}{2}$
$=1.09$ kN/m²

$1.09 \times 1.55 \times 7.2$
$= 12.2$ kN

$1.09 \times 2.6 \times 7.2$
$= 20.4$ kN

$1.09 \times 1.45 \times 7.2$
$= 11.4$ kN

1. P-Δ effects were not considered in this problem because they are not significant for this case.
2. Centre-to-centre distance between chords, h, estimated to be 7.2-0.1=7.1 m
3. Specified wall weight for each floor (q_w) is 0.33 kPa
4. There is no roof dead load and the first storey walls considered in the example support a specified floor dead load of 0.5 kN/m
5. For shearwall A, $(P_D)_T = 0.33 \times 2.75 \times \dfrac{7.2}{2} = 3.27$ kN,
   $(P_D)_P = 0.33 \times 2.75 \times \dfrac{7.2}{2} = 3.27$ kN
6. For shearwall B, $(P_D)_T = 0.5 \times \dfrac{7.2}{2} + (0.33 \times 2.75 + 0.33 \times 2.60) \times \dfrac{7.2}{2} = 8.16$ kN
   $(P_D)_P = 0.5 \times \dfrac{7.2 + 1.2}{2} + (0.33 \times 2.75 + 0.33 \times 2.60) \times \dfrac{7.2}{2} = 8.46$ kN

Shearwall member	Factored loads	
	Shearwall A	Shearwall B
Shear in upper and lower struts, V_f^*	12.2/2 = 6.09 kN	(20.4 + 12.2) / 2 = 16.3 kN
Chord force [2] $T_f = \dfrac{M}{h} - 0.9P_D$ $P_f = \dfrac{M}{h} + 1.25P_D$	$T_f = \dfrac{6.09 \times 2.75}{7.1} - 0.9\,(3.27)$ $= -0.58$ kN $P_f = \dfrac{6.09 \times 2.75}{7.1}$ $= 2.36$ kN**	$T_f = \dfrac{6.09 \times 2.75 + 16.3 \times 2.60}{7.1} - 0.9\,(8.16)$ $= 0.994$ kN $P_f = \dfrac{6.09 \times 2.75 + 16.3 \times 2.60}{7.1} + 1.25\,(8.46)$ $= 18.9$ kN
Linear shear in sheathing $v_f = V_f / L_s$	0.846 kN/m	2.27 kN/m

Note:

    * Since there are two shearwalls of equal dimensions per storey, each shearwall is designed to resist half of the applied factored shear force at each level.

    **If $T_f < 0$ the compression force P_f does not need to take into account the factored dead load tributary to the compression chords.

Design of Sheathing

Consider plywood sheathing on one side of the wall. Try 7.5 mm Canadian softwood plywood (CSP) with 2.84 mm diameter nails spaced at 150 mm at panel edges. All panel edges are blocked and there are hold-down connections at the ends of the shearwall segments.

Factored shear to be resisted, $V_f = 16.3$ kN

For S-P-F framing

$$J_{sp} = 0.8$$

For wind load

$$K_D = 1.15$$

Shear resistance, V_r

$$
\begin{aligned}
V_r &= \phi \, v_d \, (K_D \, K_{Sr}) \, J_{ub} \, J_{sp} \, J_{hd} \, L_s \\
&= 0.7 \times 4.9 \times 1.15 \times 1 \times 1 \times 0.8 \times 1 \times 7.2 \\
&= 22.7 \text{ kN} > 16.3 \text{ kN} \qquad \textit{(Acceptable)}
\end{aligned}
$$

Use 7.5 mm CSP with 2.84 mm diameter 50 mm (2 in. common) nails spaced at 150 mm.

Design of Shearwall-to-Shearwall Connections

For the floors, roof, and walls to act as a system, the shearwalls and diaphragms must be positively connected (Figure 12.20). This may be accomplished by toe nailing the roof joists and their blocking to the top plate of the shearwalls, and by direct nailing through the sole or sill plate of the shearwalls to the first and second floors as shown in Section B-B.

Assume that 3½ inch common nails are to be used. (For the diaphragm-to-wall and wall-to-diaphragm connections, the 1.3 J_D factor does not apply).

FIGURE 12.20

***Connections of
shearwalls to floor
and roof diaphragms –
general***

Section A-A

Section B-B

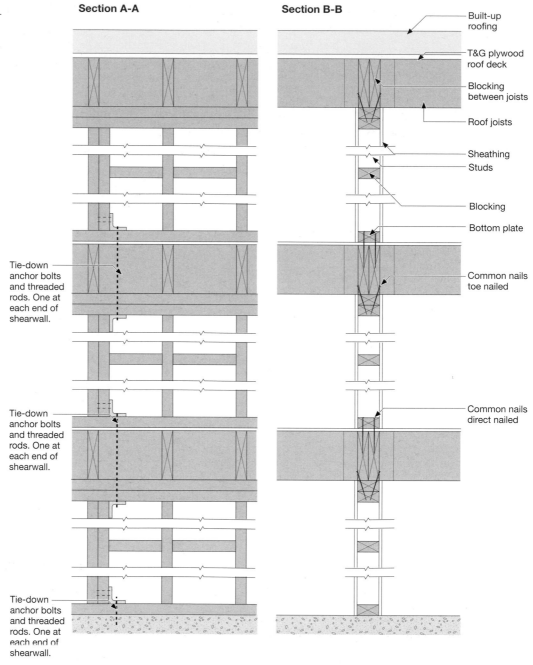

Built-up
roofing

T&G plywood
roof deck

Blocking
between joists

Roof joists

Sheathing

Studs

Blocking

Bottom plate

Common nails
toe nailed

Common nails
direct nailed

Tie-down
anchor bolts
and threaded
rods. One at
each end of
shearwall.

Tie-down
anchor bolts
and threaded
rods. One at
each end of
shearwall.

Tie-down
anchor bolts
and threaded
rods. One at
each end of
shearwall.

1. Spacing requirements for toe nailing of blocking to top plate of shearwall A.

   Try 3-1/2" common wire nails. Toe-nails are started at approximately one-third of the nail length from the end of the piece and driven at an angle about 30° to the grain of the member. Only the top member of the top plate is considered in the design. The head-side member thickness:

$$t_1 = \frac{3.5 \times 25.4}{3\cos 30°} = 34.2 mm$$

   The length of penetration into the point-side member:

$$t_2 = \frac{38}{\cos 30°} = 43.9 mm$$

   Material properties:

$$f_2 = 50G\ (1 - 0.01d_F)$$
$$= 50 \times 0.42 \times (1 - 0.01 \times 4.06)$$
$$= 20.1$$

$$f_1 = 50G\ (1 - 0.01d_F)$$
$$= 50 \times 0.42 \times (1 - 0.01 \times 4.06)$$
$$= 20.1$$

$$f_3 = 110G^{1.8}\ (1 - 0.01d_F)$$
$$= 110 \times 0.42^{1.8} \times (1 - 0.01 \times 4.06)$$
$$= 22.1$$

$$f_y = 50\ (16 - d_F)$$
$$= 50 \times (16 - 4.06)$$
$$= 597$$

   The unit lateral strength resistance, n_u, is the smallest value calculated in accordance with items (a), (b), and (d) to (g) (Clause 10.9.4.2 CSA O86-09):

$$n_u = 1070\ N$$

$$N_u = n_u(K_DK_{SF}K_T)$$
$$= 1070 \times (1.15 \times 1 \times 1)$$
$$= 1230\ N$$

$$J_F = J_EJ_AJ_BJ_D = 1 \times 0.83 \times 1 \times 1 = 0.83$$

   The factored lateral resistance of nails:

$$N_r = \phi N_u n_s n_F J_F$$
$$= 0.8 \times 1230 \times 1 \times n_F \times 0.83$$
$$= 0.816 n_F\ kN$$

Number of nails required:

$$n_F = \frac{v_f L_s}{\phi N_u n_s J_F} = \frac{0.846 \times 7.2}{0.816} = 7.5$$

Number of nails required:

Pairs of nails = 7.5/2 = 3.8

Spacing required per pair = 7.2/4 = 1.8 m

Use four pairs of 3-1/2" nails, spaced at 1.8 m.

2. Spacing requirements for nailing of bottom plate of shearwall A to blocking of second floor.

   Use Nail Selection Tables of *WDM*. The factored lateral resistance of nails:

$$N_r = N'_r n_s n_F K' J_F$$

$$K' = K_D K_{SF} K_T = 1.15 \times 1 \times 1 = 1.15$$

$$J_F = J_E J_A J_B J_D = 1 \times 1 \times 1 \times 1 = 1$$

   Try 3-1/2" common wire nails. The nailing reaches the maximum nail penetration of 51 mm and therefore the corresponding basic factored lateral resistance is:

$$N'_r n_s\ is\ 0.854\ kN$$

   Number of nails required:

$$n_r = \frac{v_f L_s}{N'_r n_s K' J_F} = \frac{0.846 \times 7.2}{0.854 \times 1.15 \times 1}$$
$$= 6.2$$

Spacing required = 7.2/7 = 1.03 m

Use seven staggered 3-1/2" nails, spaced at 1.0 m.

3. Spacing requirements for toe nailing of blocking to top plate of shearwall B.

   Number of nails required:

$$n_F = \frac{v_f L_s}{\phi N_u n_s J_F} = \frac{2.27 \times 7.2}{0.816} = 20.0$$

Pairs of nails = 20.0 / 2 = 10

Spacing required per pair = 7.2 / 10 = 0.7 m

Use ten pairs of 3-1/2" nails, spaced at 0.7 m.

4. Spacing requirements for nailing of bottom plate of shearwall B to blocking of first floor.

Number of nails required:

$$n_F = \frac{v_f L_s}{N'_r n_s K' J_F} = \frac{2.27 \times 7.2}{0.854 \times 1.15 \times 1}$$
$$= 16.6$$

Spacing required = 7.2 / 17 = 0.424 m

Use seventeen staggered 3-1/2" nails, spaced at 0.4 m.

Note: In conventional construction, nails are typically spaced at 600 mm on centre. Designers will often specify conventional spacing requirements if they are more conservative than the calculated solution.

12.7 Seismic Design Considerations for Shearwalls and Diaphragms

Seismic design forces for shearwalls and diaphragms are determined using the appropriate procedures specified in the National Building Code of Canada (NBCC). For further information on calculating earthquake load and effects refer to the NBCC and the NBC Structural Commentaries, as well as Chapter 3 of this book. The seismic design forces that must be considered in design are dependent on the type of seismic force resisting system (SFRS) used and the magnitude of the seismic forces.

Structures in moderate to high seismic zones

This section applies to structures in locations where $I_E F_a S_a(0.2)$ is equal to or greater than 0.35.

In moderate to high seismic zones wood-based seismic force resisting systems (SFRS) are designed using the appropriate NBCC procedures and corresponding values of the ductility-related force modification factor R_d, and the overstrength-related force modification factor R_o. The seismic design forces for diaphragms depend on the type of SFRS they are supported on.

For wood diaphragms supported on wood shearwalls, seismic forces applied to the diaphragm are increased to reflect the lateral load capacity of the wood shearwall. The seismic design force for diaphragm need not exceed 1.2 times the factored seismic force calculated using the $R_d R_o$ of the wood shearwalls. The ductility of wood shearwalls and diaphragms is achieved through the ductile yielding of nails that connect panel sheathing to framing members.

For wood diaphragms supported on wood-based SFRS other than wood shearwalls, the seismic design forces may be determined using the $R_d R_o$ factors for the vertical SFRS provided:

- the diaphragms are designed and detailed to exhibit ductile behaviour, and
- the diaphragms will yield before the supporting SFRS.

However, such seismic design loads shall not be less than loads determined using $R_d R_o$=2.0.

Otherwise when diaphragms are designed not to yield before the supporting SFRS, they are designed to resist a seismic force which is 1.2 times the product of the factored seismic force using the $R_d R_o$ for the SFRS and the over-capacity coefficient of the SFRS. Such seismic design loads need not exceed the value of load determined using $R_d R_o$=1.3.

For wood diaphragms supported on non-wood SFRS, if the diaphragms are designed and detailed to exhibit ductile behaviour and will yield before the supporting SFRS, the seismic design forces for diaphragms are the seismic loads determined using the $R_d R_o$ factors for the vertical SFRS. However, such seismic design loads shall not be less than loads determined using $R_d R_o$=2.0.

Otherwise when diaphragms are designed not to yield before the supporting SFRS, they shall be designed to resist a seismic force which is the product of the factored seismic force using the $R_d R_o$ for the non-wood SFRS and the over-strength coefficient for the SFRS. Such seismic design loads need not exceed the value of load determined using $R_d R_o$=1.3.

The provisions for seismic design forces in diaphragms for structures in moderate to high seismic zones are summarized in Table 12.2.

TABLE 12.2

Wood diaphragm provisions used to calculate the seismic design force V_{Di} in moderate to high seismic zones

Structural System		Seismic design force for diaphragms V_{Di}	R_dR_o used in design
Wood diaphragms supported on wood shearwalls		$V_{Di} = C_{Di} \times F_i$ C_{Di} is the lesser of C_i or 1.2	5.1 for shearwalls with wood based panels 3.4 for shearwalls using gypsum and wood based panels
Wood Diaphragms supported on wood – based SFRS other than wood shearwalls	Diaphragm designed to yield	$V_{Di} = F_i$	Lesser of: 2, or R_dR_o of the SFRS
	Diaphragm designed not to yield	$V_{Di} = 1.2 \times C_i \times F_i$	R_dR_o of the SFRS Note: V_{Di} need not exceed the value of F_i determined using R_dR_o of 1.3
Wood Diaphragms supported on non-wood SFRS	Diaphragm designed to yield	$V_{Di} = F_i$	Lesser of: 2, or R_dR_o of the SFRS
	Diaphragm designed not to yield	$V_{Di} = \gamma_i F_i$ γ_i is the over-strength coefficient determined in accordance with the applicable CSA Standards	R_dR_o of the SFRS Note: V_{Di} need not exceed the value of F_i determined using R_dR_o of 1.3

For a given storey, i, the over-capacity coefficient, $C_i = \frac{V_{ri}}{V_{fi}}$, must be greater than or equal to 1. For structures with three or more storeys, the ratio of the over-capacity coefficient of the second storey and that of the first storey shall not be less than 0.9 or greater than 1.2, to address the concern of soft-storey mechanism developing at the bottom storeys.

Loads on force transfer elements must be increased as follows:

Diaphragm chords, splice joints in structural members and connection of the diaphragm around openings and other load-transfer elements, shall be designed based on seismic forces that are at least 20% greater than the seismic design forces calculated using V_{Di}.

Connections and drag struts that are transferring shear forces between the segments of the vertical SFRS and the diaphragm shall be designed based on seismic forces that are at least 20% greater than the shear force that is being transferred.

Parts of the diaphragm around wall offsets shall be designed for seismic forces that are at least 20% greater than the seismic design force of the offset SFRS.

Alternatively, forces on diaphragm load transfer elements may be calculated using the NBCC provisions determined using an R_dR_o of 1.3.

Anchor bolts and interstorey connections resisting seismic shear forces and hold-downs resisting seismic uplift forces must be designed for seismic loads that are 20% greater than the force that is being transferred.

Structures in low seismic zones

This section applies to structures in locations where $I_E F_a S_a(0.2)$ is less than 0.35.

In low seismic zones wood-based seismic force resisting systems (SFRS) are designed using the factored seismic shear load, V_{fi}, obtained using the appropriate NBCC procedures and corresponding values of R_dR_o for the seismic force resisting system. The factored resistance of a shearwall at storey i, V_{ri} must be greater than the factored seismic shear load, V_{fi}, but the shearwall over-capacity coefficient, C_i, need not be considered in design.

The provisions for seismic design forces in diaphragms for structures in low seismic zones are summarized in Table 12.3.

Loads on force transfer elements must be increased as follows:

Diaphragm chords, splice joints in structural members and connection of the diaphragm around openings and other load-transfer elements, shall be designed based on seismic forces that are at least 20% greater than the seismic design forces calculated using V_{Di}.

Connections and drag struts that are transferring shear forces between the segments of the vertical SFRS and the diaphragm shall be designed based on seismic forces that are at least 20% greater than the shear force that is being transferred.

Parts of the diaphragm around wall off-sets shall be designed for seismic forces that are at least 20% greater than the seismic design force of the offset SFRS.

Alternatively, forces on diaphragm load transfer elements may be calculated using the NBCC provisions determined using an R_dR_o of 1.3.

TABLE 12.3

Wood diaphragm provisions used to calculate the seismic design force V_{Di} in low seismic zones

Structural System		Seismic design force for diaphragms V_{Di}	R_dR_o used in design
Wood diaphragms supported on wood shearwalls		$V_{Di} = F_i$	5.1 for shearwalls with wood based panels
			3.4 for shearwalls using gypsum and wood based panels
Wood Diaphragms supported on wood – based SFRS other than wood shearwalls	Diaphragm designed to yield	$V_{Di} = F_i$	Lesser of: 2, or R_dR_o of the SFRS
	Diaphragm designed not to yield	$V_{Di} = 1.2 \times F_i$	R_dR_o of the SFRS Note: V_{Di} need not exceed the value of F_i determined using R_dR_o of 1.3
Wood Diaphragms supported on non-wood SFRS	Diaphragm designed to yield	$V_{Di} = F_i$	Lesser of: 2, or R_dR_o of the SFRS
	Diaphragm designed not to yield	$V_{Di} = \gamma_i F_i$ γ_i is the over-strength coefficient determined in accordance with the applicable CSA Standards	R_dR_o of the SFRS Note: V_{Di} need not exceed the value of F_i determined using R_dR_o of 1.3

Sample Building

This section gives design examples for the major structural components of an office and warehouse building. Some examples are based on basic principles and some refer to the selection tables in the *Wood Design Manual*. Professors and students should also note that *WoodWorks*® software can be used to verify results and to see the effects of changing spans, loads, and materials.

13

13.1   General Description

An office and warehouse building is to be designed to provide:

- office space
- a showroom for landscaping products
- a large warehouse for landscaping materials
- a garden centre retail outlet

Wood is selected as the primary structural material for a number of reasons:

- wood framing is aesthetically pleasing in the garden centre and showroom
- wood frame construction provides good insulating capability
- sheathed roofs and stud walls provided lateral resistance for the structure so that additional bracing is not required
- wood frame construction is very cost effective

The structure is situated in Richmond Hill, Ontario and is comprised of 1728 m^2 of single-storey warehouse (mercantile) floor space. A two-storey office structure with a footprint area of 441 m^2 is attached to the warehouse. The 244 m^2 annex for the garden centre is considered to be a subsidiary part of the warehouse.

Construction Materials Used in Structural Design

Roof	Warehouse and office	Built-up roofing and 38 mm rigid insulation on tongue and groove panel sheathing.
	Garden centre	Metal roofing and 38 mm rigid insulation on 38 mm tongue and groove decking.
Framework		Wood except for hollow structural steel (HSS) columns in warehouse and garden centre.
Exterior walls	Warehouse and office	Stucco panels on 38 × 184 mm stud walls.
	Office and garden centre	Glazing with glazed panels in aluminum frames on 38 × 184 mm stud walls.
Interior walls		38 × 140 mm platform framed stud wall.
Office floor		Wood I-joists supported by beams, wood panel sheathing, gypcrete topping, carpet.
Ground floor		Reinforced concrete slab and footings.

Structural Design Loading – Gravity Loads

Snow load	S	$= I_s [S_s (C_b C_w C_s C_a) + S_r]$ where:		
		S_s = Ground snow	1.5 kPa	
		C_b = Basic roof snow load factor	0.8	
		C_w = Wind exposure factor	1.0	
		C_s = Slope factor (all slopes < 15°)	1.0	
		C_a = Shape factor	1.0	
		S_r = Associated rain load	0.4 kPa	
		For strength: S = 1.0 [1.5(0.8 × 1.0 × 1.0 × 1.0) + 0.4] =		**1.60 kPa**
		For serviceability: S = 0.9 [1.5(0.8 × 1.0 × 1.0 × 1.0) + 0.4] =		**1.44 kPa**
Office floor live uniform load				**2.4 kPa**
Office floor live concentrated load				**9.0 kN**
Dead loads	Warehouse roof	Felt and gravel, 3-ply	0.26 kPa	
		Insulation	0.02 kPa	
		15.5 mm sheathing	0.08 kPa	
		Flat trusses	0.24 kPa	
		Glulam	0.05 kPa	
		Mechanical	0.20 kPa	
		Total		**0.85 kPa**
	Garden centre roof	Roofing	0.18 kPa	
		Insulation	0.02 kPa	
		38 mm deck	0.17 kPa	
		Sawn purlins	0.13 kPa	
		Glulam	0.05 kPa	
		Mechanical	0.20 kPa	
		Total		**0.75 kPa**
	Office roof	Roofing	0.26 kPa	
		Insulation	0.02 kPa	
		15.5 mm sheathing	0.08 kPa	
		Flat trusses	0.24 kPa	
		Mechanical	0.20 kPa	
		Ceiling	0.10 kPa	
		Total		**0.90 kPa**
	Floor and mezzanines	Flooring	0.10 kPa	
		12.5 mm gypcrete	0.31 kPa	
		19 mm tongue and groove plywood	0.10 kPa	
		Wood I-joists	0.10 kPa	
		Ceiling plus strapping	0.20 kPa	
		Services	0.20 kPa	
		Partitions	1.00 kPa*	
		Total		**2.00 kPa**

* 0.50 kPa Partition load used in seismic design.

Structural Design Loading – Lateral Loads

Wind	q	= Wind pressure	0.44 kPa
	I_w	= Wind importance factor – for strength – for serviceability	1.0 0.75
	C_e	= Exposure factor (Rough terrain and height < 12 m)	0.7
	C_pC_g	= External pressure coefficient x gust effect factor (Refer to NBCC – SC/4 Figures I-7 to I-14)	
	C_{pi}	= Internal pressure coefficient	-0.45 to 0.3
	C_{gi}	= Internal gust effect factor	2.0
	P	$= P_e - P_i$ $= I_w [q\, C_e(C_pC_g - C_{pi}C_{gi})]$ $= 0.308\,(C_pC_g - C_{pi}C_{gi})$ – strength $= 0.231\,(C_pC_g - C_{pi}C_{gi})$ – serviceability	
Earthquake		$S_a(0.2) = 0.18$ $S_a(0.5) = 0.11$ $S_a(1.0) = 0.065$ $S_a(2.0) = 0.021$ Ground profile classified as soft rock (Site Class C)	

Fire Protection Requirements

	1-Storey section	2-Storey section	Total
Area	1728 m²	441 m²	2169 m²
Building use	Group E, up to 3 storeys Mercantile (Major Occupancy)	Group D, up to 3 storeys Business and Personal Services (Subsidiary occupancy)	

Fire protection determination (Group E, 2 storeys, NBCC):
1. Facing 1 street.
2. Building is sprinklered.
3. Sprinkler system is electrically supervised.
4. No roof rating required.
5. Floor assemblies shall be fire separations with a Fire Resistance Rating (FRR) of not less than 45 minutes.
6. All loadbearing walls and columns supporting an assembly required to have a FRR shall have a FRR of not less than 45 minutes.
7. The north and south stud walls require a 1-hour FRR to satisfy spatial separation requirements.

Check maximum area:

Maximum permitted building area
= 3600 m² > 2169 m²   *Acceptable*

Additional Information

Standard assumptions (unless otherwise specified)	standard load duration	
	dry service conditions	
	untreated wood	
References are made by abbreviation to:	CSA O86	Canadian Standards Association Standard CSA O86, *Engineering Design in Wood*
	NBCC	*National Building Code of Canada*
	NBCC-SC/4	*User's Guide-NBC Structural Commentaries (Part 4)*
	WDM	Canadian Wood Council's *Wood Design Manual*

Site plan

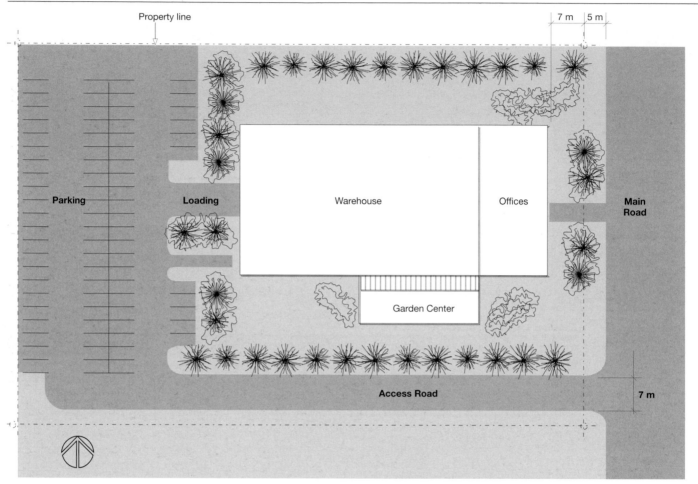

Main Floor Plan

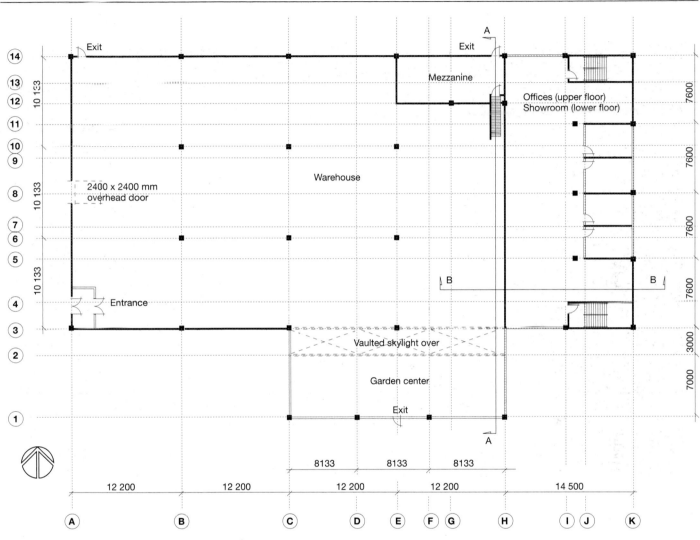

Second Floor Framing Plan

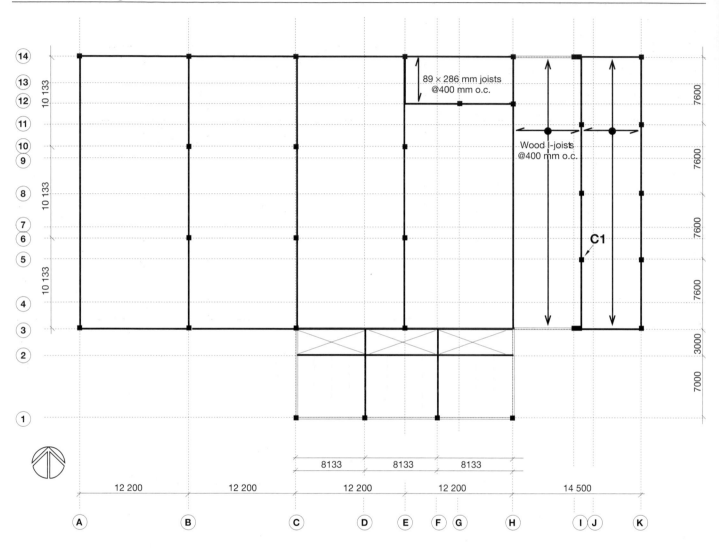

89 × 286 mm joists
@400 mm o.c.

Wood I-joists
@400 mm o.c.

C1

Roof Framing Plan

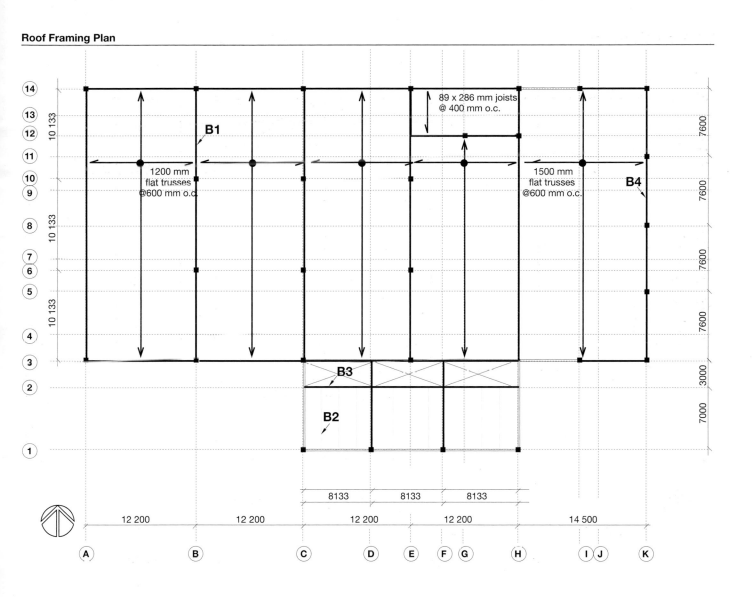

Roof Plan

Roof
drain

Roof
drain

Roof
drain

Built-up
roof system

Roof
drain

Roof
drain

Roof
drain

Control joint

Vaulted skylight

Metal roof

East elevation

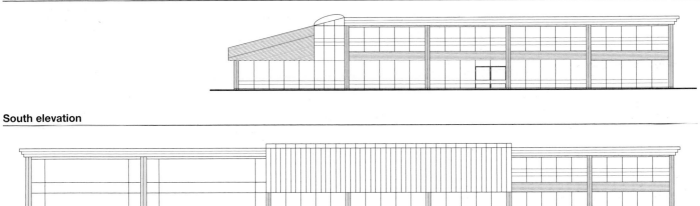

South elevation

North elevation

Section BB

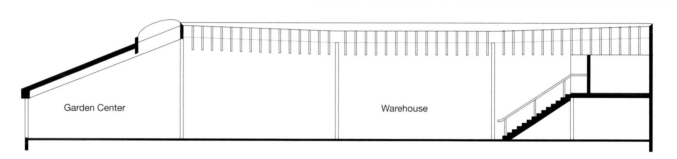

Top of roof

3.66 m

Offices

Top of mezzanine

Warehouse

3.66 m

Showroom

Top of main floor

Section AA

Garden Center   Warehouse

13.2 Glulam Roof Beam – Simply Supported at Columns

GIVEN VALUES AND ASSUMPTIONS

Design glulam roof beam B1 (simply supported at columns).

- Beam spacing = 12.2 m
- Beam span = 10.133 m
- Flat roof with no ceiling
- Flat trusses spaced at 600 mm on centre provide full lateral support
- Use 20f-E D.Fir-L glulam
- Beam free of notches

CALCULATION

For strength calculations:

Total factored load $= 1.25D + 1.5S$

$$= (1.25 \times 0.85) + (1.5 \times 1.6)$$

$$= 3.46 \text{ kPa}$$

For serviceability calculations:

Total specified load $= 0.85 + 1.44$

$$= 2.29 \text{ kPa}$$

$$w_f = 3.46 \times 12.2$$
$$= 42.2 \text{ kN/m}$$

$$w = 2.29 \times 12.2$$
$$= 27.9 \text{ kN/m}$$

$$M_f = \frac{w_f L^2}{8}$$
$$= \frac{42.2 \times 10.133^2}{8}$$
$$= 542 \text{ kN} \bullet \text{m}$$

$$V_f = \frac{w_f L}{2}$$
$$= \frac{42.2 \times 10.133}{2}$$
$$= 214 \text{ kN}$$

For L/180 deflection limit based on total specified load (governs deflection)

$$E_s I_{REQ'D} = \frac{180 \times 5w \times L^3}{384} \text{ N} \bullet \text{mm}^2$$
$$= \frac{180 \times (5 \times 27.9 \times 10\,133^3)}{384}$$
$$= 68\,035 \times 10^9 \text{ N} \bullet \text{mm}^2$$

Checklist satisfied *WDM* Section 2.5 except for condition 6 which is accounted for later.

From Beam Selection Tables for glulam (*WDM* Section 2.5)
try D.Fir-L 20f-E stress grade 175×950 mm

$$K_L \quad = 1.0 \text{ (Full lateral support)}$$

$$K_{zbg} = 0.931 \text{ (}WDM\text{ Table 2.10)} \hspace{4cm} \textit{(Governs)}$$

$$M_r \quad = 606 \text{ kN•m} \times 0.931$$

$$\quad\quad = 564 \text{ kN•m} > 542 \text{ kN•m} \hspace{3.5cm} \textit{(Acceptable)}$$

$$V_r \quad = 200 \text{ kN} < 214 \text{ kN} \hspace{4.3cm} \textit{(Not Acceptable)}$$

Recalculate V_f by subtracting loads within a beam depth from the support

$$V_f \quad = \frac{w_f(L - 2d)}{2}$$

$$\quad = \frac{42.4 \times (10\,133 - 2 \times 950)}{2}$$

$$\quad = 173 \text{ kN} < 200 \text{ kN} \hspace{4cm} \textit{(Acceptable)}$$

$$E_s I \quad = 155\,000 \times 10^9 \text{ N•mm}^2 > 68\,035 \times 10^9 \text{ N•mm}^2 \hspace{1.5cm} \textit{(Acceptable)}$$

Use 175×950 mm 20f-E D.Fir-L glulam.

Notes:

1. Load case for dead + wind does not govern in this case.
2. Concentrated load check (NBCC Article 4.1.5.9) does not govern in this case.

13.3   Glulam Roof Beam – Cantilever and Suspended

GIVEN VALUES AND ASSUMPTIONS

Design glulam roof beam B1 using cantilever and suspended span construction as an alternative to simple span construction in Section 13.2.

- Beam spacing = 12.2 m
- Beam span = 10.133 m
- Flat roof with no ceiling
- Flat roof trusses provide full lateral support on the upper surface of the beam
- Use 20f-EX D.Fir-L glulam

FIGURE 13.1

Glulam roof beam B1 using cantilever and suspended span construction

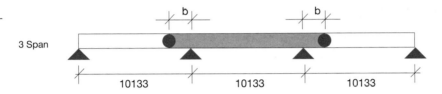

3 Span

10133   10133   10133

CALCULATION

1. Select configuration with hinges in outside bays (*WDM* Figure 2.8)

2. Determine factored load ratio, n

    For roofs: $n = \dfrac{D + 0.5S}{D + S} = \dfrac{(1.25 \times 0.85) + (0.5 \times 1.5 \times 1.6)}{(1.25 \times 0.85) + (1.5 \times 1.6)} = 0.65$

3. Determine hinge points (*WDM* Figure 2.8)

    b = 0.152 × span = 0.152 × 10.133 = 1.540 m

4. Determine maximum factored moments and shears on the suspended beam

    $M_f = \dfrac{w_f L^2}{8} = \dfrac{42.2 \times (10.133 - 1.540)^2}{8} = 390$ kN•m

    $V_f = \dfrac{w_f L}{2} = \dfrac{42.2 \times (10.333 - 1.540)}{2} = 181$ kN

5. Determine maximum factored moments and shears on the cantilevered beam (concentrated loads are end shears from suspended beams). See Figure 13.2
    M_f– for Case 1 should be equal to M_f+ for Case 2 since optimum hinge points are used

    M_f– = 329 kN•m (Case 1)

    M_f+ = 327 kN•m (Case 2)

    M_f = 329 kN•m (Case 1)

    V_f = 246 kN (Case 1)

6. Checklist satisfied (*WDM* Section 2.5) except conditions 5, 6 and 8 which are accounted for later if necessary.

   Use Beam Selection Tables (*WDM* Section 2.5) to select trial sections

   For the suspended beams try 130×912 mm

   $$K_{Zbg} = K_L = 1.0$$

   $$M_r = 415 \text{ kN} \bullet \text{m} > 390 \text{ kN} \bullet \text{m} \qquad (Acceptable)$$

   $$V_r = 142 \text{ kN} < 181 \text{ kN} \qquad (Not\ Acceptable)$$

   Re-calculate V_f by subtracting loads within a beam depth from the support

   $$V_f = \frac{w_f(L - 2d)}{2}$$

   $$= \frac{42.2 \times (8.593 - 2 \times 0.912)}{2} = 143 \text{ kN} > 142 \text{ kN} \qquad (Not\ Acceptable)$$

   Therefore check W_r:

   $$W_r = 555 \times (8.593)^{-0.18} = 376 \text{ kN}$$

   $$W_f = 42.2 \times 8.593$$

   $$= 363 \text{ kN} < 376 \text{ kN} \qquad (Acceptable)$$

7. For the cantilevered beam try 130×836 mm

   a) Check bending capacity.

      For Case 1:

      Check K_{Zbg}: The distance between points of zero moments is 6.35 m.

      $$B = 0.130 \text{ m}$$

      $$L = 6.35 \text{ m}$$

      $$K_{Zbg} = 1.03(0.130 \times 6.35)^{-0.18} \text{ but not greater than } 1.0$$

      $$= 1.0$$

      $$M_{r1} = 349 \times 1.0$$

      $$= 349 \text{ kN} \bullet \text{m}$$

   Check K_L – Lateral support is only provided on the upper surface of the beam. Therefore, where the beam is subjected to negative bending moments, lateral restraint is not provided to the compression face. Lateral restraint is provided at the supports. The unsupported length is the greater of:

   • The length of the cantilever = 1.54 m

   • The distance between the left support and the point of counter flexure = 1.89 m (Governs)

   From *WDM* Table 2.8

   $$L_e = 1.92 l_u$$

   $$= 1.92 \times 1.89$$

   $$= 3.63 \text{ m}$$

$$C_B = \sqrt{\frac{L_e d}{b^2}}$$

$$= \sqrt{\frac{3630 \times 836}{130^2}}$$

$$= 13.4$$

From *WDM* Table 2.9

$$K_L = 0.950$$

$$M_{r2} = 349 \times 0.950$$

$$= 332 \text{ kN} \bullet \text{m}$$

Therefore

$$M_r = \text{min } (M_{r1}, M_{r2}) = 332 \text{ kN} \bullet \text{m} > 329 \text{ kN} \bullet \text{m} \qquad \qquad \textit{(Acceptable)}$$

The results for three cases are listed in the Table below:

	K_{Zby}	K_L	M_r (kN•m)
Case 1	1.0	0.950	332
Case 2	1.0	0.983	343
Case 3	1.0	0.810	283

Therefore Case 3 governs:

$$M_r = 283 \text{ kN} \bullet \text{m} < 329 \text{ kN} \bullet \text{m} \qquad \qquad \textit{(Not Acceptable)}$$

b) Check shear on the cantilevered beam

$$V_r = 130 \text{ kN} < 246 \text{ kN} \qquad \qquad \textit{(Not Acceptable)}$$

Since the lowest design shear for the cantilever (181 kN) exceeds the resistive shear (130 kN), there is no need for calculating shear at a distance equal to the depth of beam away from the support.

Therefore, check W_r

$$W_f = \text{sum of total loads on the beam, maximum for Case 1}$$

$$= 921 \text{ kN}$$

$$W_r = (W_r L^{0.18}) \times L^{-0.18} \times C_v / 3.69$$

$$L = 10.133 + 2 \times 1.54$$

$$= 13.21 \text{ m}$$

$$L_1 = 1.54 \text{ m}$$

$$L_2 = 10.133 \text{ m}$$

FIGURE 13.2

Case 1: Dead + full snow load on all spans

FIGURE 13.3

Case 2: Dead + full snow load on middle span and dead + half snow load on outside spans

FIGURE 13.4

Case 3: Dead + full snow load on outside spans and dead + half snow load on middle span

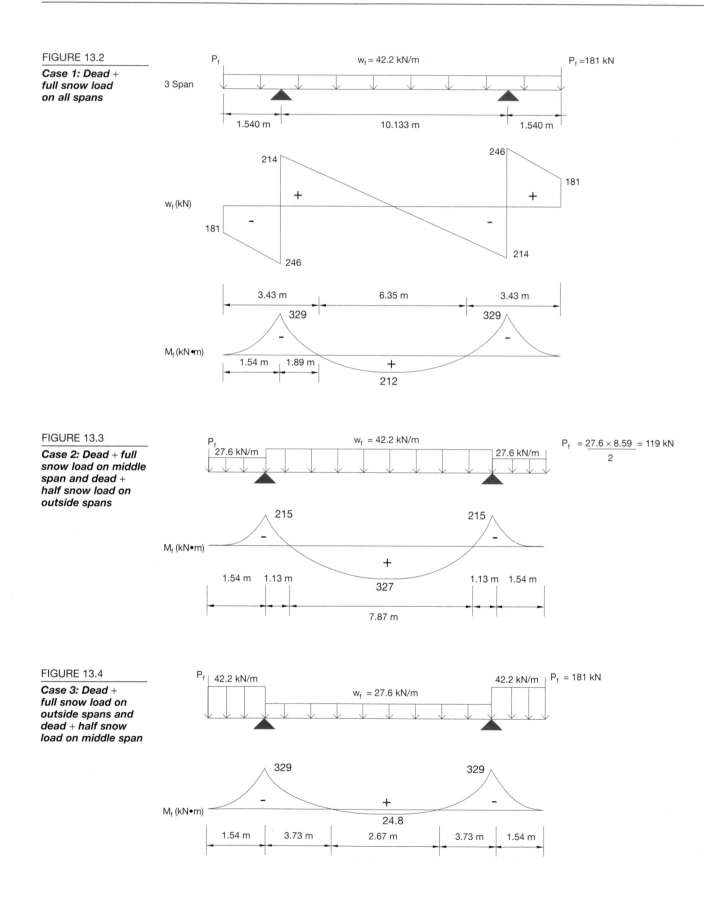

$$\frac{L_1}{L_2} = \frac{1.54}{10.133} = 0.15$$

$$r = \frac{\text{total of concentrated loads}}{\text{total of uniform loads}} = \frac{362}{558} = 0.65$$

From CSA O86 Table 6.5.7.3C

C_v = 6.63 (linearly interpolating)

W_r = 517 $(13.21^{-0.18})$ 6.63 / 3.69

= 584 kN < 920 kN   *(Not Acceptable)*

Calculate required $W_r \, L^{0.18}$

$W_r \, L^{0.18}$ = 920 × 517 / 584

= 814 kN•m$^{0.18}$

Try 215 × 912 mm

	K_{Zbg}	K_L	M_r (kN•m)
Case 1	0.974	1.0	669
Case 2	0.937	1.0	643
Case 3	1.0	0.970	666

Therefore Case 2 governs:

M_r = 643 kN•m > 327 kN•m   *(Acceptable)*

W_r = 838 $(13.21^{-0.18})$ 6.63 / 3.69

= 946 kN > 921 kN   *(Acceptable)*

Re-design suspended beams to match the cantilevered beam

Try 215 × 912 mm

K_{Zbg} = 0.922, K_L = 1.0

M_r = 633 kN•m > 390 kN•m   *(Acceptable)*

V_r = 235 kN > 181 kN   *(Acceptable)*

8.   Check deflection at the centre of the cantilevered beam due to total specified loads

FIGURE 13.5

Case 2: Dead + full snow load on middle span and dead + half snow load on outside spans

3 Span

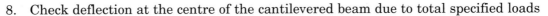
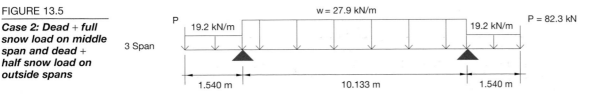

$$\text{maximum deflection} = 11.2 \text{ mm}$$

$$\text{maximum permissible deflection} = L / 180$$

$$= 10\,133 / 180$$

$$= 56.3 \text{ mm} > 11.2 \text{ mm} \qquad \textit{(Acceptable)}$$

9. Check deflection of the suspended beam due to total specified loads

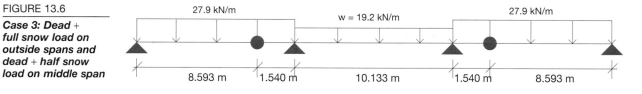

FIGURE 13.6

Case 3: Dead + full snow load on outside spans and dead + half snow load on middle span

27.9 kN/m	w = 19.2 kN/m	27.9 kN/m

8.593 m   1.540 m   10.133 m   1.540 m   8.593 m

$$\text{maximum deflection} = \text{deflection of suspended beam} + 1/2 \text{ deflection of cantilever}$$

$$= 11.72 + 1/2 \times 3.45$$

$$= 13.44 \text{ mm}$$

$$\text{maximum permissible deflection} = L / 180$$

$$= 10\,133 / 180$$

$$= 56.3 \text{ mm} > 13.44 \text{ mm} \qquad \textit{(Acceptable)}$$

Use 215 × 912 mm 20f-EX D.Fir-L glulam for both cantilever and suspended segments.

Comparison of Beam Options

Beam option	Volume m³
Simply supported	5.05
Cantilevered	5.96

In this case, the simply supported system is more economical.

13.4 Tongue and Groove Decking in Garden Centre

GIVEN VALUES AND ASSUMPTIONS

Design the tongue and groove decking in the garden centre.

- Support spacing = 2.03 m
- Controlled random pattern in east-west direction
- 3/12 roof slope = 14°
- Decking width = 133 mm
- Use Select grade spruce for appearance
- Deflection limit is L/240 for snow load, and L/180 for total specified load

CALCULATION

Specified dead load = 0.35 kPa (includes self-weight plus roofing)

$$= 0.35 / \cos 14°$$

$$= 0.36 \text{ kPa (on a horizontal projection)}$$

Specified snow load for strength calculations = 1.60 kPa

Specified snow load for serviceability calculations = 1.44 kPa

Factored loading w_f = (1.250 × 0.36) + (1.5 × 1.60) = 2.85 kPa

Specified live load w_L = 144 kPa

Total specified loading w = 0.36 + 1.44 = 1.80 kPa

Checklist satisfied (*WDM* Section 2.2). From Decking Selection Tables try 38 mm thickness

W_{FR} = 9.88 kPa > 2.85 kPa   *(Acceptable)*

$W_{\Delta R}$ = 2.12 kPa > 1.44 kPa for L/240 deflection   *(Acceptable)*

$W_{\Delta T}$ = 2.12 × 1.33 = 2.82 kPa > 1.80 kPa for L/180 deflection   *(Acceptable)*

Use 133 × 38 mm Select grade spruce decking.

13.5   Sawn Timber Roof Purlin in Garden Centre

GIVEN VALUES AND ASSUMPTIONS

Design the sawn timber roof purlin B2 in the garden centre.

- Beam spacing = 2.03 m
- Beam span – 7 m
- Beams are restrained against lateral displacement and rotation at their ends
- Use D.Fir-L No.1 sawn timber

CALCULATION

Specified dead load on a horizontal projection based on total dead load = 0.75/cos 14°

$$= 0.77 \text{ kPa}$$

For strength calculations:

Total factored load = $(1.25 \times 0.77) + (1.5 \times 1.6) = 3.36$ kPa

For serviceability calculations:

Total specified load = $0.77 + 1.44 = 2.21$ kPa

$$\begin{aligned} w_f &= 3.36 \times 2.03 \\ &= 6.82 \text{ kN/m} \end{aligned}$$

$$\begin{aligned} w &= 2.21 \times 2.03 \\ &= 4.49 \text{ kN/m} \end{aligned}$$

$$\begin{aligned} M_f &= w_f \, L^2 / 8 \\ &= 6.82 \times 7^2 / 8 \\ &= 41.8 \text{ kN} \bullet \text{m} \end{aligned}$$

$$\begin{aligned} V_f &= w_f \, L / 2 \\ &= (6.82 \times 7 \times \cos 14°) / 2 \\ &= 23.2 \text{ kN} \end{aligned}$$

For L/180, deflection limit based on total specified load

$$\begin{aligned} E_s I_{REQ'D} &= \left(\frac{180}{\cos 14°} \right) \times \frac{5 \, w \, L^3}{384} \text{ N} \bullet \text{mm}^2 \\ &= \left(\frac{180}{\cos 14°} \right) \times \frac{5 \times 4.49 \times 7000^3}{384} \text{ N} \bullet \text{mm}^2 \\ &= 3720 \times 10^9 \text{ N} \bullet \text{mm}^2 \end{aligned}$$

Checklist satisfied (*WDM* Section 2.5)

From Beam Selection Tables for sawn timber (*WDM* Section 2.5) try 140×394 mm

M_r = 46.4 kN•m > 41.8 kN•m   *(Acceptable)*

V_r = 44.7 kN > 23.2 kN   *(Acceptable)*

(Note: there is a small notch at the end of the purlin that does not affect shear capacity)

E_sI = 8560×10^9 N•mm^2 > 3720×10^9 N•mm^2 *(Acceptable)*

Use 140×394 mm No.1 D.Fir-L.

13.6   Glulam Header Beam in Garden Centre

GIVEN VALUES AND ASSUMPTIONS

Design the glulam header beam B3 in the garden centre.

- Beam span = 8.13 m
- Use 20f-E D.Fir-L glulam.
- w_f and w based on 1.5 m tributary width.
- P_f and P from B2.

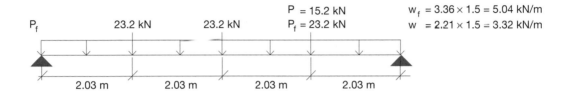

P = 15.2 kN w_f = 3.36 × 1.5 = 5.04 kN/m
P_f = 23.2 kN   w = 2.21 × 1.5 = 3.32 kN/m

23.2 kN   23.2 kN

P_f

2.03 m   2.03 m   2.03 m   2.03 m

CALCULATION

$$M_f = \frac{w_f L^2}{8} + \frac{P_f L}{2}$$

$$= \frac{5.04 \times 8.13^2}{8} + \frac{23.2 \times 8.13}{2}$$

$$= 136 \text{ kN} \cdot \text{m}$$

$$V_f = \frac{w_f L}{2} + \frac{3 P_f}{2}$$

$$= \frac{5.04 \times 8.13}{8} + \frac{3 \times 23.2}{2}$$

$$= 55.2 \text{ kN}$$

For L/180, deflection is based on total specified load

$$E_s I_{REQ'D} = 180 \times \frac{5 w L^3 + 19 P L^2}{384}$$

$$= 360 \times \frac{5 \times 3.32 \times 8130^3 + 19 \times 15\,200 \times 8130^2}{384}$$

$$= 13\,200 \times 10^9 \text{ N} \cdot \text{mm}^2$$

Checklist satisfied (*WDM* Section 2.5)

From Beam Selection Tables (*WDM* Section 2.5) try 130 × 608 mm

M'_r = 185 kN•m

From Table 2.10 (*WDM* Table 2.10)

K_{Zbg} = 1.0

Calculate K_L:

Purlin spacing, a = 2.03 m

Effective Length, L_e = 1.92a (*WDM* Table 2.8)

$\qquad$ = 1.92 × 2.03

$\qquad$ = 3.90 m

$\qquad$ = 3900 mm

$$C_b = \sqrt{\frac{L_e d}{b^2}}$$

$\qquad$ = 11.8

From *WDM* Table 2.9

K_L = 0.969

Therefore

M_r = 185 × 0.969

$\qquad$ = 179 kN•m > 136 kN•m $\hspace{6cm}$ *(Acceptable)*

V_r = 94.8 kN > 55.2 kN $\hspace{6cm}$ *(Acceptable)*

$E_s I$ = 30 200 × 10⁹ N•mm² > 13 200 × 10⁹ N•mm² $\hspace{3cm}$ *(Acceptable)*

Use 130 × 608 mm 20f-E D.Fir-L glulam.

13.7   Glulam Roof Header Beam in Office

GIVEN VALUES AND ASSUMPTIONS

Design the glulam roof header beam B4 in the office.

- Tributary width = 7.25 m
- 2-span continuous
- Beam span = 7.6 m
- Flat roof trusses provide full lateral support on the upper surface of the beam
- Use 20f–EX D.Fir–L glulam

CALCULATION

For strength calculations:

$$\text{Total factored load} = (1.25 \times 0.90) + (1.5 \times 1.6)$$
$$= 3.53 \text{ kPa}$$

For serviceability calculations:

$$\text{Total specified load} = 0.90 + 1.44$$
$$= 2.34 \text{ kPa}$$

$$w_f = 3.53 \times 7.25$$
$$= 25.6 \text{ kN/m}$$

$$w = 2.34 \times 7.25$$
$$= 17.0 \text{ kN/m}$$

FIGURE 13.7

Case 1: Dead + full snow load on all spans

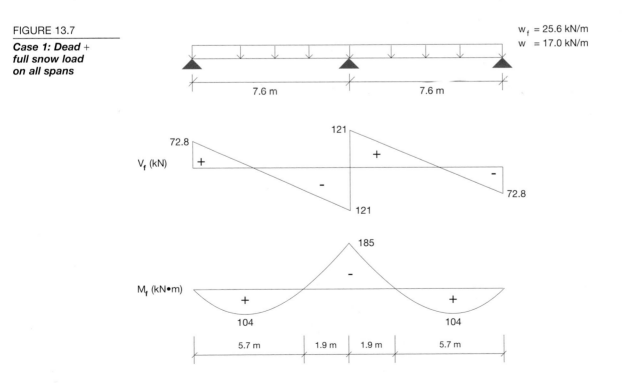

FIGURE 13.8

Case 2: Dead + full snow load on one span and dead + half snow load on the other

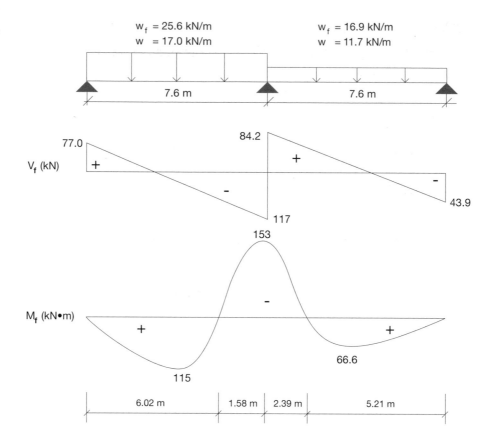

Case 2:

M_f = 153 kN•m

V_f = 117 kN

Governing:

M_f = 185 kN•m   (Case 1)

V_f = 121 kN   (Case 1)

For L/360 deflection limit based on specified snow load (Case 2 governs)

$E_sI_{REQ'D}$ = 12 000 × 10⁹ N•mm²

From Beam Selection Tables for Glulam (*WDM* Section 2.5) try 175 × 532 20f-EX D.Fir-L

K_{Zbg}= K_L = 1.0

M_r = 190 kN•m > 185 kN•m   *(Acceptable)*

V_r = 112 kN < 122 kN   *(Not Acceptable)*

Therefore check W_r:

$W_f =$ sum of total loads on the beam, maximum for Case 1

$\quad = 389$ kN

$W_r = (W_r L^{0.18}) \times L^{-0.18} \times \dfrac{C_v}{3.69}$

$\dfrac{L_1}{L_2} = 0.5$

$r \quad = 0$

From CSA O86 Table 6.5.7.3D

$C_v = 6.66$

$W_r = 455 \times (7.6 \times 2)^{-0.18} \times \dfrac{6.66}{3.69} - 503\text{kN} > 389\ kN$ *(Acceptable)*

$E_s I = 27\ 200 \times 10^9\ \text{N}\bullet\text{mm}^2 > 12\ 000 \times 10^9\ \text{N}\bullet\text{mm}^2$ *(Acceptable)*

Use 175 × 532 mm 20f-EX D. Fir-L Glulam.

13.8   Wood I-Joist in Office

GIVEN VALUES AND ASSUMPTIONS

Design the wood I-joists in the office.

- Joist spacing = 400 mm

- Joist span = 7.25 m

- Fully laterally supported by subfloor

CALCULATION

For L/480 deflection limit based on live load

$$EI_{REQ'D} = 480 \times \frac{5\, w_L\, L^3}{384}$$

$$= 480 \times \frac{5 \times 2.4 \times 0.4 \times 7250^3}{384}$$

$$= 2286 \times 10^9 \ N\bullet mm^2$$

From Table 6.13 use a 406 mm deep wood I-joist with 89 × 38 mm
(nominal 4" × 2") flanges

$$EI = 2900 \times 10^9 \ N\bullet mm^2 > 2286 \times 10^9 \ N\bullet mm^2 \qquad \textit{(Acceptable)}$$

Check for 9.0 kN concentrated load distributed over an area of 750 × 750 mm
located at mid-span for maximum effect. (NBCC Article 4.1.5.9).

Assuming that the partition and concentrated loads will not occur simultaneously,
ignore the partition load for this calculation.

$$EI_{REQ'D} = 480 \times \frac{P_L\, L^2}{48}$$

$$= 480 \times \frac{4800 \times 7250^2}{48}$$

$$= 2523 \times 10^9 \ N\bullet mm^2 < 2900 \times 10^9 \ N\bullet mm^2 \qquad \textit{(Acceptable)}$$

**For preliminary design purposes, consider a 406 mm deep wood I-joist
with 38 × 89 mm flanges. For more detailed design, consult the wood
I-joist manufacturer.**

13.9   Interior Glulam Column in Showroom

GIVEN VALUES AND ASSUMPTIONS

Design the interior glulam column C1 in the showroom.

- Unbraced length = 2.58 m
- Column effectively pinned at both ends
- Use 16c-E D.Fir-L glulam
- Column supports continuous beam

CALCULATION

Tributary area of column

$$= 7.6 \text{ m} \times 7.25 \text{ m}$$
$$= 55.1 \text{ m}^2$$

Live load reduction factor (NBCC Clause 4.1.5.8)

$$= 0.3 + \sqrt{\frac{9.8}{55.1}}$$
$$= 0.72$$

Interior support coefficient for a two span continuous beam under uniformly distributed load = 1.25.

Factored live load

$$P_L = 1.5 \times 2.4 \text{ kPa} \times 55.1 \text{ m}^2 \times 0.72 \times 1.25$$
$$= 178 \text{ kN}$$

Factored dead load

$$P_D = 1.25 \times 2.0 \text{ kPa} \times 55.1 \text{ m}^2 \times 1.25$$
$$= 172 \text{ kN}$$

Total factored load

$$P_f = 178 + 172$$
$$= 350 \text{ kN}$$

Effective lengths

$$K_e L_x = K_e L_y$$
$$= 1.0 \times 2.58$$
$$= 2.58 \text{ m}$$

Checklist satisfied (*WDM* Section 3.3)

From Column Selection Tables (*WDM* Section 3.3) try 175 × 152 mm

For $K_e L$ = 3.0 m

P_{rx} = 384 kN > 350 kN   *(Acceptable)*

P_{ry} = 440 kN > 350 kN   *(Acceptable)*

Use 175 × 152 mm 16c-E D.Fir-L glulam.

13.10   Exterior Bearing Stud Wall in Warehouse

GIVEN VALUES AND ASSUMPTIONS

Design the west exterior bearing stud wall in the warehouse (central portion of wall only).

- Stud spacing = 400 mm
- Stud length = 6.0 m
- Tributary width (gravity loads) = 6.10 m
- Studs effectively held in position by roof trusses at top, and by foundation at bottom
- Wall sheathing prevents buckling about weak axis and is fastened to meet the requirements for a Case 2 system
- Short term load duration
- Use No.1 / No.2 grade S-P-F lumber

CALCULATION

Specified dead load, D = 0.85 kPa

Specified snow load, S = 1.6 kPa (strength)

Specified wind load, W = 0.308 $(C_pC_g - C_{pi}C_{gi})$ (strength)

Specified wind load, W = 0.231 $(C_pC_g - C_{pi}C_{gi})$ (serviceability)

Specified gravity loads on the wall
Dead:

$$P_D = 0.85 \times 6.1 \times 0.4$$
$$= 2.07 \text{ kN}$$

Snow:

$$P_S = 1.6 \times 6.1 \times 0.4$$
$$= 3.90 \text{ kN}$$

Specified wind loads on the face of the wall

C_pC_g = 1.75 (from NBCC-SC/4, Figure I-8)

C_{pi} = −0.45 (from NBCC-SC/4, for Category 2 Building)

C_{gi} = 2

Strength:

$$w_f = 0.308 \times [1.75 - (-0.45 \times 2)] \times 0.4$$
$$= 0.326 \text{ kN/m}$$

Serviceability:

$$w = 0.231 \times [1.75 - (-0.45 \times 2)] \times 0.4$$
$$= 0.297 \text{ kN/m}$$

Case 1: 1.25 Dead + 1.5 Snow (K_D = 1.0)

$$P_f = 1.25 \times 2.07 + 1.5 \times 3.90 = 8.44 \text{ kN}$$

Case 2: 1.25 Dead + 1.5 Snow + 0.4 Wind (K_D = 1.15)

$\quad$ P_f = 1.25 × 2.07 + 1.5 × 3.90 = 8.44 kN

$\quad$ w_f = 0.4 x 0.326 = 0.13 kN/m

Case 3: 1.25 Dead + 0.5 Snow + 1.4 Wind (K_D = 1.15)

$\quad$ P_f = 1.25 × 2.07 + 0.5 × 3.90 = 4.54 kN

$\quad$ w_f = 1.4 × 0.326 = 0.456 kN/m $\hfill$ *(Acceptable)*

1. From the Stud Wall Selection Tables (Compression Loading) (*WDM* Section 3.2) select a size that satisfies the factored compression force for Load Case 1.

   Checklist satisfied (*WDM* Section 3.2)

   Try 38 × 140 mm

   $\quad$ P'_r = 10.1 kN > 8.44 kN $\hfill$ *(Acceptable)*

2. From the Stud Wall Selection Tables (Combined Loading) (*WDM* Section 5.2) select a size that satisfies the strength interaction equation for Load Case 2.

   Checklist satisfied (*WDM* Section 5.2)

   Try 38 × 184 mm

   $\quad$ P'_r = 10.2 kN > 8.44 kN $\hfill$ *(Acceptable)*

   $\quad$ w'_r = 0.583 kN/m > 0.13 kN/m $\hfill$ *(Acceptable)*

3. Check interaction equation for Load Case 3.

   Try 38 × 184 mm

   $\quad$ P'_r = 5.11 kN > 4.54 kN $\hfill$ *(Acceptable)*

   $\quad$ w'_r = 0.802 kN/m > 0.456 kN/m $\hfill$ *(Acceptable)*

4. Check shear and deflection

   $\quad$ V_f = w_f L / 2

   $\qquad$ = 0.456 × 6 / 2

   $\qquad$ = 1.37 kN

   $\quad$ V_r = 12.2 kN > 1.37 kN $\hfill$ *(Acceptable)*

   $\quad$ max. deflection $= \dfrac{5\,w\,L^4}{384\,E_S\,I}$

   $\qquad\qquad\qquad = \dfrac{5 \times 0.297 \times 6000^4}{384 \times 187 \times 10^9}$

   $\qquad\qquad\qquad$ = 26.8 mm = L / 224 $\hfill$ *(Acceptable)*

Use 38 × 184 mm No.1 / No.2 S-P-F spaced at 400 mm.

13.11   Bolted Connection of Header to Exterior Column

GIVEN VALUES AND ASSUMPTIONS

Design the bolted connection to resist wind uplift acting on the Glulam header beam B4 (Section 13.7) at the exterior glulam column.

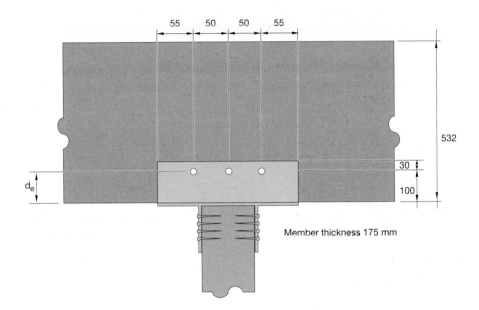

Member thickness 175 mm

Net factored uplift on the roof is 0.311 kPa.

Modification Factors

K_D = 1.15 (short term duration of load)

K_{SF} = 1.0 (dry service conditions)

K_T = 1.0 (glulam is not treated)

Therefore

K' = 1.15

CALCULATION

Q_f = 21.4 kN

V_f = 10.7 kN

The configuration is Type 10 – double shear loaded perpendicular to the grain.

Try three rows of 1/2" diameter bolts.

The capacity of the connection, Q_r, is the lesser of Q_u and QS_{rT},

Q'_u = 11.3 kN for a member thickness of 175 mm from Bolt Selection Tables *WDM* Section 7.4)

Q_u = $Q'_u \, n_c \, n_R \, K'$ = 11.3 × 3 × 1 × 1.15 = 39.0 kN

Try d_e = 100 mm, according to Claus 10.4.4.7 of CSA O86,

$$Q'S_{rT} = \phi_w \times 14 \sqrt{\frac{d_e}{1-\dfrac{d_e}{d}}} = 0.7 \times 14 \sqrt{\frac{100}{1-\dfrac{100}{532}}} = 0.109 \text{ kN/mm}$$

$$QS_{rT} = Q'S_{rT}t_mK' = 0.109 \times 175 \times 1.15 = 21.9 \text{ kN}$$

Therefore,

$$Q_r = 21.9 \text{ kN} > 21.4 \text{ kN} \qquad\qquad (Acceptable)$$

Note: Check shear resistance of glulam header beam as described in *WDM* Section 7.1

Effective depth d_e = 100 mm

From Beam Selection Tables for glulam (*WDM* Section 2.5)

$$V_r = 112 \text{ kN}$$

Modifying for effective depth and load duration

$$V_r = \left(\frac{100}{532}\right) \times 112 \times 1.15 = 24.2 \text{ kN} > 10.7 \text{ kN} \qquad\qquad (Acceptable)$$

Check spacing and edge distances from Figure 7.6 (*WDM* Section 7.4)

Spacing parallel to grain S_C = 50 mm > $3d_F$ = 38 mm   (Acceptable)

Loaded edge e_Q = 100 mm > $4d_F$ = 51 mm   (Acceptable)

Unloaded edge e_p = 532 – 100 = 432 mm > $1.5d_F$ = 19 mm   (Acceptable)

Check end and edge distance requirements for the steel plate with CSA S16.1

Use three 1/2" diameter bolts.

13.12 Shear Plate Beam-to-Column Connection in Office

GIVEN VALUES AND ASSUMPTIONS

Design the shear plate beam-to-column connection in the east office wall.

- 175 × 190 mm D.Fir-L glulam column
- 175 × 532 mm 20f–EX D.Fir–L glulam beams
- Factored reaction = 72.8 kN per beam

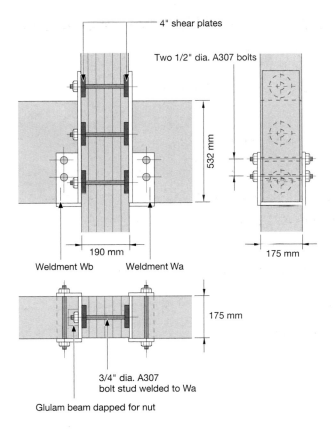

4" shear plates

Two 1/2" dia. A307 bolts

532 mm

175 mm

190 mm

Weldment Wb   Weldment Wa

175 mm

3/4" dia. A307
bolt stud welded to Wa

Glulam beam dapped for nut

Modification factors

K_D = 1.0 (standard term duration of load)

K_{SF} = 1.0 (seasoned wood, dry service conditions)

K_T = 1.0 (glulam untreated)

J_C = 1.0 (assume connector spacing, end and edge distances meet minimum
values shown in Fig. 7.16, *WDM* Section 7.8)

J_T = 1.0 (assume column thickness meets minimum values shown
in Fig. 7.16, *WDM* Section 7.8)

J_O = 1.0 (shear plates installed in side grain)

J_P = 1.0 (bolts are used)

J_S = 1.0 (steel side plates are used)

Therefore

$$K' = 1.0$$

$$J' = 1.0$$

Checklist satisfied (*WDM* Section 7.8)

CALCULATION

From Table 7.18 (*WDM* Section 7.8) try one row of 4" diameter shear plates with 3/4" diameter bolts on either side of the column.

Resistance of the glulam column

$$P_r = \phi\, p_u\, n_{Fe}\, n_R\, K'\, J'\, J_s$$
$$= 29.4 \times n_{Fe} \times 1.0 \times 1.0 \times 1.0 \times 1.0$$
$$= 29.4\, n_{Fe}$$

Required $n_{Fe} = 72.8 / 29.4$
$$= 2.48$$

Determine the number of shear plates required from Table 7.21 (*WDM* Section 7.8)

$$A_m = 175 \times 190$$
$$= 33.2 \times 10^3 \text{ mm}^2$$

$$A_s = 6 \times 175 \times 2$$
$$= 2.10 \times 10^3 \text{ mm}^2$$

$$A_m / A_s = 15.8$$

Therefore using three shear plates per row

$$n_{Fe} = 2.94 > 2.48 \qquad\qquad (Acceptable)$$

$$P_r = 29.4 \times 2.94$$
$$= 86.4 \text{ kN} > 72.8 \text{ kN} \qquad\qquad (Acceptable)$$

Check resistance of shear plates assuming bearing on threads from *WDM* Section 7.8.

$$N_{sr} = N_{su} \, n_F \, n_R$$
$$= 28 \times 3 \times 1$$
$$= 84 \text{ kN} > 72.8 \text{ kN}$$ *(Acceptable)*

Check spacing and edge distance requirements

shear plate spacing parallel to grain = 230 mm, $J_C = 1.0$ *(Acceptable)*

edge distance = 95 mm > 65 mm *(Acceptable)*

Check end and edge distance requirements for the steel plate with CSA S16.1.

Use one row of three 4" diameter shear plates with 3/4" bolts.

13.13 Timber Rivet Hanger Connection

GIVEN VALUES AND ASSUMPTIONS

Design the timber rivet hanger connection connecting sawn timber purlin B2 to glulam header B3.

- Use 65 mm rivets

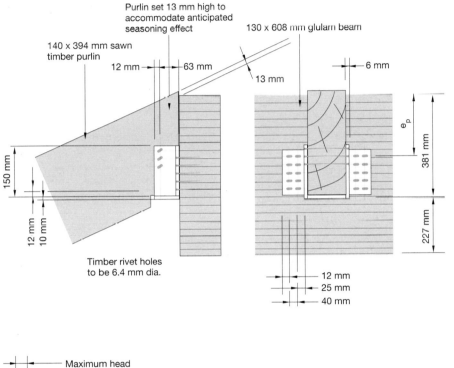

Purlin set 13 mm high to accommodate anticipated seasoning effect

130 x 608 mm glulam beam

140 x 394 mm sawn timber purlin

12 mm — 63 mm

13 mm

6 mm

e_p

381 mm

150 mm

12 mm
10 mm

227 mm

Timber rivet holes to be 6.4 mm dia.

12 mm
25 mm
40 mm

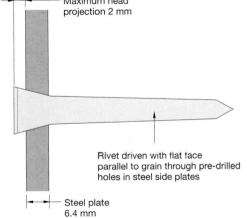

Maximum head projection 2 mm

Rivet driven with flat face parallel to grain through pre-drilled holes in steel side plates

Steel plate 6.4 mm

Modification Factors

K_D = 1.0 (standard term duration of load)

K_{SF} = 1.0 (seasoned wood, dry service conditions)

K_T = 1.0 (untreated)

H = 1.0 (D.Fir-L glulam)

J_O = 1.0 (side grain use)

J_Y = 1.0 (side plates are 6.4 mm thick)

CALCULATION

Q_f = 23.2 kN

Q_r is the lesser of:

$$Q_{ry} = Q'_y \, K_{SF} \, K_T \, J_Y \, J_O \, H$$

$$= Q'_y$$

$$Q_{rw} = Q'_w \, K_D \, K_{SF} \, K_T \, J_O \, H$$

$$= Q'_w$$

Checklist satisfied (*WDM* Section 7.7)

From the Timber Rivet Selection Tables (*WDM* Section 7.7), estimate the required number of rivets per row using a 40 mm spacing perpendicular to grain (S_Q):

Number of rivets per row, n_c	e_p $381-12-40(n_c-1)$ mm	Q'_y kN	Q'_w kN
7	129	37.7	66.5
6	169	32.3	47.3
5	209	26.9	34.0*

Note:

* Calculated using CSA O86 Clause 10.7.2.4:

Q'_w per group = $\phi \, (q_w \, L_p^{0.8} \, C_t)$

Q'_w total = 2 × (Q'_w per group)

Try five rivets per row

Q_r = 26.9 kN > 23.2 kN   *(Acceptable)*

In this example the effects of eccentricity are assumed to be negligible. Therefore, five rivets per row are sufficient.

Check end and edge distances from the selection tables

    edge distance for wood = 227 mm > 50 mm   *(Acceptable)*

    end distance for wood > 50 mm   *(Acceptable)*

    minimum end and edge distance for steel = 12 mm   *(Acceptable)*

Use two rows of five 65 mm rivets.

13.14   Lateral Loads: East-West Direction

EARTHQUAKE LOADS – EAST-WEST DIRECTION

Calculate the loads to be resisted by shearwalls along grid lines 1, 3, and 14.

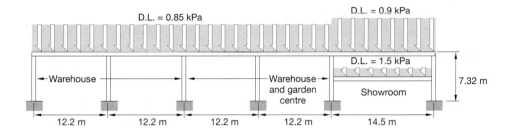

For Richmond Hill, Ontario

$S_a(0.2) = 0.18$

$S_a(0.5) = 0.11$

$S_a(1.0) = 0.065$

$S_a(2.0) = 0.021$

Ground profile classified as soft rock (Site Class C)

From Table 3.6, $F_a = 1.0$

From Table 3.7, $F_v = 1.0$

From NBCC 4.1.8.7, Equivalent Static Force Procedure may be used when $I_E F_a S_a(0.2)$ is less than 0.35.

$I_E F_a S_a(0.2) = 1.0 \times 1.0 \times 0.18 = 0.18 < 0.35$

Therefore, Equivalent Static Force Procedure may be used.

Note: In higher seismic regions, Equivalent Static Force Procedure may be used for:

- Regular structures, less than 60 m in height with fundamental periods less than 2 seconds in two orthogonal directions, or
- Structures with limited irregularities, less than 20 m in height with fundamental periods less than 0.5 seconds in two orthogonal directions.

Equivalent static force at the base of the structure (NBCC 4.1.8.11):

$$V = S(T_a) M_v I_E W / (R_d R_o)$$

V cannot be less than:

$$V_{min} = S(4.0) M_v I_E W / (R_d R_o)$$

But where $R_d \geq 1.5$, V need not be greater than:

$$V_{max} = 2/3\ S(0.2)\ I_E W / (R_d R_o)$$

$S(T_a)$ = design spectral response acceleration

= function of the fundamental period of vibration of the structure, T_a

T_a = $0.05\ (h_n)^{3/4}$

h_n = roof height

= 7.32 m

T_a = $0.05\ (7.32)^{3/4}$

= 0.22 seconds

$S(0.2) = F_a S_a(0.2)$

= 1.0×0.18

= 0.18

$S(0.5) = \min (F_v S_a(0.5)\ \text{or}\ F_a S_a(0.2))$

= $\min (1.0 \times 0.11\ \text{or}\ 1.0 \times 0.18)$

= 0.11

$S(4.0) = F_v S_a(2.0)\ /\ 2$

= $1.0 \times 0.021\ /\ 2$

= 0.0105

by interpolation:

$S(0.22) = 0.175$

M_v = 1.0 (NBCC Table 4.1.8.11)

I_E = 1.0

W = dead load + 25% snow load

R_d = 3.0 (NBCC Table 4.1.8.9)

R_o = 1.7 (NBCC Table 4.1.8.9)

In this design, it is assumed that the diaphragms are flexible and the seismic loads are distributed to the shearlines based on the tributary area per shearwall. According to NBCC-SC/4, for structures with flexible diaphragms, accidental torsion should be taken into account by moving the center of mass by $\pm 0.05\ D_{nx}$ and using the largest of the seismic loads for the design of each vertical element. D_{nx} is the plan dimension of the building perpendicular to the seismic load.

Loads at gridlines without accounting for accidental torsion (used for diaphragm design):

Area	Tributary area per shear line m²	Dead load kPa	25% snow load kPa	Load at gridlines, kN		
				1	3	14
Warehouse roof	742	0.85	0.40		927	927
Office roof	220	0.90	0.40		287	287
Garden centre roof	122	0.75	0.40	140	140	
Office floor	220	1.50			331	331
			Total	140	1685	1545

Loads at gridlines accounting for accidental offset (used for shearwall design):

$$\text{Offset} = \pm 0.05\ D_{nx}$$
$$= \pm 0.05 \times 40.4$$
$$= \pm 2.02\ m$$

Area	Offset +2.02 m Load (kN) at gridlines			Offset −2.02 m Load (kN) at gridlines		
	1	3	14	1	3	14
Warehouse roof		804	1050		1050	804
Office roof		248	325		325	248
Garden center roof	84	197		197	84	
Office floor		287	374		374	287
Total	84	1536	1749*	197*	1833*	1339

* Governing case

$$V \quad = \; S(T_a)M_vI_EW/(R_dR_o)$$
$$= \; 0.175 \times 1.0 \times 1.0 \times W/(3.0 \times 1.7)$$
$$= \; 0.0343 \; W \; kN$$

$$V_{min} = \; S(4.0) \; M_vI_EW/(R_dR_o)$$
$$= \; 0.0105 \times 1.0 \times 1.0 \times W/(3.0 \times 1.7)$$
$$= \; 0.00206 \; W \; kN$$

But need not be greater than

$$V_{max} = \; 2/3 \; S(0.2) \; I_EW/(R_dR_o)$$
$$= \; 2/3 \times 0.18 \times 1.0 \times W/(3.0 \times 1.7)$$
$$= \; 0.0235 \; W \; kN \qquad\qquad\qquad\qquad\qquad \textit{(Governs)}$$

For shearwalls at gridline 3:

For diaphragm design:

$$V_{max} = \; 0.0235 \times 1685$$
$$= \; 39.6 \; kN$$

For shearwall design:

$$V_{max} = \; 0.0235 \times 1833$$
$$= \; 43.1 \; kN$$

Because $I_EF_aS_a$ (0.2) <0.35, Clause 9.8.7 of CSA O86 for structures in low seismic zones applies. Seismic design forces for diaphragms equal to the factored seismic force calculated using R_dR_o for the wood shearwalls. Therefore,

For diaphragm design:

$$= \; 39.6/63.3$$
$$= \; 0.626 \; kN/m$$

Diaphragm chords, splice joints in structural members and other load transfer elements shall be designed for seismic loads that are at least 20% greater than the seismic design load on the diaphragm. Therefore for these load transfer elements the seismic design load:

$$= \; 0.626 \times 1.2$$
$$= \; 0.752 \; kN/m$$

For shearwall design:

$$= \; 43.1/63.3$$
$$= \; 0.681 \; kN/m$$

Connections and drag struts that are transferring shear forces between the segments of the vertical SFRS and the diaphragm shall be designed for seismic loads that are at least 20% greater than the shear force that is being transferred. Therefore for these load transfer elements the seismic design load:

$$= \; 0.681 \times 1.2$$
$$= \; 0.818 \; kN/m$$

Factored design load for seismic forces (gridline 14)

For diaphragm design:

$$= 36.4/63.3$$
$$= 0.574 \text{ kN/m}$$

For diaphragm chords and splice joints the corresponding seismic design load:

$$= 0.574 \times 1.2$$
$$= 0.689 \text{ kN/m}$$

For shearwall design:

$$= 41.2/63.3$$
$$= 0.650 \text{ kN/m}$$

For drag struts, hold-downs and anchorages the corresponding seismic design load:

$$= 0.650 \times 1.2$$
$$= 0.780 \text{ kN/m}$$

WIND LOADS – EAST-WEST DIRECTION

Calculate the loads to be resisted by shearwalls along gridlines 1, 3, and 14.

Note: Internal pressures act in opposite directions on opposite walls and therefore have no net effect on the overall lateral loads on the structure

FIGURE 13.9

Values of C_pC_g from NBCC-SC/4 Figure I-7

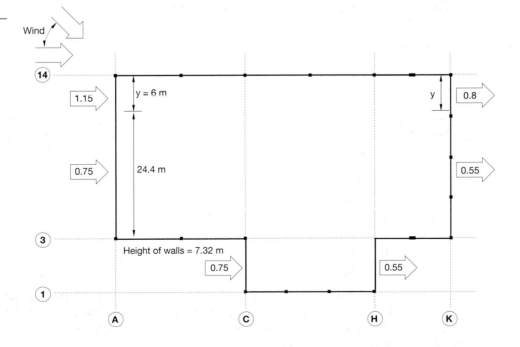

$y = \text{maximum } (2z, 6m)$

z is minimum of: $0.1 \times 40.4 \text{ m} = 4.04 \text{ m}$

$-$ or $-$

$0.4 \times 7.32 = 2.93 \text{ m} > 4\% \times 40.4 \text{ m} = 1.62 \text{ m}$

Use $y = 6 \text{ m}$

Wall studs transfer wind loads to roof diaphragm and foundation. Therefore, shearwalls must be capable of resisting half of the lateral force on the east and west walls.

Note: For wind loads, a principal load factor of 1.4 is applied.

Wall A

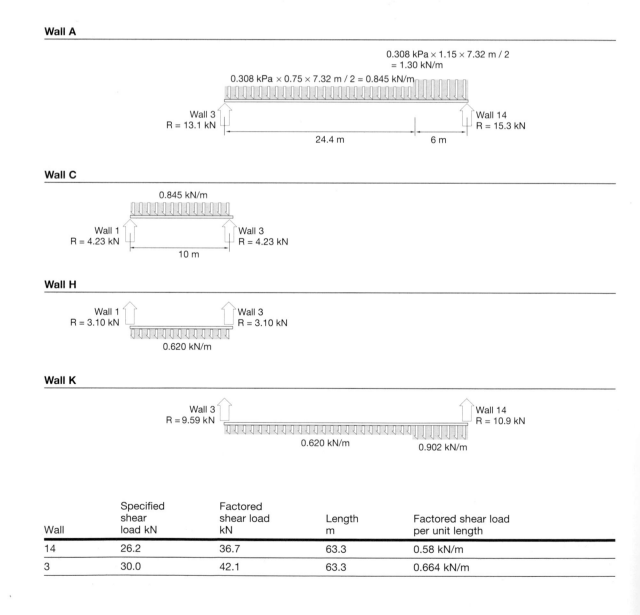

Wall	Specified shear load kN	Factored shear load kN	Length m	Factored shear load per unit length
14	26.2	36.7	63.3	0.58 kN/m
3	30.0	42.1	63.3	0.664 kN/m

SUMMARY

For factored lateral loads in the east-west direction

maximum earthquake

diaphragm design = 0.626 kN/m

shearwall design = 0.681 kN/m

for diaphragm chords and splice joints the corresponding seismic design load = 0.752 kN/m

for drag struts, hold-downs and anchorages the corresponding seismic design load = 0.818 kN/m

maximum wind = 0.664 kN/m

13.15   Lateral Loads: North-South Direction

EARTHQUAKE LOAD – NORTH-SOUTH DIRECTION

Calculate the loads to be resisted along gridlines A, H, and K.

$$V = S(T_a)M_v I_E W/(R_d R_o)$$
$$= 0.175 \times 1.0 \times 1.0 \times W/(3.0 \times 1.7)$$
$$= 0.0343 \ W \ kN$$

But need not be greater than

$$V_{max} = 2/3 \ S(0.2) \ I_E W/(R_d R_o)$$
$$= 2/3 \times 0.18 \times 1.0 \times W/(3.0 \times 1.7)$$
$$= 0.0235 \ W \ kN \qquad\qquad\qquad\qquad (Governs)$$

Loads at shear lines without accounting for accidental torsion (used for diaphragm design):

Weights and Distribution to Gridlines

	Total loads kN	Load at gridlines, kN		
		A	H	K
Warehouse roof	1854	927	927	
Office roof	573		287	287
Garden centre roof	281	70	210	
Office floor	661		331	331
		997	1755	618

Loads at shear lines accounting for accidental offset (used for shearwall design):

$$Offset = \pm 0.05 \ D_{nx}$$
$$= \pm 0.05 \times 63.3$$
$$= \pm 3.16 \ m$$

Area	Offset +3.16 m Load (kN) at gridlines			Offset –3.16 m Load (kN) at gridlines		
	A	H	K	A	H	K
Warehouse roof	807	1047		1047	807	
Office roof		161	411		411	161
Garden center roof	52	229		88	192	
Office floor		186	474		474	186
Total	**859**	**1623**	**885***	**1135***	**1884***	**347**

* Governing case

Area	Length m	Diaphragm design: V_{max} kN	V_{max}/Length kN/m	Shearwall design: V_{max} kN	V_{max}/Length kN/m
Gridline A	30.4	23.5	0.772	26.7	0.878
Gridline H	30.4	41.3	1.36	44.3	1.46
Gridline K	30.4	14.5	0.478	20.8	0.685

WIND LOADS – NORTH-SOUTH DIRECTION

Loads will be resisted by shearwalls along gridlines A, H, and K.

Assume the diaphragms are simple spans between the shearwalls.

FIGURE 13.10

*Values of C_pC_g
from NBCC-SC/4
Figure I-7*

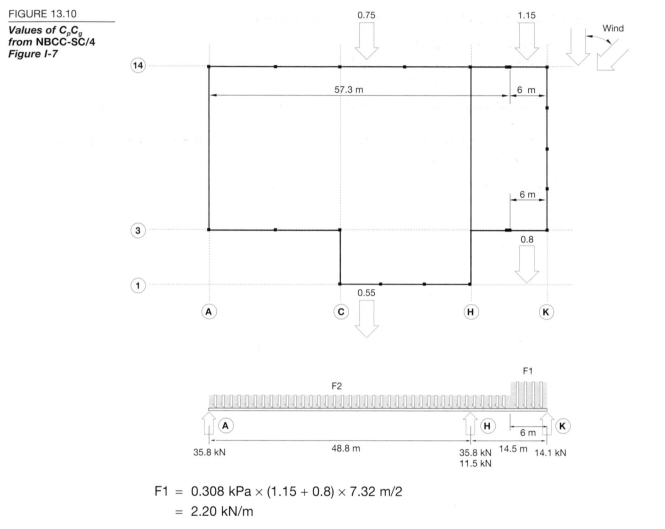

FIGURE 13.10

*Values of C_pC_g
from NBCC-SC/4
Figure I-7*

$$F1 = 0.308 \text{ kPa} \times (1.15 + 0.8) \times 7.32 \text{ m}/2$$
$$= 2.20 \text{ kN/m}$$

$$F2 = 0.308 \text{ kPa} \times (0.75 + 0.55) \times 7.32 \text{ m}/2$$
$$= 1.47 \text{ kN/m}$$

	Specified shear load kN	Length m	Factored shear load per unit length kN/m
Shearwall A	35.8	30.4	1.65
Shearwall H	47.3	30.4	2.18
Shearwall K	14.1	30.4	0.650

SUMMARY

For factored lateral loads in the north-south direction

    maximum earthquake:

        diaphragm design = 1.36 kN/m

        shearwall design = 1.46 kN/m

        for diaphragm chords and splice joints the corresponding seismic design load = 1.63 kN/m

        for drag struts, hold-downs and anchorages the corresponding seismic design load = 1.75 kN/m

    maximum wind = 2.18 kN/m

13.16   Roof Diaphragm and Chords

GIVEN VALUES AND ASSUMPTIONS

Design the roof diaphragm. In determining the shear force distribution for the roof diaphragm, wind forces in the north-south direction will govern design. Shearwalls are located at gridlines A, H, and K. The roof diaphragms over the warehouse and office area act independently. Critical wind in the design of the warehouse diaphragm is from north to northwest. Note

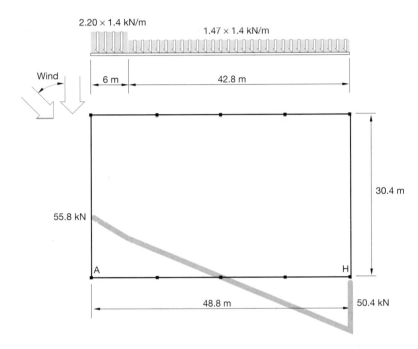

that the wind force action on the south face of the garden centre must be transferred to the diaphragm through the roof framing.

- Short term load duration
- Roof framed with S-P-F lumber

Maximum shear force in diaphragm

$$= 55.8 \text{ kN} / 30.4\text{m}$$
$$= 1.84 \text{ kN/m}$$

From the Diaphragm Selection Tables (*WDM* Section 8.2), try the following

- 12.5 mm plywood thickness
- 3.25 mm diameter nails spaced at 150 mm on centre along supported ends
- No blocking

$V_r = 3.16 \text{ kN/m} > 1.84 \text{ kN/m}$ *(Acceptable)*

Use 12.5 mm plywood with 3.25 mm diameter nails spaced at 150 mm on centre along supported panel ends and at 300 mm along intermediate trusses.

DESIGN OF CHORDS

- Use S-P-F dimension lumber
- Nailed on edge along perimeter of roof diaphragms

$$M_f = 620 \text{ kN} \bullet \text{m}$$

$$h = 30.2\text{m}$$

$$T_f = P_f$$
$$= 620 / 30.2$$
$$= 20.5 \text{ kN}$$

Design the chord member for tension assuming that the cross-sectional area will not be reduced due to nailing.

Checklist satisfied (*WDM* Section 4.2) with the exception of load duration which is accounted for below.

From the Tension Member Selection Tables (*WDM* Section 4.2), try 38×140 mm No.1 / No.2 grade S-P-F adjusted for short term load duration

$$T_r = 34.2 \times 1.15$$
$$= 39.3 \text{ kN} > 20.5 \text{ kN} \qquad\qquad (Acceptable)$$

Since the chord is fully laterally braced by the wall sheathing, buckling of the chord due to compression is not possible and tension controls the design.

Use 38×140 mm No.1 / No.2 grade S-P-F chord nailed on edge.

The diaphragm chord must be adequately spliced along the full length of the diaphragm to ensure continuity.

DESIGN OF SHEARWALL AND DIAPHRAGM CONNECTIONS

The details shown below may be used to transfer shear and lateral forces between the roof diaphragm and the stud walls. The spacing of nails must be calculated so that the resistance of the connection exceeds the applied forces.

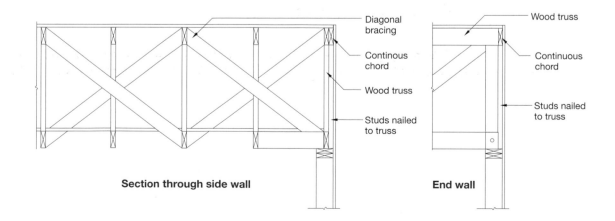

Section through side wall   **End wall**

13.17   Shearwall, Chords and Tie-Down Connections

GIVEN VALUES AND ASSUMPTIONS

Design the shearwalls, chords and tie-down connection for the west wall in the warehouse.

For transmitting lateral forces from the roof diaphragm to the foundation, shearwalls are located as shown below.

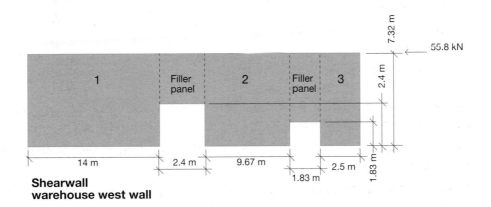

Shearwall
warehouse west wall

V_f = 55.8 kN at the top of the wall

The shear force per unit length along the bottom of the wall may be calculated as

$$v_f = \frac{55.8}{14 + 9.67 + 2.5}$$
$$= 2.13 \text{ kN/m}$$

DESIGN OF SHEATHING

Checklist satisfied (*WDM* Section 8.3)

From the Shearwall Selection Table (*WDM* Section 9.3) try the following

* 9.5 mm thick plywood nailed directly to the S-P-F studs
* 2" nails spaced at 150 mm on centre along panel edges
* Blocking

$$v_r = 3.48 \text{ kN/m} > 2.13 \text{ kN/m}$$ *(Acceptable)*

Use 9.5 mm plywood with 2" nails spaced at 150 mm on centre along panel edges and at 300 mm on centre along intermediate studs and blocking.

DESIGN OF TENSION AND COMPRESSION CHORDS FOR SHEAR PANEL 3

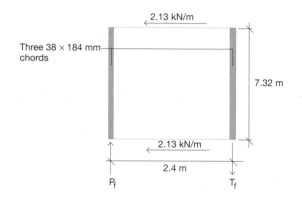

Wind forces in the south direction will govern design of tension and compression chords for shear panel 3.

Check the chord member for tension.

The gravity loads that acts to resist overturning:

Total factored load from the roof = 0.9D + 0.5S
$$= (0.9 \times 0.85) + (0.5 \times 1.6)$$
$$= 1.57 \text{ kPa}$$

The factored dead load of the wall = 0.9 x 0.33 = 0.297 kPa (assume a specified dead load of 0.33 kPa).

The force in the tension chord is

$$T_f = \frac{2.13 \times 2.5 \times 7.32}{2.4} - (1.57 \times 6.1) \times \frac{2.5}{2} - (0.297 \times 7.32) \times \frac{2.5}{2}$$

$$= 1.59 \text{ kN}$$

Assume the chords will be anchored using 1/2" diameter bolts.

Checklist satisfied (*WDM* Section 4.2) with the exception of load duration which is accounted for below.

From the Tension Member Selection Tables (*WDM* Section 4.2), check three 38 × 184 mm No.1/ No.2 grade S-P-F. The tabulated resistance must be modified for short term loading and area reduction due to bolt holes:

$$T_r = 3 \times 41.5 \times 1.15 \times \frac{184 - (12.7 + 2) \times 1}{184}$$

$$= 132 \text{ kN} > 1.59 \text{ kN}$$ *(Acceptable)*

Check the chord member for compression.

The gravity loads that go to the compression chord:

Total factored load from the roof = 1.25D + 0.5S
$$= (1.25 \times 0.85) + (0.5 \times 1.6)$$
$$= 1.86 \text{ kPa}$$

The factored dead load of the wall = 1.25 x 0.33 = 0.413 kPa

The compression in the chord member is

$$P_f = \frac{2.13 \times 2.5 \times 7.32}{2.4} + (1.86 \times 6.1) \times \left(\frac{2.5}{2} + \frac{1.83}{2}\right) + (0.413 \times 7.32) \times \frac{2.5}{2}$$

$$= 44.6 \text{ kN}$$

Check the capacity of three 38 × 184 mm No.1/No.2 grade S-P-F studs 7.32 m long.

$$P_r = \phi F_C A K_{Zc} K_C$$

$$\phi F_C = 11.6 \text{ MPa from } \textit{WDM Table 3.2}$$

$$A = 38 \times 184 = 6992 \text{ mm}^2$$

$$K_{Zc} = 6.3 (184 \times 7320)^{-0.13} = 1.01$$

$$C_c = \frac{7320}{184} = 39.8$$

$$F_c/E' = 63.9 \times 10^{-6} \text{ from } \textit{WDM Table 3.3}$$

$$K_c = [1.0 + 63.9 \times 10^{-6} \times 1.01 \times 39.8^3]^{-1} = 0.198$$

$$P_r = 3 \times 11.6 \times 6992 \times 1.01 \times 0.197$$

$$= 48.5 \text{ kN} > 44.6 \text{ kN} \hspace{4em} \textit{(Acceptable)}$$

Note that if the tension force is negative, which means the gravity loads are sufficient to resist the overturning force, the gravity loads don't need to be accounted for when calculating the compression force in the chord.

Therefore, three 38 × 184 mm No.1/No.2 grade S-P-F studs are adequate for use as chord members for shear panel 3.

DESIGN OF ANCHORAGE CONNECTION FOR SHEAR PANEL 3

Chord members will be anchored to the foundation with a bolted bracket as shown below.

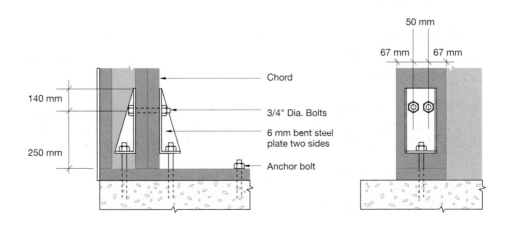

Modification Factors

$$K_D = 1.15 \text{ (short term load duration)}$$

$$K_{SF} = 1.0 \text{ (service conditions are dry, material is seasoned)}$$

$$K_T = 1.0 \text{ (lumber is not treated)}$$

Therefore

$$K' = 1.15$$

CALCULATION

$$P_f = 1.59 \text{ kN}$$

The configuration is Type 9 – double shear with steel side plates loaded parallel to grain.

Try one row of one 1/2" diameter bolt.

For a single row of fastener, P_r is equal to the row shear resistance, PR_{rT}:

$$PR_{rT} = PR_F \, n_c \, n_R \, K'$$

From the Bolt Selection Tables (*WDM* Section 7.4)

PR_F = 15.7 kN for bolt spacing of 250 mm and for a member thickness of 114 mm

PR_{rT} = 15.7 × 1 × 1 × 1.15 = 18.1 kN > 1.59 kN   *(Acceptable)*

Check end and edge distance requirements from Figure 7.6 (*WDM* Section 7.4)

loaded end distance = 250 mm > 64 mm   *(Acceptable)*

Edge distance = 184/2 = 92 mm > 1.5 bolt diameters = 19 mm   *(Acceptable)*

Anchor bolts that fasten the bottom plate to the foundation must also be designed for tension and shear.

Use one 1/2" diameter bolt.

Appendix

A.1 Index